Infrared Absorption

OF INORGANIC SUBSTANCES

KATHERYN E. LAWSON

Physical Sciences Research Department
Sandia Corporation
Albuquerque, New Mexico

New York
REINHOLD PUBLISHING CORPORATION
Chapman & Hall, Ltd., London

Library of Congress Catalog Card Number: 61–11885

Printed in the United States of America

To the Memory of
My Father
LEON LEWIS EMANUEL
(1901–1940)

Preface

Since 1952, an increasing number of detailed studies of the infrared absorption spectra of inorganic materials have appeared in the literature. In many of these studies characteristic frequencies which are useful in the analysis and identification of inorganic substances have been observed. In addition, some of the studies have afforded valuable information on the nature of the structures and of the intermolecular forces.

The present work represents a compilation and review of empirical data and interpretations of the infrared absorption spectra of inorganic substances. No effort has been made to cover the theory of spectra nor, in any great detail, the experimental methods, both of which have been treated extensively in the literature. Rather, it is intended that this volume should serve as a source book of spectral information for persons engaged in this phase of spectroscopy.

Part I summarizes current experimental techniques with reference to the controlling factors and cites the varied applications of infrared spectroscopic studies of inorganic materials. In Part II, as many correlations and assignments as are available from the experimental data of various observers are presented. The inorganic substances discussed have been grouped into four main categories based on the number of elements involved: elemental substances, binary compounds, ternary compounds, and compounds containing more than three elements. A glossary and an extensive annotated bibliography with index follow.

The author wishes to thank those who have assisted in the preparation of this work, and particularly Dr. G. A. Crosby, Dr. R. S. Claassen, Dr. F. P. Hudson, and Mr. H. A. Stein, who read portions of the manuscript critically. Thanks are also due to The American Chemical Society, The American Institute of Physics, The Faraday Society, The National Research Council of Canada, D. Van Nostrand Co., Inc., Pergamon Press Ltd. and *Physical Review* for permission to use certain copyrighted material. Finally, the author expresses appreciation to her husband for assistance and encouragement throughout the entire course of this work.

K. Lawson

Albuquerque, New Mexico
March, 1961

Contents

	PREFACE	v
PART I	INTRODUCTION	1
PART II	SPECTRA-STRUCTURE CORRELATIONS	14
	GLOSSARY	77
PART III	BIBLIOGRAPHY OF UNCLASSIFIED REFERENCES	86
	INDEX TO BIBLIOGRAPHY	188

PART I

Introduction

INFRARED ABSORPTION SPECTRA associated with various structural groups of organic materials have been so thoroughly studied that identification of many organic compounds and mixtures presents very little problem.   This method of analysis has the advantages of being rapid and of requiring only small amounts of sample.   The ease of solubility of organic materials in non-aqueous solvents has, to some extent, been responsible for the large volume of work which has been completed with these substances.

On the other hand, studies involving inorganic materials have not met with corresponding success.   Until recently inorganic samples, suitable for analysis, were difficult, if not impossible, to prepare.   Consequently, such data as were available on the vibrational spectra of inorganics were obtained primarily by Raman or reflectance methods.   In the past six to eight years, however, techniques have been developed which yield discrete spectra resulting in a considerable increase in accumulated data.   A number of valuable correlations are now available and fundamental studies on inorganic structures and intermolecular forces have been initiated. This section presents a survey of the usual techniques employed in infrared spectroscopy of inorganic substances and describes some of the many applications of the spectral data.

1

TECHNIQUES

Manuals, books, and review articles[1-7] containing extensive descriptions and discussions of instrumentation, and instruction books for the various commercial instruments, are available to the infrared spectroscopist. This section has, therefore, been confined strictly to methods of sample preparation and related factors.

Infrared absorption spectra may be obtained on gases, liquids, or solids. The practicality of infrared spectrophotometry as an analytical tool for gases is well established. Gases are particularly easy to investigate in the infrared region because concentrations are controllable by simply varying the pressure. In addition, spectra of gaseous materials are less affected by intermolecular forces than are those of solid and liquid samples.

The freedom of rotation of gaseous molecules generally introduces fine structure into the absorption bands as a result of rotational energy changes along with the usual vibrational energy changes. This frequently makes the spectra more complicated, but aids in the assignment of characteristic frequencies and consequently in identification of the molecule.

Special sampling techniques and cell construction for use in vapor-phase spectroscopy are described in the literature. For example, Taylor, Benedict, and Strong[8] described a porcelain-lined

1. Harrison, G. R., Lord, R. C., and Loofbourow, J. R., "Practical Spectroscopy," Prentice-Hall, New York, 1948.
2. Jones, R. N., and Sandorfy, C., "Infrared and Raman Spectrometry: Applications," in A. Weissberger's "Technique of Organic Chemistry," Vol. IX, Interscience, New York, 1956.
3. Lord, R. C., McDonald, R. S., and Miller, F. A., *J. Opt. Soc. Amer.*, **42**, 149 (1952).
4. Robinson, D. Z., *Anal. Chem.*, **23**, 273 (1951); **24**, 619 (1952).
5. West, W., "Spectroscopy and Spectrophotometry," in A. Weissberger's "Physical Methods of Organic Chemistry, Technique of Organic Chemistry," Vol. I, Part II, 2nd Ed., Interscience, New York, 1949.
6. Willard, H. H., Merritt, L. L., and Dean, J. A., "Instrumental Methods of Analysis," 3rd Ed., D. Van Nostrand, New Jersey, 1958.
7. Williams, V. Z., *Rev. Sci. Instr.*, **19**, 135 (1948).
8. Taylor, J. H., Benedict, W. S., and Strong, J., *J. Chem. Phys.*, **20**, 1884 (1952).

absorption cell of the Pfund type capable of heating 3 meters of gas to temperatures above 500° C. Similarly, Randall, Greene, and Margrave [9] described a simple cell for measuring the spectra of magnesium halides at 1000° C and nickel chloride at 850° C.

The liquid state of inorganic substances is seldom used in obtaining spectra, since few inorganics normally occur in the liquid state, and it is not usually convenient to transform a solid or gas to a liquid simply for the purpose of analysis. However, some progress has been made in the study of inorganic materials in solution. The usual solvent for inorganic determinations is water. Aside from the fact that water attacks the more common infrared cell materials, it also has a strong absorption at wavelengths greater than 1.5 microns. Cells of silver, barium, and thallium halides have made possible the measurement of infrared spectra of aqueous solutions. Non-aqueous solutions of inorganic substances are rarely used for infrared measurements, since solubilities of inorganic compounds in the common solvents are quite low. The current trend of molten salt spectroscopy accompanied by the newer designs of the necessary high-temperature cells will in all probability increase the number of spectral observations in the liquid phase. One notable advance in this direction is the platinum screen technique of Greenberg and Hallgren [10] for the infrared study of fused salts. The salt under consideration is placed in a fine-mesh platinum screen which has been electrically heated to the appropriate temperature. The screen is then placed vertically into the spectrometer so that excess salt runs off, leaving a uniform film supported in the interstices. The technique has been used at temperatures up to 800° C in vacuum and in the atmosphere. Some of its advantages are: (1) the infrared radiation penetrates only the sample, not the cell material; (2) spectra can be obtained over varying temperatures; (3) the corrosive action of the salt at the high temperature does not appreciably affect the screen; and (4) elimination of moisture from the screen is relatively easy when

9. Randall, S. P., Greene, F. T., and Margrave, J. L., *J. Phys. Chem.*, **63**, 758 (1959).
10. Greenberg, J., and Hallgren, L. J., *J. Chem. Phys.*, **33**, 900 (1960).

compared to elimination of moisture from other matrix materials used in normal infrared studies.

The most extensively studied physical state for the examination of inorganic compounds via infrared spectroscopy is the solid state. Solids may be handled in a number of ways: powder film, mull, or alkali-halide pellet techniques are most frequently used.   In the powder film technique a thin film of the finely pulverized sample is deposited upon a salt plate by evaporation of the liquid from a solution or suspension of the solid.   The particle size is quite important, the optimum size being that which prevents excessive scattering and yet transmits adequately for measurement of the absorption.   Generally, methods which are required to give the ideal particle size are rather complicated.

Hackskaylo [11] introduced a refinement of the film technique which produced well-resolved spectra, free of extraneous absorption bands which arise from the solvent or the dispersing medium. Solutions of soluble inorganic salts (e.g., potassium thiocyanate and ammonium heptamolybdate) were brushed onto salt plates which were heated to a temperature intermediate between the decomposition point of the compound and the vaporization temperature of the solvent.   As the solvent evaporated, a thin film of suitable particle size remained on the plate.   The technique was extended to insoluble compounds.   Actually, in some instances, soluble compounds behaved more favorably if treated as insoluble ones.   A slurry or thin paste is prepared by mixing the compound with a liquid of low vaporization temperature.   The mixture is spread onto salt plates and the liquid allowed to vaporize.   As the evaporation proceeds, crystals explode into smaller particles and leave a fluffy coating of solid on the plate.   Excess solid is removed by smoothing over with another salt plate.

Thin crystalline samples of the alkali hydroxides have been prepared by melting a small amount of the compound between cleaved halves of an alkali halide plate and allowing recrystallization to occur after pressing the halves together.[12]   The hydroxide

11. Hackskaylo, M., *Anal. Chem.*, 26 (9), 1410 (1954).
12. Wickersheim, K. A., *J. Chem. Phys.*, 29, 1197 (1958).

forms a thin filler in a crystalline sandwich. The samples ranged in thickness from 10 to 30 microns. Samples of LiOH, NaOH, and KOH were coarse-grained with single crystal grains up to two millimeters in diameter. This structure was not exhibited by cesium or rubidium hydroxide. For all hydroxides except lithium hydroxide, moisture was excluded by sealing the edges of the plates. The formation of alkali carbonate was minimized by working in a carbon dioxide-free atmosphere. Interaction between the salt plate and the hydroxide was considered negligible.

The mull technique has found rather wide usage in infrared spectroscopy. The procedure involves grinding the sample with a viscous liquid, which has few absorption peaks in the region under study. The solid particles are suspended in the liquid medium, the refractive index of which is higher than that of air, in order that light scattering may be reduced to a minimum. The common mulling agents are mineral oil, perfluorokerosene, and hexachlorobutadiene. The problem of excluding moisture and carbon dioxide during the grinding process has been dealt with in a number of ways, among which is conducting the entire process in a cold, dry box or room. Erley [13] proposed the use of 2,2-dimethoxypropane as a drying agent for samples which are slightly acid or are stable in a slightly acid environment. For such a mull, the grinding process will generally remove the products of the interaction between the drying agent and water, since they are volatile. One inhibiting feature is the fact that 2,2-dimethoxypropane is a combustion hazard when stored at room temperature and must be handled with extreme care.

More recently, the alkali halide pellet or disk technique has been applied to the infrared examination of inorganic compounds. The solid being investigated is ground to micron size with the alkali halide, usually potassium bromide, and the mixture pressed into a clear pellet or disk at room temperature *in vacuo* under pressures of about 20,000 pounds per square inch for 5 or more minutes. This technique was originally accepted with enthusiasm, since potassium bromide has no absorption peaks in the 2–25 micron

13. Erley, D. S., *Anal. Chem.*, **29** (10), 1564 (1957).

range.   More discrete spectra were obtained, the pellets could be stored in a dry box for future reference, and the possibility of quantitative analysis was suggested.   This early enthusiasm was soon curtailed as various investigators encountered anomalous behavior in the infrared spectra of inorganic samples prepared by the pellet technique.

Kalbus [14] made an extensive study of the factors influencing the appearance of the spectra.   Difficulties encountered when the alkali halide pellet technique was used were attributed to anion exchange between the inorganic compound and the alkali halide and to pressure or orientation effects on the sample as a result of compression.   Some of the factors affecting the exchange were enumerated—ionic size and type, magnitude and time of application of pressure, particle size, grinding time, surface moisture, and sample solubility.   Table 1 summarizes the data obtained.

The relative merits of the mull and pellet procedures were discussed in considerable detail by Baker.[15]   Although this work was concerned primarily with spectra of organic compounds, some of the findings may be extended to the field of inorganic spectroscopy.   Baker suggested that discrepancies between spectra of organic compounds prepared by the two techniques are due either to an induced physical isomerization of the compound or to the fact that it becomes amorphous in the alkali halide pellet.   Several factors influence these changes: the crystal energy of the organic phase; the energy of grinding of both sample and matrix; the matrix lattice energy and particle size; the ability of the sample to recrystallize in the pellet; and the relative stability of its polymorphic forms.   Each of these factors is discussed at length and experimental data substantiating the arguments are presented. Despite the serious limitations of the pellet procedure, it possesses certain advantages over other methods of sample preparation. When used with caution and together with other techniques, valuable qualitative information can be obtained.   In particular, steps

14. Kalbus, G. E., *Dissertation Abstracts,* **17,** 2413 (1957).   See also Meloche, V. W., and Kalbus, G. E., *J. Inorg. Nucl. Chem.,* **6,** 104 (1958).
15. Baker, A. W., *J. Phys. Chem.,* **61,** 450 (1957).   See also literature citations therein.

TABLE 1. BEHAVIOR OF INORGANIC SALTS CONTAINED IN POTASSIUM BROMIDE PELLETS [a]

(After Meloche and Kalbus [14])

Anion	Cation	Behavior
CO_3^{-2}	Normal: Ag, Sr, Cd, Co(III), Mn(II), Li, Fe(II), Mg, K, Na, Ca, Ba, Pb	No exchange
	Basic: Cu, Mg, Ni, Cr(III), Be, Zn	No exchange
NO_3^-	Ag, Ni(II), Cd, Mg, Co(II), Li, Bi(III), Zn, Fe(III), Hg(II), Pb	Exchange evident
	Na, Al, Ca, Cr(III), Cu(II), Sr, Ba, Th(IV), Hg(I)	No exchange
PO_4^{-3}	Anhydrous: K, Ca, Sr, Ag, Cd, Ba, Bi(III), Pb	No exchange
	Hydrated: Li, Na, Mg, Mn(II), Fe(III), Ni, Co(II), Cu, Zn	No exchange
SO_4^{-2}	Anhydrous: Hg(I), Hg(II), Pb, Cu(II), Ag	Exchange evident
	Hydrated: Cu, Zn	Exchange evident
	Anhydrous: Na, Sr, Ba	No exchange
	Hydrated: Mn(II), Co(II), Li, Mg, Ni, Ca	No exchange
CrO_4^{-2}, NO_3^-, MoO_4^{-2}, CI^-, Br^-, I^-	NH_4^+	No exchange [b]
CO_3^{-2}	NH_4^+	Bands of $KHCO_3$, not of K_2CO_3
SCN^-	NH_4^+	Exchange facilitated by $CHCl_3$; eliminated in dry state

[a] Samples of 0.8–1.5 mg. of the inorganic salt weighed to the nearest 0.05 mg. were added to 300 ± 30 mg. of potassium bromide.
[b] Exchange from halides, if it did occur, could not be observed, since the absorption bands would appear too close to the original bands to be distinguishable.

which eliminate moisture and minimize distortions due to grinding and pressure yield clear-cut spectra which are not otherwise obtainable.

For some inorganic salts, particularly hydrates and hygroscopic materials, the elimination of moisture is extremely difficult, if not impossible. Tai and Underwood [16] combined the technique of freeze drying with the KBr-disk method to obtain good spectra of a number of inorganic sulfates. An aqueous solution of the sample under study was placed in a tube which was rotated in a dry ice-acetone bath until a thin layer of frozen matter formed. The sample tube was then connected to a vacuum system and pumped-on for at least 12 hours. The water was removed rapidly enough to keep the solutions frozen without external cooling. The pumping time can be greatly reduced by warming the tubes after the first two hours, provided the sample is sufficiently heat-stable. After all the water was removed, the freeze-dried product was pressed into a potassium bromide pellet. Generally, prior to formation of the pellet, both the alkali halide and sample should be dried as completely as possible.

The particle size of the matrix must be small enough to obtain pellet transparency and to prevent too violent a grinding action on the particles of the sample. The particle size of the sample should be of the order of one micron. This ideal condition is difficult to attain by hand grinding. For most samples, Harshaw KBr (250–300 mesh) pulverized with the sample in a mechanical vibrator (such as the Wig-L-Bug amalgamator) yields an appropriate particle size. Although it is not absolutely necessary to dry the mixture after the grinding process, a minimum of contact with moisture should be permitted. Distortions of spectra due to amount of pressure and loading time are generally, though not always, minimized by using pressures not in excess of 20,000 pounds per square inch for a loading time of 5 to 15 minutes.

It may be worth while to mention at this point that crystal changes giving rise to distorted spectra have also been encountered in mulls, although less frequently than in pellets. Spectra

16. Tai, H., and Underwood, A. C., *Anal. Chem.*, **29** (10), 1430 (1957).

obtained from vigorously hand-mulled samples are different, in a number of cases, from those obtained from vigorously machine-mulled samples.[15] Although anomalous behavior in alkali halide pellet spectra has been observed and attributed to cation exchange, mixed crystal formation, or surface absorption, some evidence also exists for interchange when oil mulls are pressed between salt plates, particularly when sufficient moisture is present to foster the reaction.[17] Thus, any comparison of solid-state spectra, whether obtained by mull or pellet technique, should make allowance for possible crystal changes and interaction.

The growth of suitable single crystals of appropriate thicknesses has made possible the examination of many elemental substances and ionic and intermetallic compounds. Unfortunately, the techniques for growing such crystals are by no means suited to general use. Furthermore, the spectra of crystals are often complicated by the presence of peaks due to reflection and scattering. These complications are of general occurrence and, unless they are accurately controlled, lead to difficulties in interpreting the infrared spectra of the substance.

Samples which cannot be dealt with by any of the above means may possibly be handled by the recently developed diamond cell microtechnique.[18] A small crystal weighing as little as 4×10^{-6} gram can be crushed into a thin film between diamond surfaces and the assembly mounted into a commercial infrared beam-condensing unit. Minimum pressures to produce the film range from 1 to 100 atmospheres. The inertness of the diamond surface permits the handling of corrosive materials. By using sapphire instead of diamond, the useful range of the cell can be extended to frequencies higher than 1900 cm^{-1}.

17. Padgett, W. M., Talbert, J. M., and Hammer, W. F., *J. Chem. Phys.*, **26**, 959 (1957).
18. Method of Lippincott, Welsh, and Weir, as reported in *Chem. Eng. News*, **38**, No. 39, 120 (1960).

APPLICATIONS

Review of the literature reveals a variety of applications of the infrared spectra of inorganic materials. These include (1) qualitative [14, 19-21] and quantitative analysis; [4] (2) study of molecular structure; (3) measurement of band intensities; [22] (4) study of solid-state reactions to determine whether a product is a new compound or a physical mixture of reactants; [23] (5) calculation of thermodynamic quantities; [24] (6) investigation of impurity levels in semiconductors; [25-27] and (7) determination of isotope ratios in tracer experiments. [28] Other applications can be found in the review articles cited in the bibliography. Only the qualitative and quantitative analyses and molecular structure studies will be discussed here as examples of the application.

As early as 1952, Miller and Wilkins [19] demonstrated the usefulness of spectral data for the qualitative analysis of inorganic mixtures by assigning characteristic frequencies for 33 polyatomic ions present in over a hundred different pure inorganic compounds. The quality of the spectra ranged from sharp, intense bands to ill-defined ones. The effect of varying the positive ion associated with a given anion was observed. Individual sulfates demonstrated enough variation among themselves to make distinction possible. On the other hand, nitrates showed no appreciable shifting as the cation was varied. However, it was suggested that a combination of infrared absorption, emission, and x-ray analysis

19. Miller, F. A., and Wilkins, C. H., *Anal. Chem.*, **24**, 1253 (1952).
20. Brame, E. G., Cohen, S., Margrave, J. L., and Meloche, V. W., *J. Inorg. Nucl. Chem.*, **4**, 90 (1957); Brame, E. G., Margrave, J. L., and Meloche, V. W., *J. Inorg. Nucl. Chem.*, **5**, 48 (1957).
21. Brame, E. G., Johnson, F. A., Larsen, E. M., and Meloche, V. W., *J. Inorg. Nucl. Chem.*, **6**, 99 (1958).
22. Mecke, R. J., *J. Chem. Phys.*, **20**, 1935 (1952).
23. Duval, C., and Lecomte, J., *Compt. rend.*, **234**, 2445 (1952).
24. Giguere, P. A., and Liu, I. D., *Can. J. Chem.*, **30**, 948 (1952).
25. Burstein, E., *et al.*, *J. Phys. Chem.*, **57**, 849 (1953).
26. Kaiser, W., *et al.*, *Phys. Rev.*, **91**, 1380 (1953); *Naturwiss.*, **40**, 497 (1953).
27. Tanenbaum, M., and Briggs, H. B., *Phys. Rev.*, **91**, 1561 (1953).
28. Kluyver, J. C., and Milatz, J. M., *Physica*, **19**, 401 (1953).

be used in the qualitative analysis of mixtures containing more than two components, since this combination provides more valid information than one method alone. Kalbus [14] examined 122 inorganic compounds and found that identification was generally possible for carbonates, nitrates, and sulfates, but was not as specific for others. Brame *et al.*[20-21] undertook the task of securing spectra of a variety of inorganic materials—peroxides, peroxide hydrates, superoxides, oxides, nitrides, carbides, borides, and octacyano complexes of tungsten and molybdenum—for identification purposes. The results of the spectral studies showed characteristic absorption bands for some of the structures, but failed to do so for others. The important correlations made are discussed here in Part II.

Quantitative analysis of inorganic substances has not developed as rapidly as qualitative. The absorption spectrum of a mixture is generally an additive function of each component, so that theoretically it should be possible to determine the component concentrations. Experimentally, difficulties are encountered due largely to the presence of scattered energy from the sources employed in the spectrophotometers used. A number of adjustments and modifications of instruments and methods have been proposed to correct for the stray energy. Other sources of errors are reflection losses, solvent absorption, non-homogeneity of sample, misalignment of cells, and non-linearity in the detecting and recording systems of the instrument.

An evaluation of infrared spectrophotometers for quantitative analysis has been made by Robinson.[4] It was pointed out that errors occur in the measurement of transmission, and in the reading of the zero and 100% lines. The effect of such errors can be calculated. If a plot is made of the per cent transmission versus the per cent error in concentration, assuming a probable error of 1% in the zero line, 100% line, and the transmission, a minimum occurs at about 40% transmission. Any transmission between 25% and 60% gives about the same error.

Two other factors are involved in the adaptation of infrared techniques for quantitative analysis, namely, the law of additivity of optical density and the Beer-Lambert law. The law of additivity of optical density simply states that the optical density of a mixture is the sum of the optical densities of its components:

$$\left(\log \frac{I_0}{I}\right)_{\text{mixture}} = \sum_{i=1}^{N} \left(\log \frac{I_0}{I}\right)_i$$

where $\left(\log \dfrac{I_0}{I}\right)$ is the optical density and there are N components. For the law of additivity to hold, Beer's law must hold for all components but one. The fact that the transmission of light through a medium containing a number of molecules is a function of the number of molecules in the light beam is the basis of every concentration measurement. If there is no appreciable molecular interaction and if the light is monochromatic, Beer's law is an approximation of this function. Deviations from Beer's law generally occur when the spectrometer slits are wider than the width of the absorption band measured, since under this condition it is possible to have changes in absorption coefficients over a slit width.

A useful technique in infrared quantitative analysis is the method of differential analysis. By this method small differences in similar substances can be detected by comparing them simultaneously in a double-beam spectrophotometer. Some method should be employed to eliminate the effect of differences in cell thickness; for example, measuring the solution in the sample cell against the solvent in the blank cell, followed by measuring the solution in the blank cell against the solvent in the sample cell.

The availability of microsampling techniques makes possible the analysis of microquantities of solids, liquids, and gases. Essentially, to effect analysis of microquantities the thickness of the sample in the beam or the sample area must be reduced. When the sample thickness is reduced, a loss in recorder deflection occurs, unless scale expansion devices are used with the spectrometer. Reduction in sample area by means of a small cell lowers the amount of energy available to the detector. One approach to the problem has been the use of beam-condenser optics, which reduce the size of the beam as it passes through the sample, thus making possible the analysis of smaller samples.

Spectra obtained as a function of temperature have proved useful in studies of molecular structure. In addition, study of the polarized spectra of crystalline samples give valuable information in this regard. For molecules of appropriate symmetry, vibrations which are in a direction parallel to an axis of orientation can be differentiated from those which are perpendicular. Interpretation of polarized spectra provides information about the crystal structure also. These spectra have, indeed, been useful in locating bonds which are difficult to find by x-ray diffraction methods. Here again, technical difficulties arise in obtaining and properly orienting the crystalline film or sample. The experimental data indicate that the radiation absorbed in a band is polarized along a given axis. This is not always easily or correctly related to the direction of the bond or to the direction of the bond vibration. Consequently, information provided by infrared polarized radiations of a sample is most valuable when used to complement information secured by other means of analysis.

PART II

Spectra-Structure Correlations

THE CORRELATION OF STRUCTURE OF MOLECULES with their spectra is one of the ultimate aims of infrared analysis. In this section is presented a discussion of the vibrational spectra of a variety of inorganic materials for which absorption data are available. The materials are divided into categories based on the number of kinds of atoms present. Where more than one kind of atom is present, further subdivision is based on the principal non-metallic constituent. Miscellaneous structures, such as intermetallic compounds, are discussed under the subheading "Other Binary (or Ternary) Compounds." Some consideration is also given to metal-organic complexes. In view of the immense volume of empirical data that exists in the literature, there are unavoidable omissions of source material, particularly with respect to publications prior to 1950. However, an attempt has been made to cite as many review articles and references to the earlier work as possible. Although this review represents extensive coverage of the important achievements in the field, the reader should regard this section only as an aid in locating the types of spectral studies reported in the literature for various inorganic materials, realizing that any further usage or interpretation should be made in conjunction with the original accounts.

ELEMENTAL SUBSTANCES

Vibrations of linear non-polar molecules, e.g., O_2, N_2, H_2, cause no change of electric moment—a condition necessary for absorption in the infrared. Therefore, such molecules should possess no rotation-vibration spectra. However, these symmetrical diatomic molecules have been found to have absorption bands when measured under certain conditions.[29] The intensity of the absorption is proportional to the square of the gas pressure. Absorbing gases, when pressurized with infrared-inactive gases, exhibit an induced absorption which has an intensity proportional to the pressure of the inactive gas. Apparently then, this pressure-induced absorption is due to the interaction of the radiation field with an induced dipole moment resulting from the distortion of molecules upon collision.

Considerable interest has centered around the absorption of hydrogen. In the region 660–1250 cm^{-1} compressed hydrogen shows a remarkable absorption, which has been ascribed to the pure rotation spectrum by Ketelaar *et al.*[30] The fundamental vibrational absorption of hydrogen, induced by intermolecular forces, has been studied over a wide range of pressures and temperatures. As the temperature is lowered, resolution of the band is improved. Allin, Hare, and MacDonald[31] investigated the infrared absorption of hydrogen in the liquid and solid states. The molecule is distorted asymmetrically by intermolecular forces as the temperature drops, giving rise to induced infrared absorption. In the crystalline state, this distortion is produced not only by random orientation of the freely rotating molecule but also by the lattice vibrations of the crystals. Variations in the fundamental absorption of solid hydrogen at $13.6 \pm 0.2°K$ occurs with changes

29. Welsh, H. L., Crawford, M. F., MacDonald, J. C. F., Chishom, D. A., *Phys. Rev.*, **83**, 1264 (1951).
30. Ketelaar, J. A. A., Colpa, J. P., and Hooge, F. N., *J. Chem. Phys.*, **23**, 413 (1955).
31. Allin, E. J., Hare, W. F. J., and MacDonald, R. E., *Phys. Rev.*, **98**, 554 (1955).

in the ortho-para ratio.[32]   More structure is observed as the per cent composition of para-hydrogen is decreased.

While there are published works on other non-metallic molecules—ozone,[33, 34] sulfur,[35] oxygen and nitrogen[36, 37]—most of the work on elemental substances has been devoted to metallic and semiconducting structures.   The optical constants of many polyvalent metals show a marked dependence on frequency in the infrared region at wavelengths greater than 10 microns.   Theoretical discussions of the optical properties of metals appear in the book literature.[38, 39]

A number of inconsistencies in the measured optical constants exist in the literature.   These arise, in general, from the fact that the methods used in determining the constants are all too often dependent on the previous chemical and mechanical treatment of the surface.   Haas[40] has tabulated the optical constants of a number of metals and alloys at various wavelengths extending into the infrared.

Infrared absorption measurements have also been used as a means of investigating the anomalous skin effect[41, 42] in metals. According to classical theory, the absorptivity of a metal should

32. Hare, W. F. J., Allin, E. J., and Welsh, H. L., *Phys. Rev.*, **99**, 1887 (1955).
33. Nexsen, W. E., *Dissertation Abstr.*, **16**, 771 (1956).
34. Paetzold, H. K., *Z. Naturforsch.*, 11a, 128 (1956).
35. Barrow, G. M., *J. Chem. Phys.*, **21**, 219 (1953).
36. Yaroslavskii, N. G., and Karyalin, A. V., *Doklady Akad. Nauk S.S.S.R.*, **85**, 1103 (1952).
37. Coulon, R., Oskengorn, B., Robin, St., and Vodar, B., *J. phys. rad.*, **14**, 63 (1953).
38. Seitz, F., "The Modern Theory of Solids," Chapter XVII, McGraw-Hill Book Co., Inc., New York (1940).
39. Givens, M. P., "Optical Properties Of Metals," p. 313ff. in "Solid State Physics," Vol. 6, F. Seitz and D. Turnbull, Editors, Academic Press, Inc., New York (1958).
40. Haas, G., "Optical Constants of Metals," Section 6–102 in "American Institute of Physics Handbook," D. E. Gray, Editor, McGraw-Hill Book Co., Inc., New York (1957).
41. Pippard, A. B., *Proc. Roy. Soc. (London)*, **191A**, 385, 399 (1947).
42. Reuter, G. E. H., and Sondheimer, E. H., *Proc. Roy. Soc. (London)*, **195A**, 336 (1948).

decrease without limit as the mean free path of the conduction electrons increases. Observed absorptivities of metals, however, are of the same order of magnitude at liquid helium temperature as at room temperature. The classical theory is valid as long as the mean free path, l, is small compared to the depth of penetration, δ, of the electromagnetic field. When $l > \delta$, anomalous behavior results. Biondi[43] has measured the optical absorption of copper and silver at 4.2°K in the region 33,333–3030 cm^{-1} (0.3–3μ), where $l > \delta$. Consistent with the anomalous skin effect, infrared absorptivity was independent of wavelength at values greater than 1.5μ.

Notable contributions to the understanding of phenomena associated with semiconductors have been made through infrared absorption spectroscopy. By studying the temperature dependence of the absorption spectrum of such materials in terms of existing theories, it has been possible to obtain valuable information for the assignment of the appropriate band structures. Furthermore, examination of the infrared absorption spectra of semiconductors before and after heat treatments and irradiation provides clues to the nature of the mechanisms responsible for absorption. Extensive coverage of the theory and experimental findings appear in a recent book by Moss.[44]

BINARY COMPOUNDS

Borides, Carbides, and Nitrides

Information on the physical and chemical properties of borides, carbides, and nitrides is very limited; this is particularly true of spectral information. The infrared spectra of Mo_2B, ZrB_2, TiB_2, B_4C, SiC, Li_3N, Cu_3N, BN, AlN, CrN, Mg_3N_2 and Zr_3N_2 have been investigated in the region 624–5000 cm^{-1}.[20] Of the boride structures studied, only the tetragonal molybdenum boride showed band structure. A weak, broad band with its center at 1389 cm^{-1}

43. Biondi, M. A., *Phys. Rev.*, **102**, 964 (1956).
44. Moss, T. S., "Optical Properties of Semiconductors," Academic Press, Inc., New York (1959).

was found.   Only two carbides—rhombohedral boron carbide and hexagonal silicon carbide—were examined.   Although this is hardly sufficient data to establish that the observed band is characteristic, it is interesting to point out that a shift toward longer wavelengths occurs as the mass is increased.   The 1053 cm^{-1} medium intensity band of B_4C is shifted, as would be expected from the mass effect, to an 833.3 cm^{-1} band of medium intensity for SiC. The shift is small and may be attributed partly to differences in crystal structure as well as to the mass effect.

Two strong intensity bands were noted for all nitride samples except copper nitride and chromium nitride.   Copper nitride exhibits strong absorption in the neighborhood of 625 cm^{-1}, the limit of the rock-salt scanning region used; chromium nitride showed no absorption for the region.   For the series Li_3N, BN, AlN a progressive shift toward longer wavelength of the strong intensity bands with mass increase was observed.   Similarly, an absorption band shift was noted for Mg_3N_2 and Zn_3N_2.   The predicted change in position of the bands as a result of mass effect was not followed when the entire group of nitrides was considered.   Presumably, the differences in crystal structure between the two sets of nitride samples make the mass effect prediction invalid.   For different crystal structures, relative positions of the atoms are changed. This results in changes of the force constants involved and consequent shifts in the absorption frequencies.   Notwithstanding the crystal structure effect, the strong intensity bands observed apparently represent a metal-nitrogen vibration, particularly since the shift of the main band was of reasonably large magnitude. Table 2 shows the crystal structures and band centers located for the samples studied.

Halides

Inorganic halides have been used widely as prism and cell window material for the infrared region.   For a number of these compounds, the infrared absorption spectrum has been determined under a variety of conditions.   The approximate range of transmission of the halides most commonly used for prism and window construction is given in Table 3.   The useful range of

TABLE 2. CRYSTAL STRUCTURE AND ABSORPTION BAND CENTERS
OF BORIDES, CARBIDES, AND NITRIDES

(After Brame *et al.*[20])

Compound	Crystal Structure [a]	Absorption Bands [b]	
Mo_2B	tetragonal	7.2(1389)w	
B_4C	rhombohedral	9.5(1053)m	12.9(775.2)w
SiC	hexagonal	12.0(833.3)m	
Li_3N	hexagonal	6.8(1471)sh	7.0(1429)s
		11.6(862.1)m	15.2(657.9)m
Bn	hexagonal	7.28(1374)s	12.3(813)m
AlN	hexagonal	8.45(1183)w	9.46(1057)w
		14.0(714.3)m	
Mg_3N_2	cubic	4.8(2083)m	7.1(1408)m
		15.2(657.9)m	
Zn_3N_2	cubic	9.1(1099)m	11.15(897.1)w
Cu_3N	cubic	16.0(625)s	

[a] Wyckoff, R. W. G., "Crystal Structure," Vol. I., Interscience Publishers, New York, 1951.
[b] The location of the band centers is given in microns and cm^{-1}; the wave number (cm^{-1}) location is in parentheses. The band intensity is represented by the lettering: sh = shoulder; w = weak; m = medium; s = strong.

TABLE 3. APPROXIMATE RANGE OF INFRARED TRANSMISSION OF SOME
COMMONLY USED PRISM AND WINDOW MATERIALS [a]

Material	Range of Transmission	
	Wavelength, μ	Wavenumber, cm^{-1}
LiF	0.11–6	90,910–1667
CaF_2	0.12–8.5	90,090–1176
NaCl	0.2–15	50,000–667
KBr	0.21–28	49,750–357
KRS–5(TlBr + TlI)	0.6–40	16,670–250
CsBr	0.3–40	33,333–250
CsI	–55	–182

[a] Taken in part from: Willard, Merritt, Dean, *"Instrumental Methods of Analysis,"* p. 156, D. Van Nostrand Company, Inc., Princeton, N. J., 1958.

transmission is determined by other factors and will, in general, be somewhat narrower than the ranges given.

Fluorides. The hexafluorides of S, Se, Te, Mo, W, U, Np, Pu, Re, and Ir have been shown to have the O_h symmetrical structures of regular octahedra.   Accordingly, there are six fundamental vibrations: three Raman-active modes of species a_{1g}, e_g, and f_{2g}; two infrared-active modes of species f_{1u}; and an inactive f_{2u} mode. Observed and calculated values of these fundamentals have been reported in the literature [45-51] and are tabulated in Table 4.   Spectra of certain fluorides of sulfur, namely, sulfur monofluoride,[52] sulfur tetrafluoride,[53] and sulfur hexafluoride,[46, 54, 55] have been measured in the infrared region.   Sulfur monofluoride exhibits the following vibrations: 1332 cm^{-1}, combination band of 807 and 526; 807 cm^{-1}, asymmetric F—S stretching; 745 cm^{-1}, symmetric F—S stretching; and 526 cm^{-1}, S—S stretching.   Both infrared and Raman work on the tetrafluoride seems to indicate that the SF$_4$ molecule belongs to point group C$_{2v}$.   The spectrum of the hexafluoride has a number of unexplainable peaks, perhaps due to the presence of SF$_4$ and S$_2$F$_{10}$.   However, the observation of the predicted infrared and Raman bands, together with electron diffraction data, is compatible with the octahedral model for SF$_6$.

45. Burke, T. G., Smith, D. F., and Nielsen, A. H., *J. Chem. Phys.*, **20**, 447 (1952).
46. Gaunt, J., *Trans. Faraday Soc.*, **49**, 1122 (1953).
47. Gaunt, J., *Trans. Faraday Soc.*, **51**, 893 (1955).
48. Hawkins, N. J., Mattraw, H. C., and Sabol, W. W., *J. Chem. Phys.*, **23**, 2191 (1955).
49. Malm, J. G., Weinstock, B., and Claasen, H. H., *J. Chem. Phys.*, **23**, 2192 (1955).
50. Gaunt, J., *Trans. Faraday Soc.*, **50**, 209 (1954).
51. Mattraw, H. C., Hawkins, N. J., Carpenter, D. R., and Sabol, W. W., *J. Chem. Phys.*, **23**, 985 (1955).
52. Matutano, J. R. B., and Otero, C., *Anales real Soc. espan. fis. y quim. (Madrid)*, **51B**, 223 (1955).
53. Dodd, R. E., Woodward, L. A., and Roberts, H. L., *Trans. Faraday Soc.*, **52**, 1052 (1956).
54. de Lattre, A., *J. Chem. Phys.*, **20**, 520 (1952).
55. Edelson, D., and McAfee, K. B., *J. Chem. Phys.*, **19**, 1311 (1951).

Table 4. Fundamental Vibrational Frequencies (cm^{-1}) of Some Hexafluorides [a]

	ν_1	ν_2	ν_3	ν_4	ν_5	ν_6	References [b]
MoF$_6$	741(736)	645(641)	741(742)	260(269)	322(319)	234(240)	45,(46,47)
WF$_6$	772(769)	672(670)	712(712)	258(256)	316(322)	215(216)	45,(46,47)
ReF$_6$	753	600	716	393	246	170	50
IrF$_6$	696	643	718	276	260	205	51
UF$_6$	656(668)	511(532)	640(626)	200(189)	200(202)	130(144)	45,(46,47)
NpF$_6$	648(665)	528(536)	624(623)	200(186)	206(202)	164(136)	49,(48)
PuF$_6$	628(625)	523(522)	615(617)	203(205)	211(211)	171(176)	49,(48)
SF$_6$	775	644	932	613	524	344	46,47
SeF$_6$	708	662	780	437	405	260	46,47
TeF$_6$	701	674	752	327	313	197	46,47

[a] ν_1, ν_2, ν_5–Raman-active, ν_3, ν_4–infrared active, ν_6–inactive.
[b] The references in parentheses refer to the values listed in parentheses.

Considering their similarity to methane, CH_4, it seems natural to assume that the tetrafluorides of carbon, silicon, and germaium (CF_4, SiF_4, and GeF_4, respectively) would form a regular tetrahedron with each of the four fluoride atoms at the vertices and the remaining atom in the center.   For the regular tetrahedron (point group, T_d) there are four fundamental vibrational frequencies, two of which are infrared-active.   Indeed, for these three tetrafluorides, two intense infrared bands have been located.[56]   The number of total bands observed for GeF_4 is small when compared with those observed for CF_4 and SiF_4.   For all three compounds, the ν_4 fundamental is the only one in which PQR band structure is discernible with prism instruments.   The fundamental vibrational frequencies are recorded in Table 5.

TABLE 5.   FUNDAMENTAL VIBRATIONAL FREQUENCIES OF CF_4, SiF_4, AND GeF_4

	CF_4[a]	SiF_4[b]	GeF_4[c]
ν_1	904 cm^{-1}	800 cm^{-1}	738 cm^{-1}
ν_2	435	268	205
ν_3	1283	1031	800
ν_4	632	391	260

[a] Woltz, P. J. H., and Nielsen, A. H., *J. Chem. Phys.*, 20, 307 (1952).
[b] Jones, Kirby-Smith, Woltz, P. J. H., and Nielsen, A. H., *J. Chem. Phys.*, 19, 242 (1951).
[c] Caunt, A. D., Short, L. N., and Woodward, L. A., *Trans. Faraday Soc.*, 48, 873 (1952).

The trifluorides of nitrogen and phosphorus were investigated by Wilson and Polo[57] for the region 250–5000 cm^{-1}.   Chemically, NF_3 and PF_3 are quite dissimilar in their tendency to form addition compounds.   For example, PF_3 forms a ferrohemoglobin complex, $HbPF_3$, and a nickel complex, $Ni(PF_3)_4$, while NF_3 does not.   This would seem to indicate that the two molecules have significantly different electronic structures.   These investigators measured the absolute intensities of the infrared vibration bands

56. Woltz, P. J. H., and Nielsen, A. H., *J. Chem. Phys.*, 20, 307 (1952).
57. Wilson, M. K., and Polo, S. R., *J. Chem. Phys.*, 20, 1716 (1952).

of NF_3 and PF_3 in an attempt to gain information on the structure. If one assumes for these molecules the C_{3v} symmetry of ammonia, NH_3, then six normal vibrational modes may be described: $\nu_1(a_1)$, a totally symmetric stretching vibration; $\nu_2(a_1)$, a totally symmetric bending vibration; $\nu_3(e)$, a doubly degenerate stretching frequency; and $\nu_4(e)$, a doubly degenerate bending frequency. All four fundamentals are allowed in the infrared and Raman spectrum. The spectrum of neither molecule was rich in overtone and combination bands, and assignment was reasonably straightforward. Pace and Pierce [58] observed the infrared and Raman spectra of NF_3 and obtained data which substantiate the findings of Wilson and Polo (Table 6).

TABLE 6. FUNDAMENTAL VIBRATIONAL FREQUENCIES (cm^{-1}) OF NF_3 AND PF_3

	PF_3[a]	NF_3[a]	NF_3[b]	
			Infrared	Raman
$\nu_1(a_1)$	892	1032	1031	1050
$\nu_2(a_1)$	487	647	642	667
$\nu_3(e)$	860	905	907	905
$\nu_4(e)$	344	493	497	515

[a] Wilson and Polo.[57]
[b] Pace and Pierce.[58]

Most molecules of the XY_3 type have been found to have the planar or pyramidal structures, the Y atoms being equivalent. For NF_3 and PF_3 the pyramidal model is indicated; however, for BF_3 spectral data favor the plane symmetrical structure.[59] For the trifluorides of chlorine and bromine, ClF_3 and BrF_3, respectively, there is strong indication that neither model applies.[60] Rather, a planar T-shaped model seems more plausible. For such a structure, six fundamental vibrations are allowed: three totally

58. Pace, E. L., and Pierce, L., *J. Chem. Phys.*, **23**, 1248 (1955).
59. See discussion in Herzberg, F., "Infrared and Raman Spectra of Polyatomic Molecules," p. 298, D. Van Nostrand Co., Inc., New York, 1945.
60. Claasen, H. H., Weinstock, B., and Malm, J. G., *J. Chem. Phys.*, **28**, 285 (1958).

symmetric vibrations of species a_1, two fundamentals of species b_1, and one of species b_2.   All six were observed in the spectra of ClF_3 (vapor): $\nu_1(752)$, $\nu_2(528)$, $\nu_3(326)$, $\nu_4(703)$, $\nu_5(434)$, and $\nu_6(364)$; while only two were observed in the spectra of BrF_3 (vapor): $\nu_1(674)$ and $\nu_4(613)$.   The calculated values for BrF_3 are $\nu_1(662)$, $\nu_2(528)$, $\nu_3(300)$, $\nu_4(601)$, $\nu_5(384)$, $\nu_6(289)$.

The spectrum of gaseous BrF_5 was recorded in the KBr region and a tetragonal pyramidal structure suggested on the basis of the data obtained along with supporting data from the Raman spectrum of liquid BrF_5.[61]   No definite structural assignment could be made because insufficient data were obtained on the low-frequency infrared-active fundamentals.   Measurements are necessarily made at low pressures, because BrF_5 strongly attacks the cell windows.   Nine Raman lines (684, 629, 569, 539, 480, 410, 365, 310, 241) were designated as fundamentals, strongly suggesting the C_{4v} square pyramid structure in preference to a trigonal bipyramid model.   The infrared spectra of liquid BrF_5 and liquid BrF_3 were reported by Haendler and co-workers.[62]   Only a limited region of the infrared was studied because of the extreme activity of the samples.   Three bands were located for both compounds: BrF_3– 1337, 1250, 1154 cm^{-1} and BrF_5–1355, 1298, 1187 cm^{-1}.   Another pentafluoride, PF_5, was studied by Pemsler and Planet.[63]   The data obtained suggest a trigonal bipyramid structure for the molecule.

Spectral studies on other fluorides [64-67] warrant citation but will not be discussed in detail here.   Fluorides of hydrogen and its isotopes will be treated at the end of this section with the corresponding compounds of the other halogens.

61. Burke, T. G., and Jones, E. A., *J. Chem. Phys.*, **19**, 1611 (1951).
62. Haendler, H. M., BuKata, S. W., Millard, B., Goodman, E. I., and Littman, J., *J. Chem. Phys.*, **22**, 1939 (1954).
63. Pemsler, J. P., and Planet, W. G., *J. Chem. Phys.*, **24**, 920 (1956).
64. Nielsen, A. H., and Jones, E. A., *J. Chem. Phys.*, **19**, 1117 (1951) ClF.
65. Edelson, D., *J. Am. Chem. Soc.*, **74**, 262 (1952) S_2F_{10}.
66. Gaunt, J., and Ainscough, J. B., *Spectrochim. Acta*, **10**, 57 (1957) SbF_5; *ibid.*, 52 NbF_5.
67. Jones, D. A., Jones, R. V., and Stevenson, R. W., *Proc. Phys. Soc. (London)*, **65B**, 906 (1952) LiF, CuF_2, CaF_2, CdF_2, SrF_2, PbF_2, BaF_2.

Chlorides, Bromides, and Iodides. The vibrational spectra of a number of inorganic halides were reviewed in the classic work of Herzberg. More recently, several articles containing theoretical discussions of the optical properties and lattice vibrations of alkali halides and other non-metallic crystals have appeared.[68] Infrared absorption information on the alkali halides was obtained indirectly through the use of their reflection spectra and the findings were analyzed by Lax and Burstein.[69] An explanation for the auxiliary bands appearing in the infrared absorption spectra of these compounds was proposed, on the assumption that an appreciable deformation of charge distribution exists about the atoms during their lattice vibration.

In the region of the fundamental vibration frequency, spectra for NaCl, NaBr, NaI, KCl, KBr, RbCl, and CsCl have been taken of the molten salts in an atmosphere of argon using optics of cesium bromide or iodide.[70] The calculated frequencies in cm^{-1} are: NaCl (366), NaBr (302), NaI (258), KCl (281), KBr (213), RbCl (228), CsCl (209). It was possible from the data obtained, along with other data on lithium halides, to extrapolate values for five other compounds: KI (173), RbBr (166), RbI (128), CsBr (139), CsI (101).

The polarized infrared spectrum of hydrated cupric chloride, $CuCl_2.2H_2O$, was investigated in an attempt to determine whether water is predominantly ionically or covalently bonded to the metal ions in such complex structures.[71] If the bonding is ionic, it would be expected that the water dipole would point toward the metal; if the bonding is covalent, approximately tetrahedral MOH angles would be anticipated. The polarized infrared spectral data favor the latter.

68. Dexter, D. L., "Theory of the Optical Properties of Imperfections in Nonmetals," p. 353ff. in "Solid State Physics," Vol. 6, F. Seitz and D. Turnbull, Editors, Academic Press, Inc., New York, 1958. See also references cited therein.
69. Lax, M., and Burstein, E., *Phys. Rev.*, **97**, 39 (1955).
70. Rice, S. A., and Klemperer, W., *J. Chem. Phys.*, **27**, 573 (1957).
71. Rundle, R. E., Nakamoto, K., and Richardson, J. W., *J. Chem. Phys.*, **23**, 2450 (1955).

Molecules of divalent metals and halogens have been investigated to some extent.	Klemperer and Lindeman [72] reported the frequency of the antisymmetric motion in gaseous mercuric chloride, bromide, and iodide.	These are linear symmetrical triatomic molecules for which knowledge of the three fundamental frequencies is sufficient to calculate the force constants.	The vibrational frequencies (in cm^{-1}) observed are: $HgCl_2$, ν_1 (360), ν_2 (70), ν_3 (413); $HgBr_2$, ν_1 (225), ν_2 (41), ν_3 (293); HgI_2, ν_1 (156), ν_2 (33).

Gaseous magnesium bromide and magnesium chloride have been examined spectrally at an elevated temperature of 1000° C.[73] Based on electron diffraction measurements these molecules are also linear and should exhibit two infrared-active fundamentals at frequency ν_3 for the antisymmetric stretching vibration and ν_2 for the bending vibration.	Only one absorption peak was observed for these halides and it has been ascribed to the antisymmetric stretching vibration.	Similar results were obtained with nickelous chloride at 850° C.

Halides of Hydrogen and Its Isotopes.	Rather extensive studies have centered around the hydrogen halides and their deuterium and tritium analogs.[74-86]	Many of the studies are concerned pri-

72. Klemperer, W., and Lindeman, L., *J. Chem. Phys.*, 25, 397 (1956).
73. Randall, S. P., Greene, F. T., and Margrave, J. L., *J. Phys. Chem.*, 63, 758 (1959).
74. Shelton, R. D., and Nielsen, A. H., *J. Chem. Phys.*, 19, 1312 (1951).
75. Coulon, R., *J. phys. radium*, 13, 371 (1952).
76. Mills, I. M., Thompson, H. W., and Williams, R. C., *Proc. Roy. Soc. (London)*, A218, 29 (1953).
77. Benesch, W., and Elder, T., *Phys. Rev.*, 91, 308 (1953).
78. Keller, F. L., and Nielsen, A. H., *J. Chem. Phys.*, 22, 294 (1954).
79. Hornig, D. F., and Osberg, W. E., *J. Chem. Phys.*, 23, 662 (1955).
80. Mayburg, R. H., Gordon, S., and Katz, J. J., *J. Chem. Phys.*, 23, 1277 (1955).
81. Palik, E. D., *J. Chem. Phys*, 23, 217 (1955).
82. Adams, R. M., and Katz, J. J., *J. Opt. Soc. Am.*, 46, 895 (1956).
83. Jones, L. H., and Robinson, E. S., *J. Chem. Phys.*, 24, 1246 (1956).
84. Van Horne, B. H., and Hause, C. D., *J. Chem. Phys.*, 25, 56 (1956).
85. Kuipers, G. A., Smith, D. F., and Nielsen, A. H., *J. Chem. Phys.*, 25, 275 (1956).
86. Hiebert, G. L., and Hornig, D. F., *J. Chem. Phys.*, 28, 1316 (1958).

marily with the evaluation and re-evaluation of data for the calculation of molecular constants. Others have been conducted for the purpose of explaining some rather interesting physical and chemical problems. The phenomenon of pressure broadening of absorption lines constitutes a major problem in infrared atmospheric transmission and in quantitative gas analysis in the infrared region. Some qualitative features of molecular interactions in pressure-broadening phenomena have been determined using HCl and CH_4 gases with He, Ne, A, Kr, Xe, SF_6, O_2, H_2, N_2, CO, CO_2, N_2O, SO_2, and HCl as broadeners.[77] The data seem to indicate (1) an interaction between the induced dipole of the broadener molecule and some undefined property of the absorbing gas regardless of the foreign gas used, and (2) an interaction between the quadrupole moment of the broadener and the dipole of the absorber when unsymmetrical foreign molecules were used to broaden the absorption lines of a polar molecule. The increased absorption in the infrared associated with the pressure-broadening effect has been used to calculate relative optical collision diameters.

The infrared absorption spectrum of hydrogen fluoride has been studied to gain information concerning the degree of polymerization under various conditions. The intensity of the 1025 cm^{-1} band increases with pressure to the extent that polymeric formation is undoubtedly the prevailing situation.[75] Examination of HF from $3000–4250 \text{ cm}^{-1}$ at temperature from $32–88°$ C, and pressures from atmospheric to vacuum give results that indicate only a few polymeric species, even under the optimum polymer formation conditions of low temperature and high pressure.[74]

Fundamental vibrations of hydrogen halide crystals at $-250°$ C were determined, to delineate the structures of the low-temperature phases present.[79] Both HCl and HBr were shown to form zigzag hydrogen-bonded chains, the angles between adjacent molecules being $107°$ and $97°$ for the HCl and HBr, respectively. Apparently HI has a different structure, but this was not conclusively determined. Mixed crystals of HCl and HBr at $63°$ K give rise to a spectrum which consists of a band characteristic of chains of similar molecules plus a line resulting from the end molecule in any chain.[86] This structure is repeated in the HCl and HBr regions. The fundamental frequency of HBr with the H bonded to HCl is higher than when it is bonded to another HBr molecule; and that of HCl is lower when the H is bonded to HBr than to another HCl.

The ionic crystalline monohydrates of the hydrogen halides have been investigated in the infrared region at −195° C. The spectra of OH_3F, OH_3Cl, OH_3Br, OH_3I, and OD_3Cl exhibit fundamental frequencies consistent with a symmetrical pyramidal structure[87] (Table 7).

TABLE 7.   FUNDAMENTAL FREQUENCIES (cm^{-1}) OF IONIC CRYSTALS
HYDROGEN HALIDE MONOHYDRATES

(After Ferriso and Hornig[87])

	OH_3F	OH_3Cl	OH_3Br	OH_3I	OD_3Cl
ν_1 or ν_3	3150	3235	3250	3350	2445
ν_2	1150	1150	1150	1160	785
ν_3 or ν_1	2468	2590	2610	2635	2000
ν_4	1705	1700	1705	1705	1255

Oxides

The classic work of Herzberg summarizes the earlier observations of the vibrational spectra of oxides and peroxides. Included among these are oxides of carbon, hydrogen, nitrogen, fluorine, and chlorine and hydrogen peroxide. No attempt will be made here to review these observations, except as necessary for discussion. Attention will be directed toward the more recent studies which have been conducted to gain further insight into the vibrational frequencies and structure of these and related molecules.

Compounds of Hydrogen and Its Isotopes. In addition to the spectra of water and deuterium oxide, infrared spectra of tritium oxide, THO, and TDO have been obtained.[88] Vapor-phase

87. Ferriso and Hornig, D. F., *J. Chem. Phys.*, **23**, 1464 (1955).
88. Staats, P. A., Morgan, H. W., and Goldstein, J. H., *J. Chem. Phys.*, **24**, 916 (1956).

studies in the 700–7000 cm^{-1} region yield the following assignments: T$_2$O: ν_2–1017.2 cm^{-1}, ν_3–2438 ± 5 cm^{-1}; THO: ν_2–1358.8 cm^{-1}, ν_3–3895 ± 10 cm^{-1}; TDO: ν_3–2829 ± 5 cm^{-1}. The values given are observed frequency plus the anharmonicity correction, and are in agreement with calculated values of ω except for ν_2 of THO, the calculated value of which was found to be 16 cm^{-1} higher than the value given here. This discrepancy was not explained and is greater than the estimated error in locating the center of the band.

The matrix isolation technique has been used to study the hydrogen bonding of water. The technique warrants some discussion. It generally consists of the dispersion of a chemically reactive material in a large amount of inert solid substance, the matrix, at a temperature sufficiently low to retard or prevent molecular diffusion of the sample. A glass or crystalline solid of suitable inertness, rigidity, transparency, and volatility can serve as the matrix. Theoretically, any molecule which is difficult to prepare because of its high reactivity or is unstable under the more conventional means may be handled in this way. The method has been tested using the free radical NO$_2$, and the hydrogen bonding molecules—HBr, HCN, HN$_3$, NH$_3$, and H$_2$O—with nitrogen, argon, and xenon as matrices at 20° K.[89] The vibrational frequencies obtained when these molecules are isolated in the matrix in molar ratios of inactive to active material ranging from 100:1 to 500:1 are essentially the same as the frequencies in the gas phase. Using nitrogen at 20° K as a matrix, the stretching and bending modes of the hydrogen-bonded polymers of water were studied by Thiel, Becker, and Pimental.[90] Absorption frequencies for the monomers are 3725, 3627, 1600 cm^{-1}; for the dimers, 3691, 3546, 1620 cm^{-1}; and for the higher polymers, 3510, 3355, 3318, 3222, and 1633 cm^{-1}. The three possible structures of the dimeric molecule are as shown:

89. Becker, E. D., and Pimentel, G. C., *J. Chem. Phys.*, **25**, 224 (1956).
90. Thiel, M. V., Becker, E. C., and Pimentel, G. C., *J. Chem. Phys.*, **27**, 486 (1957).

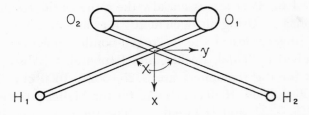

| *open* | *cyclic* | *bifurcated* |

The observed frequencies agree with the cyclic structure for the dimer rather than the open or bifurcated configuration. A slight decrease in the absorption coefficients of the bending modes was noted in the higher polymers, while an increase by a factor of about twelve was observed in the stretching modes. This intensity can hardly be explained on the basis of the enhanced ionic character of the O—H group only, and thus lends support to the currently accepted assumption of linearity of the H—bond.

Hirota[91] has studied the rotational structure of the infrared absorption spectrum of hydrogen peroxide vapor. The H_2O_2 molecule is known to have C_2 symmetry. Its vibrational motions are (1) a symmetric O—H stretch, a symmetric H—O—O deformation, and an O—O stretch of class A except for internal rotation and (2) an antisymmetric O—H stretch and an antisymmetric H—O—O deformation of class B. The internal rotation of H_2O_2 was treated on the assumption that its potential energy can be approximated by a Fourier expansion. Considering the H_2O_2 molecule to have the structure:

with the z axis chosen through the centers of mass of two OH bonds, and with χ the angle between the projections of these bonds on the plane perpendicular to the z axis, then using the two-

91. Hirota, E., *J. Chem. Phys.*, **28**, 839 (1958).

term Fourier expansion: $V = (V_1/2)(1+\cos\chi) \div (V_2/2)(1+\cos 2\chi)$, and data obtained from infrared and microwave spectra, Hirota calculated values for V_1 and V_2. These values were respectively 244 cm^{-1} (700 cal/mole) and 319 cm^{-1} (910 cal/mole). The doublet structure of the infrared absorption spectrum was attributed to the existence of a double minimum in the hindering potential, V. The height of the potential barrier for the *cis*-configuration was definitely greater than that for the *trans*-configuration.

Spectra of air in the region 400–5000 cm^{-1} have been obtained with varying conditions of pressure, temperature, and concentration of carbon dioxide and water.[92] New lines originating from levels of high energy were observed in the pure rotation spectrum and the ν_2 vibrational region of water and in the 2000 cm^{-1} and 500–909 cm^{-1} region of the absorption spectrum of carbon dioxide. The observations were made with a high resolution spectrometer and represented the first attempt to study superheated steam under such resolution.

Oxides of Carbon. A number of studies have been made on carbon monoxide and carbon dioxide. The purposes of these have been largely (1) to determine molecular constants,[93-95] (2) to investigate absorption after thermal excitation,[96] (3) to study spectra of the chemisorbed oxide,[97-98] and (4) to measure quantitatively infrared intensities of the pressurized and unpressurized gases.[99] The Raman spectra and the infrared spectra of carbon

92. Taylor, J. H., Benedict, W. S., and Strong, J., *J. Chem. Phys.*, **20**, 1884 (1952).
93. Rossman, K., Rao, K. N., and Nielsen, H. H., *J. Chem. Phys.*, **24**, 103 (1956).
94. Nielsen, A. H., and Lagemann, R. T., *J. Chem. Phys.*, **22**, 36 (1954).
95. Rossman, K., France, W. L., Rao, K. N., and Nielsen, H. H., *J. Chem. Phys.*, **24**, 1007 (1956).
96. Tourin, R. H., *J. Chem. Phys.*, **20**, 1651 (1952).
97. Yang, A. C., and Garland, C. W., *J. Phys. Chem.*, **61**, 1504 (1957).
98. Eischens, R. P., Pliskin, W. A., and Francis, S. A., *J. Chem. Phys.*, **22**, 1986 (1954).
99. Renner, S. S., and Weber, D., *J. Chem. Phys.*, **19**, 807, 817, 1351 (1951).

suboxide have been reported independently by Rix[100] and Long.[101]

Oxides of Nitrogen.   Perhaps the most widely studied oxides are those of nitrogen.   These oxides are difficult to prepare in pure form free from water and other nitrogen oxides.   However, their interesting chemical and physical behavior has led to extensive investigation of their molecular structures.   Bands suitable for analytical purposes have been found in the 650–2500 cm^{-1} range for many of these compounds.   The spectrum of N_2O_5 has been recorded with a fast-scanning spectrometer.[102]   A strong band was observed at 1240 cm^{-1} and another band at 1315 cm^{-1}.   Initially the band at 1315 cm^{-1} was weak while the 1240 cm^{-1} band was intense.   As the scanning was continued the 1315 cm^{-1} band became more intense, while the 1240 cm^{-1} band diminished in intensity.   This is strong indication that the 1315 cm^{-1} band is that of HNO_3 formed by interaction of the N_2O_5 molecule with water.

Nitric oxide is a particularly interesting compound, being a stable diatomic molecule possessing an unpaired electron.   The lowest electronic configuration for the molecule gives a $^2\Pi$ state as ground state.   The components of the ground state are only slightly separated, giving rise to a unique infrared spectrum. Fletcher and Begun[103] observed the fundamental vibration of $N^{15}O$ (1760–1920 cm^{-1}) under high resolution and calculated molecular constants which were in good agreement with those obtained by earlier studies.   They also observed the spectra of the isotopic N_2O molecules: $N^{14} N^{15} O^{16}$, $N^{15} N^{14} O^{16}$, and $N^{15} N^{15} O^{16}$ in the 500–4000 cm^{-1} region.[104]   Frequencies of three fundamental bands and fifteen overtone and combination bands were tabulated.   Approximate zero-order frequencies were calculated for

100. Rix, H. D., *J. Chem. Phys.*, **22**, 429 (1954).
101. Long, D. A., Murfin, F. S., and Williams, R. C., *Proc. Roy. Soc. (London)*, **A223**, 251 (1954).
102. Nightingale, R. E., Downie, A. R., Rotenberg, D. C., Crawford, B. C., and Ogg, R. A., *J. Phys. Chem.*, **58**, 1047 (1954).   (See also literature citations therein.)
103. Fletcher, W. H., and Begun, G. M., *J. Chem. Phys.*, **27**, 579 (1957).
104. Begun, G. M., and Fletcher, W. H., *J. Chem. Phys.*, **28**, 414 (1958).

the isotopic molecules, using known anharmonic constants and isotopic relations. Table 8 shows the agreement between observed and calculated values.

TABLE 8. ZERO-ORDER FREQUENCIES (cm^{-1}) OF ISOTOPIC NITROUS
OXIDE MOLECULES

(After Begun and Fletcher [104])

$N_2^{14}O$		$N^{14}N^{15}O$		$N^{15}N^{14}O$		$N_2^{15}O$	
Obs.	Calc.	Obs.	Calc.	Obs.	Calc.	Obs.	Calc.
1300.3	1299.7	1295.6	1298.5	1285.1	1281.4	1280.3	1280.6
596.5	596.5	582.8	582.8	593.2	592.9	578.9	579.2
2276.9	2277.0	2228.6	2226.9	2254.5	2256.7	2206.3	2205.9

Oxides of Halogens and Sulfur. The absorption spectra of ClO, BrO, and IO were observed by Durie and Ramsay [105] during photolysis of mixtures of chlorine, bromine, or iodine with oxygen. Nielsen and Woltz [106] have interpreted the spectrum of ClO_2 in the 250–5000 cm^{-1} region as follows: polymer band–290 cm^{-1}; ν_1–943.2 cm^{-1}; ν_2–455 cm^{-1}; ν_3–1110.5 cm^{-1}. The ν_2 bending mode at 455 cm^{-1} has the doublet character required if the molecular model is to be an obtuse triangle, as suggested by electron diffraction measurements. The band at 290 cm^{-1} was difficult to assign, but the suggestion was made that it may be ascribed to a polymeric form of ClO_2.

The dioxide of sulfur at 95° K has crystal structure C_{2v}^{17} with two molecules per unit cell (orthorhombic). In such a structure the SO_2 each occupy sites of C_2 symmetry. The fundamental vibrations, ν_1 (a_1) and ν_2 (a_1), yield one infrared active component, while the b_1 fundamental, ν_3, is split into two components by the crystalline field, both of these components being infrared-active. Wiener and Nixon [107] measured the infrared transmission of solid SO_2 at

105. Durie, R. A., and Ramsay, D. A., *Can. J. Phys.*, **36**, 35 (1958).
106. Nielsen, A. H., and Woltz, P. J. H., *J. Chem. Phys.*, **20**, 1878 (1952).
107. Wiener, R. N., and Nixon, E. R., *J. Chem. Phys.*, **25**, 175 (1956).

93° K. Spectral studies performed by Giguere and Falk[108] are in agreement (Table 9).

TABLE 9. INFRARED ABSORPTION FREQUENCIES OF SULFUR DIOXIDE (cm^{-1})

Assignment	Gaseous* SO_2	Solid SO_2 (Wiener and Nixon)	Solid SO_2 (Giguere and Falk)
ν_2, bending	518	521	528–35 (doublet)
$\nu_1 - \nu'$		1142	
ν_1, symmetric stretch	1151	1147	1144
$\nu_3 - \nu''$		1316	
ν_3, asymmetric stretch	1361	1308⎱ doublet 1330⎰	1310–22 (doublet)
$\nu_1 + \nu_3$		2460⎱ doublet 2436⎰	2455

* Polo, S. R., and Wilson, M. K., *J. Chem. Phys.*, 22, 900 (1954).

An interesting study of the absorption of SO_2 and CO_2 in aqueous solution was made by Jones and McLaren.[109] Solutions were prepared by bubbling the gas through water at room temperature. The infrared and Raman spectra show that in the aqueous phase, SO_2 is present mostly as SO_2 rather than as H_2SO_3. This is consistent with data obtained by conductance and vapor pressure measurements and from ultraviolet absorption data. The results obtained are as shown below with comparable data from Herzberg on the gas phase. (After Jones and McLaren.[109])

		Aqueous	Gaseous
SO_2	ν_3	1332 cm^{-1}	1361 cm^{-1}
	ν_1	1157	1151
CO_2	ν_3	2342	2349

108. Giguere, P. A, and Falk, M., *Can. J. Chem.*, 34, 1833 (1956).
109. Jones, L. H., and McLaren, E., *J. Chem. Phys.*, 28, 995 (1958).

The frequency shift for CO_2 is not appreciable; however, for SO_2 the shift from gaseous to aqueous phase is 29 cm^{-1}. Carbon dioxide, a linear, symmetric molecule, having no dipole moment, will not interact as strongly with water as will SO_2, which is a nonlinear, symmetric molecule with a dipole moment. This is actually manifested in the observed difference in magnitude of the v_3 shift in the two molecules.

Oxygen Compounds of Metals. The infrared spectra of Li_2O_2, $Li_2O_2 \cdot 8H_2O$, Na_2O_2, $Na_2O_2 \cdot 8H_2O$, $Na_2O_2 \cdot 8D_2O$, NaO_2, KO_2, $CaO_2 \cdot 8H_2O$, SrO_2, and BaO_2 were obtained by Brame and co-workers [110] in order to search for a possible existence of the O_3^- ion as well as to investigate the peroxide and peroxide hydrate structures. No characteristic sharp bands were observed for peroxide, O_2^{-2}, or superoxide, O_2^{-1}. This is consistent with the theory that both ions are homopolar and consequently have no infrared-active vibrations. There were no absorption bands attributable to the O_3^{-2} ion. Similarly, Giguere and Harvey [111] were unable to show any evidence of discrete O_3^{-2} ions in the infrared spectrum of K_2O_3.

Brame and his co-workers [112] were able to locate at least one strong absorption band in each of four oxide samples investigated. This band, observed in B_2O_3, Al_2O_3, Cr_2O_3, and Ga_2O_3, was probably due to a metal-oxygen vibration, the band shifting to longer wavelengths with increase of mass in the series.

The infrared spectrum of osmium tetroxide, OsO_4, has been obtained under conditions of its own vapor pressure and temperatures up to about 130° C.[113] Four bands—$v_1(a_1)$ 971 cm^{-1}*; $v_2(e)$ 328 cm^{-1}; $v_3(f_2)$ 959.7 cm^{-1}; and $v_4(f_2)$ 328 cm^{-1}—were positively attributed to OsO_4. It was assumed that the molecular

110. Brame, E. C., Cohen, S., Margrave, J. L., and Meloche, V. W., *J. Inorg. and Nucl. Chem.*, **4**, 90 (1957).
111. Giguere, P. A., and Harvey, K. B., *J. Am. Chem. Soc.*, **76**, 5891 (1954).
112. Brame, E. G., Margrave, J. C., and Meloche, V. W., *J. Inorg. Nucl. Chem.*, **5**, 48 (1957).
113. Hawkins, N. J., and Sabol, W. W., *J. Chem. Phys.*, **25**, 775 (1956).

* Data of Langseth and Quiller, Z. *Physik. Chem.*, **B27**, 79 (1934).

model is an XY_4 model of T_d point group symmetry. If this is the proper model, one would expect to find in the 660–580 cm^{-1} region the overtone band, $2\nu_4$, the combination band, $\nu_2 + \nu_4$, and the difference bands involving the stretching frequency less the deformation frequency. The spectrum obtained was quite simple, having the two stretching vibrations, ν_1 and ν_3, of almost equal values and the two deformations, ν_2 and ν_4, of equal value and containing none of the overtone or combination bands.

Other Binary Compounds

The infrared spectra of gaseous hydrogen sulfide, H_2S, and the deuterated species, HDS and D_2S, have been studied under high resolution in a number of regions. The reader is referred to the original works and the references cited therein.[114-121] The H_2S, HDS, and D_2S molecules have spectra which are similar to those obtained for the corresponding oxygen analogs. Actually, the Group VI elements O, S, Se, and Te form with hydrogen a series of asymmetric top molecules with interesting spectral similarities. Hydrogen selenide, when examined in the far infrared, exhibits bands suggesting that the molecule is an almost accidentally symmetric rotor with apex angle $2\alpha \approx 90°$ and $a \approx b \approx 2c$, where a, b, and c are reciprocals of the moments of inertia.[122]

114. Allen, H. C., and Plyler, E. K., *J. Research Natl. Bur. Standards*, 52, 205 (1954) H_2S (6290 cm^{-1}); *J. Chem. Phys.*, 22, 1104 (1954) H_2S (5100 cm^{-1}); *J. Chem. Phys.*, 25, 1132 (1956) H_2S (1250 cm^{-1}).
115. Innes, K. K., Cross, P. C., and Bair, E. J., *J. Chem. Phys.*, 21, 545 (1953) H_2S (8700 cm^{-1}) and (11000 cm^{-1}).
116. McCubbin, T. K., *J. Chem. Phys.*, 20, 668 (1952) H_2S (100–143 cm^{-1}).
117. Allen, H. C., Blaine, C. R., Plyler, E. K., and Cross, P. C., *J. Chem. Phys.*, 24, 35 (1956) H_2S (2200–2800 cm^{-1}).
118. Ordway, G. L., Cross, P. C., and Bair, E. J., *J. Chem. Phys.*, 23, 541 (1955) H_2S (7480–7880 cm^{-1}).
119. Savage, C. M., and Edwards, T. H., *J. Chem. Phys.*, 27, 179 (1957) H_2S (3846 cm^{-1}).
120. Crosby, G., Bair, E. J., and Cross, P. C., *J. Chem. Phys.*, 23, 1660 (1955) HDS (6140 cm^{-1}).
121. Allen, H. C., Plyler, E. K., and Blaine, L. R., *J. Research Nat'l. Bur. Standards*, 59, 211 (1957) D_2S (2000 cm^{-1} and 2778 cm^{-1}).
122. Palik, E. D., *J. Chem. Phys.*, 23, 980 (1955).

The most nearly symmetric member of the entire series is hydrogen telluride, H_2Te. The particular chemical instability of the gas presents experimental difficulties in obtaining its high resolution spectrum. However, Rossmann and Straley[123] have succeeded in stabilizing it for a long enough period to obtain spectra and data sufficient to calculate molecular constants. They identified two overlapping fundamentals, ν_1 and ν_3, extending from 1800–2200 cm^{-1} and a fundamental ν_2 centering at about 870 cm^{-1}. The angle H-Te-H was reported as 89°30' with H-Te distance equal to 1.7×10^{-8} cm, $I_A = I_B = 4.6 \times 10^{-40}$ g cm^2 and $I_c = 9.2 \times 10^{-40}$ g cm^2.

The infrared spectra of H_2S in phases III, II, and I have been studied at 66°K, 112°K, and 140°K, respectively, and that of D_2S in phase III at 66°K.[124] Extremely sharp lines were observed in the spectra of phase III, suggesting an ordered structure which presumably consisted of eight molecules in a primitive unit cell of D_{4h} symmetry. Broader bands, indicating disordered arrangement of the hydrogen atoms, were noted in phases II and I. The three phases are related as shown below:

Phase III 103.6°K Phase II 126.2°K Phase I 187.6°K
(H_2S or   (H_2S) ——————→   (H_2S) ——————→ melt
D_2S)   107.8°K Phase II 132.8°K Phase I 187.1°K
                          (D_2S) ——————→   (D_2S) ——————→ melt

From the spectra of the crystalline form it was concluded that the fundamental frequencies of gaseous D_2S must be very nearly 855 cm^{-1} for ν_2 and 1910 cm^{-1} for ν_3. Examination with a polarizing microscope showed phase III to be anisotropic, while phases II and I are perhaps isotropic.

XH₃ Molecules. Molecules of the type XH_3, where X is N, As, P, or Sb and H is hydrogen or deuterium, have been examined in

123. Rossmann, K., and Straley, J. W., *J. Chem. Phys.*, **24**, 1276 (1956).
124. Reding, F. P., and Hornig, D. F., *J. Chem. Phys.*, **27**, 1024 (1957).

the infrared region to some extent.[125-128]   The ammonia molecule, NH_3, is a symmetrical pyramidal structure of point group C_{3v} and, as such, has two totally symmetric a fundamentals and two doubly degenerate e fundamentals.   All are active in the infrared and Raman.   Infrared absorption spectra of ammonia containing equimolar proportions of deuterium and hydrogen seem to indicate a disproportionation.   The infrared region seems particularly suitable to determine the molecular species arising from partial deuteration of ammonia.   The 700–1000 cm^{-1} region contains only one fundamental vibrational mode for NH_3 and ND_3.   The intensities are strong and the only other observations in this region are the relatively much weaker rotational components.   Arsine, AsH_3, has band structure in the region 857–1130 cm^{-1}.   Phosphine, PH_3, has two fundamentals, ν_1, and ν_3, which lie near 2381 cm^{-1}. The four fundamentals of stibine, SbH_3, and the two high-frequency fundamentals of deutero-stibine have been observed and sufficient analysis made to determine the size and shape of the molecule and to correct the band centers for anharmonicity and thus indicate the normal frequencies of the molecule with a reasonable degree of accuracy (Table 10).

TABLE 10.   FUNDAMENTAL BANDS OF XY_3 MOLECULES (cm^{-1})

	NH_3[a]	ND_3[a]	PH_3[b]	SbH_3[c]	SbD_3[c]		SbH_3[c]	SbD_3[c]
ν_1	3335.9	2419	2322.9	1890.9	1358.8	ω_1	1988.9	1409.4
	3337.5							
ν_2	931.58	748.6	992.0	781.5	561.1	ω_2	795.9	568.5
	968.08	749.0						
ν_3	3414	2555	2327.7	1894.2	1362.0	ω_3	1974.5	1403.5
ν_4	1627.5	1191.0	1122.4	830.9	592.5	ω_4	844.7	599.5

[a] Herzberg; [b] (127); [c] (128).

125. Stedman, D. F., *J. Chem. Phys.*, **20**, 718 (1952) (NH_3–ND).
126. Nielsen, H. H., *Discussions Faraday Soc.*, No. 9, 85 (1950) AsH_3.
127. McConaghie, V. M., and Nielsen, H. H., *J. Chem. Phys.*, **21**, 1836 (1953) PH_3.
128. Haynie, W. H., and Nielsen, H. H., *J. Chem. Phys.*, **21**, 1839 (1953) SbH_3 + SbD_3.

XN₃ Molecules. The infrared spectra of gaseous and solid hydrazoic acid, HN₃, and deuterohydroazoic acid, DN₃, have been investigated by Dows and Pimentel.[129] In the solid state of both species, hydrogen bonding was manifested through frequency shifts of the N—H and N—D stretching vibrations, 216 and 151 cm⁻¹, respectively. In carbon tetrachloride solutions of HN₃ up to 0.3M, hydrogen bonding was not evident. The structure of HN₃ is known from data obtained from infrared and microwave studies.[130] An angle of 112° exists between the N—H bond and the three colinear nitrogen atoms,

The molecule has C$_s$ symmetry with five in-plane vibrations (type a′) and one out-of-plane vibration (type a′′), all of which are active in both infrared and Raman. The molecule approaches the symmetric top model and, if treated as such, one might expect the out-of-plane vibration to be a perpendicular band and the in-plane vibrations to be hybrids of superimposed parallel and perpendicular bands. The parallel bands should be similar to those of a linear molecule, i.e., the Q branch should be weak. Calculations of the separations of the P and R branch maxima indicate 26 cm⁻¹ for both HN₃ and DN₃, while the Q branch separation of the perpendicular bands should be 36 cm⁻¹ apart for HN₃ and 22 cm⁻¹ apart for DN₃. Table 11 shows the frequencies observed for gaseous and solid states of HN₃ and DN₃. (On warming solid hydrazoic acid, an irreversible phase transition occurs above about 120°K.)

Upon substitution with deuterium, the ν_3 fundamental acquires more of a bending motion. The combination band $\nu_3 + \nu_4$ is not appreciably affected and is observed both in HN₃ and DN₃; however, the first overtone of ν_4 is observed only in HN₃ and that of ν_3 observed only in DN₃. Hydrogen bonding is suggested from the following observations in going from the gaseous to the solid

129. Dows, D. A., and Pimentel, G. C., *J. Chem. Phys.*, **23**, 1258 (1955).
130. Amble, E., and Dailey, B. P., *J. Chem. Phys.*, **18**, 1422 (1950).

TABLE 11.   FREQUENCIES OF GASEOUS AND SOLID HN_3 AND DN_3

(After Dows and Pimentel [129])

Assignment	$HN_3(g)$	$HN_3(SII)$	$HN_3(SI)$	$DN_3(g)$	$DN_3(SII)$	$DN_3(SI)$
ν_1	3336 m	3120 vs	3090	2480 m	2329 s	2308
$\nu_2 + \nu_4$	3250 w	3305 w				
$2\nu_3$				2358 m	2442 m	2412
$\nu_2 + \nu_7$		2435 w			2380 w	
$\nu_3 + \nu_4$	2402 m	2402 m		2170 w	2202 w	
$2\nu_4$	2304 s	2298 w	2349			
ν_2	2140 vs	2169 vs	2162	2141 vs	2165 vs	2155
ν_3	1274 m	1280 m	1299	1183 m	1229 m	1230
ν_4	1150 vs	1182 s	1180	955 s	958 s	977
$\nu_2 - \nu_4$	950 vw					
ν_6	672 w			638 w		
ν_5	522 w			498 w		
ν_7		266 (?)			215 (?)	

states: (1) bands associated with N—H and N—D stretching modes shift to lower frequencies and are more intense relative to other bands, and (2) all fundamentals ν_1, ν_2, ν_3, and ν_4 shift to higher frequencies.

Gray and Waddington [131] have observed the fundamental vibrational frequencies of the azide ion, N_3^-, with various cations: Li, Na, K, Rb, Cs, Ca, Sr, and Ba. The symmetric stretching vibration, ν_1, and the first overtone of the ν_2 deformation mode were observed in the Raman, while the fundamental ν_2 and the asymmetric stretching frequency, ν_3, were observed in the infrared. The ν_1 symmetrical stretching frequency for the compounds containing monovalent cations decreased from 1368.7 cm^{-1} for lithium to 1328.6 cm^{-1} for cesium. For the divalent cations the range was 1380.5 cm^{-1} for calcium to 1354.4 cm^{-1} for barium. The values ν_2 and ν_3 for the entire series of compounds were 642 ± 8 cm^{-1} and $2076 \pm$ cm^{-1}, respectively. Ammonium azide, which has been studied in some detail by Dows and co-workers,[132]

131. Gray, P., and Waddington, T. C., *Trans. Faraday Soc.*, **53**, 901 (1957).
132. Dows, D. A., Whittle, E., and Pimentel, G. C., *J. Chem. Phys.*, **23**, 1475 (1955).

has the values: v_1–1345 cm^{-1}, v_2–661 (650) cm^{-1}, and v_3–2041 cm^{-1}. An additional assignment of a combination band in NH_4N_3 at 1830 cm^{-1} has thrown some light on the question of the free rotation of the ammonium ion in the solid state. The behavior of the ammonium ion in a lattice has received considerable attention. Studies made with solid NH_4Cl and NH_4Br suggest that the ion does not undergo free rotation in the lattice.[133] On the other hand, studies with NH_4I indicate a temperature-dependent, one-dimensional free rotation between the two ions.[134]

On the basis of proton magnetic resonance studies, the ammonium ion is hindered with respect to rotation in solids.[135] Dows *et al.*[132] investigated the ammonium azide molecule in an attempt to gain an understanding of the contrasting behavior already reported for the ammonium halides. The crystal structure of ammonium azide, NH_4N_3, at room temperature is D_{2h}^7 with four molecules per unit cell. Four azide ions surround each ammonium ion at approximately tetrahedral angles. Two slightly different distances (2.94Å and 2.99Å) exist between the nitrogen atom of each ammonium ion and the nearest nitrogen atoms of the four neighboring azide ions. The ammonium ion has site symmetry C_2. According to the site group approximation, nine nondegenerate infrared and Raman-active vibrations are expected. The linear, symmetric azide ions are equally distributed between two sets of C_{2h} symmetry sites. Both sets give equivalent results; however, the frequencies for the two kinds of azides are not necessarily identical. In the approximation, four nondegenerate vibrations are allowed: two arising from the degenerate bending mode of the hypothetical free azide ion, one active only in the Raman, and one active only in the infrared. A torsional motion of the ammonium ion, v_6(420 ± 20 cm^{-1}), shows that it does not rotate freely in crystalline NH_4N_3. A combination band at 1830 cm^{-1}, involving v_6 and v_4, the NH bending mode, was also assigned. The relative magnitudes of the frequencies of these torsional modes of NH_4^+ are consistent, at least qualitatively, with the hydrogen bond ener-

133. Wagner, E. L., and Hornig, D. F., *J. Chem. Phys.*, **18**, 305 (1950).
134. Plumb, R. C., and Hornig, D. F., *J. Chem. Phys.*, **21**, 366 (1953).
135. Gutowsky, H. S., Pake, and Bersohn, *J. Chem. Phys.*, **22**, 643 (1954).

gies inferred from frequencies of the N—H stretching modes in ammonium azide, chloride, and bromide.

The technique of infrared spectroscopy has been used further to study the species formed in the glow-discharge decomposition of hydrazoic acid, HN_3, when the products are allowed to condense on a surface cooled to $90°K$.[136] Spectra were taken at several temperatures up to $230°K$, and absorption bands attributable to HN_3, NH_4N_3, NH_3 and two intermediates were observed. The intermediate species were assumed to be N_2H_2 and $(NH)_x$, where x may be as high as 4.

Other Binary Nitrogen Compounds. The hydrazine molecule, N_2H_4, has been examined in the infrared from $400-6667$ cm^{-1}. The spectra of the liquid and of the solid at $-70°C$ were observed. The symmetry of the molecule is C_2 and one expects twelve non-degenerate fundamental modes: four N—H stretching vibrations, six N—H deformation vibrations, an N—N stretching mode, and a torsional oscillatory mode. The identification and assignment of vibrational bands were not complete because of extensive overlapping in the observed spectra.

The molecule N_4S_4 has been studied in sufficient detail to make complete assignment of the frequencies of its normal vibrational modes.[137] The data were analyzed in terms of several proposed structures and were found to be consistent with a cage structure of D_{2d} symmetry. Force constants were calculated for the N—S bond stretch, and the N—N bond stretch, the N—N—S angle bend, the N—N bond to N—N bond, the N—S bond to N—S bond, and the N—N—S angle to N—N—S angle.

XH₄ Molecules. Molecules and ions of this type where X is C, Si, Ge, N, P, or Al and H is hydrogen and/or its isotopes have been examined in the infrared region by several investigators.[138-140] Some of the observed frequencies are tabulated in Table 12.

136. Dows, D. A., Pimentel, G. C., and Whittle, E., *J. Chem. Phys.*, **23**, 1606 (1955).
137. Lippincott, E. R., and Tobin, M. C., *J. Chem. Phys.*, **21**, 1559 (1953).
138. Meal, J. H., and Wilson, M. K., *J. Chem. Phys.*, **24**, 385 (1956).
139. Pistorius, C. W. F. T., *J. Chem. Phys.*, **27**, 965 (1957).
140. Morgan, H. W., Staats, P. A., and Goldstein, J. H., *J. Chem. Phys.*, **27**, 1212 (1957).

TABLE 12. SOME OBSERVED FREQUENCIES (cm^{-1}) OF XH$_4$ TYPE MOLECULES AND IONS

	Symmetry	$\nu_1(a_1)$	$\nu_2(e)$	$\nu_3(f_2)$	$\nu_4(f_2)$
CH$_4$[a]	T$_d$	2914.2	1520	3020	1305
CD$_4$[a]	T$_d$	2084.7	1075	2259.3	995.86
SiH$_4$[a]	T$_d$	2180	970	2183	910
SiH$_4$[b]	T$_d$	2187	974.6	2190.6	914.2
SiD$_4$[b]	T$_d$	1545	689	1597	681
GeH$_4$[a]	T$_d$	1990	833	2110	933
NH$_4^+$[a]	T$_d$	3040	1680	3145	1400
NH$_4^+$[c]	T$_d$		1649	3146	1404
ND$_4^+$[a]	T$_d$	2214	1215	2346	1065
ND$_4^+$[c]	T$_d$		1186	2350	1066
NT$_4^+$[c]	T$_d$		976	2022	913
NHT$_3^+$[c]				3084 (?)	1345 (?)
NDT$_3^+$[c]				2319 (?)	
PH$_4^+$[a]	T$_d$	2304	1040	2370	930
AlH$_4^-$[a]	T$_d$	1790	799	1741	769
SiHD$_3$[b]	C$_{3v}$	1573	683	2182(a$_1$)	851(e)
				1598(e)	683(a$_1$)
SiH$_2$D$_2$	C$_{2v}$	1587	944(a$_1$)	2189(a$_1$)	862(b$_1$)
			844(a$_2$)	2183(b$_2$)	743(b$_2$)
				1601(b$_1$)	682.5(a$_1$)

[a] (139)   [b] (138)   [c] (140)

Note: For the structures of symmetry type other than T$_d$, the species representation, wherever it differs from that of T$_d$, is indicated parenthetically to the right of the observed frequency.

Digermane and Disilane. These two compounds, Ge$_2$H$_6$ and Si$_2$H$_6$, are analogous to ethane, C$_2$H$_6$. A knowledge of their molecular structures and intermolecular forces would contribute to the understanding of the chemistry of germanium and silicon compounds, just as knowledge of ethane structure has to the chemistry of carbon compounds. The spectrum of gaseous Si$_2$H$_6$ was observed in the 350–4000 cm^{-1} region [141] and that of gaseous and solid Ge$_2$H$_6$ observed in the 400–4000 cm^{-1} region.[142] Like ethane, one expects the structure of these molecules to be D$_{3h}$ or D$_{3d}$ (or

141. Gutowsky, H. S., and Stejskal, E. O., *J. Chem. Phys.*, **22**, 939 (1954).
142. Dows, D. A., and Hexter, R. M., *J. Chem. Phys.*, **24**, 1029 (1956).

free rotation about the Si—Si or Ge—Ge axis). Four of the five infrared-active fundamentals of disilane were observed and assigned: $\nu_5 - 2154.4$ cm^{-1}, $\nu_6 - 842.7$ cm^{-1} (both parallel bands) and $\nu_7 - 2181.1$ cm^{-1}, $\nu_8 - 945.7$ cm^{-1} (both perpendicular bands). The infrared fundamentals of gaseous digermane are: $a_{2u} - 2078, 755$, $e_u - 2114, 898, 407$ cm^{-1}; $a_{1u} - 144$ cm^{-1}; $a_{1g} - 2070, 765, 229$ cm^{-1}; and $e_g - 2150, 875, 417$ cm^{-1}. The solid spectrum at 90°K showed only the fundamentals active in the gas phase.

Binary Intermetallic Compounds. The binary intermetallic compounds of interest are those which have been studied primarily with reference to their electrical properties. Absorption processes are generally more easily interpreted and understood than are the electrical properties of these materials. Consequently, increasing emphasis is being placed on the study of infrared absorption of intermetallics. A number of review articles [143] and books [38, 39, 44] cover the work already published in this field. Blunt, Frederikse, and Hosler [144] have investigated n and p-type magnesium stannide, Mg_2Sn, between 2 and 15μ. Both n and p-type show a relatively strong absorption with a maximum at approximately 1333 cm^{-1} at room temperature (300°K). The room-temperature absorption is much larger than absorption at low temperature due to the high concentration of intrinsic carriers ($\sim 4 \times 10^{17}$ cm^{-3}). For p-type samples, no absorption band was found in any of the low temperature spectral curves; however, a faint absorption was still observable in the n-type samples at 85°K and 5°K. The value of the energy gap, obtained by extrapolating the absorption edge to $\alpha = 0$, is ~ 0.22 ev at 300°K, 0.30 ev at 85°K, and 0.33 ev at 5°K. Electrical measurements give a value of 0.33 ev at 0°K. The value deduced from photoconductivity threshold 2381 cm^{-1} is about 0.03 ev lower.

143. Hrostowski, H. J., "Infrared Absorption of Semiconductors," Chapter 10 in Semiconductors, N. B. Hannay, Editor, Reinhold Publishing Corporation, New York, 1959.

144. Blunt, R. F., Frederikse, H. P. R., and Hosler, W. R., *Phys. Rev.*, **100**, 663 (1955).

The Group III-Group IV [145-149] and Group III-Group VI [150] compounds have been studied by a number of investigators, with the result that, at least for some of the structures, important correlations between absorption and band structure exist. The IIIB–VB compounds (InSb, GaSb, and AlSb) have the zincblende structure, equivalent to the diamond structure when the two components are the same. Indium antimonide has a small forbidden energy gap and high electron mobility. Between 3333 and 1429 cm^{-1} the absorption edge changes from sample to sample [147, 151, 152] in both n and p-types. The absorption edge shift with temperature is greater for n-type samples than for p-type.

Samples of p- and n-type gallium antimonide [149] and aluminum antimonide [148] do not show the anomalous absorption edge change from sample to sample observed with indium antimonide. For GaSb, the absorption edge occurs at approximately 5556–6667 cm^{-1}. Measurements taken at 10°K, 80°K, and 300°K, show clearly the shift of absorption edge, while the long wavelength tail changes very little with the temperature variation. The forbidden energy gap is 0.775 ev at 0°K. For AlSb, a sharp absorption edge is observed at 12,220 cm^{-1}, corresponding to a forbidden energy gap of 1.52 ev at room temperature.

Typical of the studies made in an attempt to determine energy gaps, carrier mobilities, and other properties of importance in semiconductor application is the work of Black *et al.*[153] on M_2^{VB} –

145. Avery, D. G., Goodwin, D. W., Lawson, W. D., and Moss, T. S., *Proc. Phys. Soc. (London)*, **67B** (1954) InSb.
146. Cunnell, F. A., Edmond, J. T., and Richards, J. L., *Proc. Phys. Soc. (London)*, **67B**, 848 (1954) AlSb, GaSb, InSb, InAs, InP, GaAs.
147. Breckenridge, R. G., Blunt, R. F., Hosler, W. R., Frederikse, H. P. R., Becker, J. H., and Oshinsky, W., *Phys. Rev.*, **96**, 571 (1954) InSb.
148. Blunt, R. F., Frederikse, H. P. R., Becker, J. H., and Hosler, W. R., *Phys. Rev.*, **96**, 578 (1954) AlSb.
149. Blunt, R. F., Hosler, W. R., and Frederikse, H. P. R., *Phys. Rev.*, **96**, 576 (1954) GaSb.
150. Harbeke, G., and Lautz, G., *Optik*, **14**, 547 (1957) Ga$_2$Te$_3$, In$_2$Te$_3$.
151. Tanenbaum, M., and Briggs, H. B., *Phys. Rev.*, **91**, 1561 (1953).
152. Burstein, E., *Phys. Rev.*, **93**, 632 (1954).
153. Black, J., Conwell, E. M., Seigle, L., and Spencer, C. W., *J. Phys. Chem. Solids*, **2**, 240 (1957).

TABLE 13.   OPTICAL PROPERTIES OF M_2^{VB}–N_3^{VIB} COMPOUNDS

(After Black, Conwell, Seigle, and Spencer [153])

Compound [a]	Lattice	Space Group	Short Wave-Length Edge, μ	Remarks	Optical Energy Gap (ev at 300°K)
As_2Te_3 *	Monoclinic	$C_{2h}^3(A\text{-}m)$	1.1	Polycrystalline	1.0
Sb_2Se_3	Orthorhombic	$D_{2h}^{16}(Pbnm)$	< 2	0.1 mm thick sample; $T \cong 30\%$ from 2–15 μ	1.7
Sb_2Se_3	Orthorhombic	$D_{2h}^{16}(Pbnm)$	~ 1.0	21%T, illumination $\parallel$ to cleavage plane, 6%T, $\perp$	1.2
Sb_2Te_3	Rhombohedral	$D_{3d}^5(R\bar{3}m)$		Poor T, 0.04 mm thick sample transmitted a little from 3.6–5 μ	0.3
Bi_2S_3 *	Orthorhombic	$D_{2h}^{16}(Pbnm)$		0.6 mm thick sample. Results indicate better samples need be used.	1.3
Bi_2Se_3	Rhombohedral	$D_{3d}^5(R\bar{3}m)$		Transmits < 5% from 3.5–5 μ; 0.03 mm thick sample, illumination $\perp$ to plane.	(0.4 at liq. N_2°T.) 0.35
Bi_2Te_3	Rhombohedral	$D_{3d}^5(R\bar{3}m)$	Falls slowly below 8.2	~ 0.1% T, illumination to cleavage plane at 300°K, 1.4–4% T at liq. N_2°T. (0.06 mm thick)	0.16 (78°K)
As_2Se_3 *			0.77	Amorphous	1.6

[a] All samples were single crystals except those whose formulas appear with an asterisk.

N_3^{VIB} compounds. Data obtained by optical and electrical measurements are tabulated in Table 13.

TERNARY COMPOUNDS

Boron and Carbon Compounds

Boric Acid. Polycrystalline mulls and single crystals of boric acid, $B(OH)_3$, and deuteroboric acid, $B(OD)_3$, have been examined in the 500–3600 cm^{-1} region by Bethel and Sheppard and the results compared with earlier work.[154] The data support a slightly distorted C_{3h} crystal site symmetry for the molecule and C_{6h} for the layer structure of boric acid. The results of this work have been confirmed by the independent works of Hornig and Plumb [155] and Servoss and Clark.[156]

In the work of Hornig and Plumb, spectra were obtained at 25° and $-195°C$ of $B(OH)_3$ as randomly oriented crystallites and at 25°C as a single crystal. The spectra were interpreted as skeletal vibrations of $B(OH)_3$ molecules plus vibrations of the hydrogens associated with the hexagonal O—H...O rings. The symmetry about the boron atoms is almost trigonal. The masses and forces in the boric acid molecule are similar to those in the boron trifluoride molecule, BF_3, and consequently one might expect similar skeletal frequencies and the same isotope effect (Table 14).

Borates. Samples of Mg, Ca, Ni, Mn, Sr, and Ba orthoborates and of Na, Pb and Ba metaborates absorb in the 2000–700 cm^{-1} region.[157] The spectra indicate that the BO_2 ion does not exist; rather, the ion is present as the polymerized unit, $(BO_2)_n$, where n depends on the age of the sample. For freshly prepared samples, one may postulate $n = 2$ or 3, but the exact structure cannot be accurately determined. For aged samples, the extent of polymerization is certainly greater. The aqueous borate ion has been observed in Raman spectra and from the number, shape, and position

154. Bethel, D. E., and Sheppard, N., *Trans. Faraday Soc.*, **51**, 9 (1955).
155. Hornig, D. F., and Plumb, R. C., *J. Chem. Phys.*, **26**, 637 (1957).
156. Servoss, R. R., and Clark, H. M., *J. Chem. Phys.*, **26**, 1175 (1957).
157. Duval, C., and Lecomte, J., *Bull. soc. chim. France*, 101, 1952; *J. Opt. Soc. Amer.*, **44**, 261 (1954).

TABLE 14. COMPARISON OF SKELETAL FREQUENCIES (cm^{-1}) OF $B(OH)_3$
AND BF_3

(After Hornig and Plumb [155])

Vibration	$B(OH)_3$	BF_3 (Herzberg)
ν_1	885	888
ν_2	666(B^{10})	720(B^{10})
	632(B^{11})	691(B^{11})
ν_3	1490	1497(B^{10})
		1446(B^{11})
ν_4	552	482(B^{10})
		480(B^{11})

of the lines the ion has been described as $B(OH)^-$ with tetrahedral symmetry.[158]

Borates of lanthanum, scandium, and indium having B^{10}/B^{11} ratios varying from the natural abundance 18/82, up to about 96/4, yield four fundamental frequencies which fall within the ranges: $\omega_1 = 939$ cm^{-1}, $\omega_2 = 740$–790 cm^{-1}, $\omega_3 = 1265$–1330 cm^{-1}, and $\omega_4 = 606$–675.[159] Lanthanum borate, unlike the other two salts, has less than threefold site symmetry and was the only one of the three borates for which the totally symmetric frequency ω_1 was observable.

Metal Carbonates. The infrared spectra of various carbonates, basic carbonates, bicarbonates and related materials have been studied by Hunt and co-workers [160] and by Miller and Wilkins.[19] A strong band in the 1450–1410 cm^{-1} region and a less intense one in the 880–850 cm^{-1} region are characteristic of normal carbonates. For the 880–850 cm^{-1} band, an almost linear relationship exists between the observed frequency and the logarithm of the mass of the cation. Lithium carbonate was the only compound which did not follow this relationship. The studies with bicarbonates, basic carbonates, and related materials suggest that suffi-

158. Edwards, J. O., Morrison, G. C., Ross, V. F., and Schultz, J. W., *J. Am. Chem. Soc.*, **77**, 266 (1955).

159. Steele, W. C., *J. Chem. Phys.*, **25**, 1184 (1956).

160. Hunt, J. M., Wisherd, M. P., and Bonham, L. C., *Anal. Chem.*, **22**, 1478 (1950).

cient spectral changes occur to make possible use of infrared spectra for aids in identification purposes. However, considerably more study is needed to make significant correlations. Louisfert and Pobequin [161] have successfully differentiated between crystal forms of calcium carbonate by means of infrared absorption and found the method to be more sensitive than the usual x-ray diffraction methods.

The infrared absorption spectra of carbonates which crystallize in the aragonite-type lattice show considerable fine structure in the 880–800 cm^{-1} region when the carbon isotope ratio is altered. In the aragonite-type lattice the nearest neighbor carbonate ions occupy positions vertically above one another, the plane of the ion being taken as horizontal. The distance between nearest neighbors is decidedly less than in the calcite-type lattice, where the nearest neighbors are in the same plane. Decius [162] has observed fine structure in Nujol mull spectra of two compounds, barium carbonate and potassium nitrate, which crystallize in the aragonite-type lattice. This structure is present when the N^{15} or C^{13} content is increased to the order of 50%, but is not observed with sodium nitrate, which has a calcite-type structure. A force-constant coupling the out-of-plane bending modes of nearest neighbors in the aragonite-type lattice was postulated. Calculated and observed spectra are in good agreement.

Metals Carbonyls. Interesting structural problems arise in the infrared study of the metal carbonyls, $M_x(CO)_y$. In particular, the question occurs as to whether these compounds have M—C≡O or M=C=O structures or, in some cases, bridged carbonyl structures. It is commonly accepted that the CO molecule, which absorbs in the 2100 cm^{-1} region, has partial triple bond character. Crawford and Cross [163] quote absorption of $Ni(CO)_4$ at 2039 cm^{-1}. Jones [164] has also observed nickel carbonyl absorptions at 2057 cm^{-1} and 2128 cm^{-1}. Other metal carbonyls have reportedly shown similar band pairs in the triple-bond region. This offers strong,

161. Louisfert, J., and Pobequin, T., *Compt. rend.*, **235**, 287 (1952).
162. Decius, J. C., *J. Chem. Phys.*, **23**, 1290 (1955).
163. Crawford, B., and Cross, P. C., *J. Chem. Phys.*, **6**, 525 (1938).
164. Jones, L. H., *J. Chem. Phys.*, **28**, 1215 (1958).

although not unequivocal, evidence that the M—C≡O structure exists in metal carbonyls. The appearance of additional absorption bands near 1830 cm^{-1} in certain metal carbonyls [165-167] seems to indicate the existence of bridged ring systems in which some of the carbonyl groups are ketonic while others exist as —C≡O units. The bridge carbonyl structure has been further suggested from x-ray diffraction data. Dahl and Rundle [168] have investigated the infrared spectra of iron tetracarbonyl with a view to elucidating the structure of the molecule. Solution spectra obtained were essentially the same as reported by others. An alkali halide pellet spectrum showed two distinct bands in the 1800 cm^{-1} region and a large increase in the intensity ratio of the 1800 cm^{-1} to 2000 cm^{-1} bands compared to the ratio in solution. An intense band at 1875 cm^{-1} was found in the polarized infrared spectrum of a single crystal. The intensity of the 1800 cm^{-1} band throws some doubt on the possibility of its being a combination or overtone—a suggestion that has been made by some investigators. On the basis of this work there is some evidence for the association of some carbonyls with more than one iron atom in the crystalline state. On the other hand, the question of differences in solid and solution spectra cannot be ignored in the interpretation, and consequently the structure of iron tetracarbonyl cannot be considered as delineated.

Infrared spectral studies throw some light on the structure of carbonyl derivatives of cobalt. An investigation of cobalt hydrocarbonyl, $HCo(CO)_4$, dicobalt octacarbonyl, $Co_2(CO)_8$, cobalt carbonyl anion, $[Co(CO)_4]^-$, and tetracobalt dodecacarbonyl, $Co_4(CO)_{12}$, leads to the following inferences: (1) the hydrogen of $HCo(CO)_4$ is very weakly bound to the rest of the molecule; (2) $Co_2(CO)_8$ is structurally a transconfiguration of two trigonal bipyramids joined at the edge so that the apical and equatorial carbonyls are shared as bridge carbonyls; (3) $Co_4(CO)_{12}$ has a somewhat simpler structure but also possesses bridge carbonyls; and

165. Sheline, R. K., *J. Am. Chem. Soc.*, **73**, 1615 (1951).
166. Cable, J. W., and Sheline, R. K., *Chem. Rev.*, **56**, 1 (1956).
167. Friedel, R. A., Wender, I., Shufler, S. L., and Sternberg, H. W., *J. Am. Chem. Soc.*, **77**, 3951 (1955).
168. Dahl, L. F., and Rundle, R. E., *J. Chem. Phys.*, **27**, 323 (1957).

(4) the cobalt carbonyl anion shows only one band in the carbonyl region and may be represented by a tetrahedral model.[167] For the tetracobalt dodecacarbonyl molecule, infrared data show bands attributable to both terminal and bridge carbonyl groups, the ratios of the areas under the bands corresponding to a 2:1 terminal to bridge relationship.

The structure of the $M(CO)_6$ molecules appears to be more definite. Only one intense $C≡O$ stretching frequency is observed in the vapor phase of $Cr(CO)_6$. This indicates strongly an equivalence of all the CO bonds and implies a regular octahedral structure for the $Cr(CO)_6$ molecule and other hexacarbonyls.[169] Assuming for these molecules an O_h symmetry, it can be shown that thirteen fundamental vibrations are allowed, four of which are infrared-active. Three of these have been observed directly by means of infrared spectroscopy; the fourth, occurring at about 100 cm^{-1}, is beyond the cutoff of the usual commercially available instruments.[170] Calculated and observed spectral frequencies are in good agreement.[171]

Halogen Compounds

Compounds of halogen, hydrogen, and some other element. The ternary compounds of the form MH_3X (or MD_3X), where M is Si or Ge, have been found to have the expected C_3 symmetry. Thus, there are six fundamentals: three totally symmetric a_1 vibrations and three doubly degenerate e vibrations. All fundamentals, overtones, and combinations are allowed in both the Raman and infrared. The M—H vibration is almost independent of the rest of the molecule and occurs at approximately 2100–2200 cm^{-1}. Substitution of deuterium for hydrogen in the molecule gives the expected lower frequency vibration. The M—X vibration, involving masses of more equal magnitude, is dependent on the rest of the molecule, as would be expected. The observed fundamen-

169. Shufler, S. C., Sternberg, H. W., and Friedel, R. A., *J. Am. Chem. Soc.*, **78**, 2687 (1956).
170. Hawkins, N. J., Mattraw, H. C., Sabol, W. W., and Carpenter, D. R., *J. Chem. Phys.*, **23**, 2422 (1955).
171. Murata, H., and Kawai, K., *J. Chem. Phys.*, **27**, 605 (1957).

tal frequencies of SiH_3F, SiH_3Cl, SiH_3Br, GeH_3Cl, and GeD_3Cl are shown in Table 15.

TABLE 15.   OBSERVED FUNDAMENTAL FREQUENCIES (cm^{-1}) OF MH_3X MOLECULES

		SiH_3F[a]	SiH_3Cl[a]	SiH_3Br[a]	SiH_3Br[b]	GeH_3Cl[c]	GeD_3Cl[c]
a_1	M—H stretch	2206	2201	2200	2200	2121.2	1522
	MH_3 bend	990	949	930	927	847.7	614
	M—X stretch	872	551	430	428	422.6	421
e	M—H stretch	2196	2195	2196	~2100[d]	2129.4	1530
	M—H_3 bend	943.4	954.4	950.4	946	874.6	630
	M—H_3 rock	728.1	664.0	632.6	629	604.1	434

[a] Newman, C., O'Loane, J. K., Polo, S. R., and Wilson, M. K., *J. Chem. Phys.*, **25**, 855 (1956).
[b] Mayo, D. W., Opitz, H. E., and Peake, J. S., *J. Chem. Phys.*, **23**, 1344 (1955).
[c] Lord, R. C., and Steese, C. M., *J. Chem. Phys.*, **22**, 542 (1954).
[d] Estimated from data in reference (b) by authors in Reference (a).

The absorption spectra of several compounds of nitrogen, hydrogen and halogen have been observed in the 400–3333 cm^{-1} region. As an example, the crystalline and liquid states of N_2H_5Cl, N_2D_5Cl, N_2H_5Br and N_2D_5Br were studied by Decius and Pearson.[172] From x-ray diffraction data, N_2H_5Cl has been found to be an orthorhombic crystal of space group C_{2v}^{19} with 16 molecules per unit cell. All fundamental frequencies are allowed in both the infrared and Raman. If one ignores intermolecular coupling, the following frequencies are expected: five hydrogen stretching modes in the 3200–2400 cm^{-1} region, four H—N—H deformations in the 1400–1600 cm^{-1} region; four NH_3^+ or NH_2 bending modes in the 1000–1200 cm^{-1} region, an N—N stretching frequency below 1000 cm^{-1}, and a torsional mode at a considerably lower frequency.

According to these authors, rather broad, complex absorption was observed in the hydrogen stretching region for the N—H or N—D stretch. The arrangement of $N_2H_5^+$ ions in the unit cell is not known, but it was suggested that hydrogen bonds between —NH_3^+ groups of one ion and the nitrogen of the —NH_2 group

172. Decius, J. C., and Pearson, D. P., *J. Am. Chem. Soc.*, **75**, 2436 (1953).

of another ion perhaps are important in the structure determination. The possibility of hydrogen bonding to the halide ions was eliminated, since bromide ion would not be expected to take part in such bonding; yet the spectra of N_2H_5Cl and N_2H_5Br were quite similar. The bending and deformation region revealed a number of peaks, the total not exceeding that predicted by site symmetry selection rules. However, it was not possible to make detailed assignments. Data and assignments for the spectra of N_2H_5Cl and N_2D_2Cl are shown in Table 16.

TABLE 16. VIBRATIONAL MODES AND FREQUENCIES (cm^{-1}) OF N_2H_5Cl
AND N_2D_2Cl

(After Decius and Pearson [186])

Vibrational Mode	N_2H_5Cl Liquid, 95°	N_2H_5Cl Solid, 25°	N_2D_2Cl Solid, 25°
N—N stretch	950	975	940
NH_3^+ bend	1080	1101	790
	1100	1124	805
Bend	1220	1246	1000
Bend	1405	1417	1100
Deformation	1495	1500	1133
Deformation		1584	
Deformation	1600	1638	1190
NH_3^+ stretch		2716	
NH_3^+ stretch		2950	2170
NH_3^+ stretch		3034	
NH_2 stretch		3150	2390
NH_2 stretch		3261	2440

Absorption and reflection spectra of NH_4Cl, NH_4F, NH_4Br, and NH_4I at 20° and $-150°$ were recorded in the 1400–3400 cm^{-1} region by Bovey.[173] The data support the following symmetries for the low-temperature form of the ammonium ion: T_d in NH_4Cl, V_d in NH_4Br and NH_4I, and C_3 or C_{3v} in NH_4F. Martinez and Wagner[174] have reported a similar vibrational study of phosphonium and deutero-phosphonium iodides at $-78°C$, room temperature,

173. Bovey, L. R. H., *J. Opt. Soc. Am.*, **41**, 836 (1951).
174. Martinez, J. V., and Wagner, E. L., *J. Chem. Phys.*, **27**, 1110 (1957).

and 190°C in the range 400–4000 cm^{-1}. The low-temperature spectra could be interpreted on the basis of a V_d site symmetry for the PH_4^+ ion and the room temperature spectra were compatible with the x-ray structure, D_{4h}^7.

Infrared absorption spectra of bifluorides ($NaHF_2$, KHF_2, and NH_4HF_2) are identical when obtained in KCl discs, but different when obtained as Nujol mulls.[175] This behavior has been attributed to the formation of mixed crystals in the alkali halide technique. Discs of KCl, KBr, KI, and NaBr give somewhat different spectra, but for a given matrix, absorption is essentially the same for the three bifluoride molecules. Two infrared-active vibrations were reported for the bifluoride ion: the antisymmetric stretching vibration near 1500 cm^{-1} and the deformation vibration near 1200 cm^{-1}. This is in accord with the vibrational frequencies found by Cote and Thompson[176] and Newman and Badger[177] for the HF_2^- ion in potassium bifluoride.

Compounds of halogen, oxygen and some other element.   The ternary compounds of the form ZO_xX_y where x is a halogen atom, x and y are small integers (1–3), and Z is another element (possibly a different halogen), have been examined to some extent in the infrared region. Twelve absorption bands have been observed and identified for the nitrosyl fluoride molecule, NOF, in the 260–5500 cm^{-1} region[178] (Table 17). The assumed model for NOF, like that of NOCl and NOBr, is a non-linear unsymmetrical structure with nitrogen at the apex of a comparatively flat triangle.

The thionyl halides, SOF_2 and $SOCl_2$, are known to have C_s symmetry from electron diffraction, microwave, and vibrational studies. Assignments for the fundamentals of SOF_2, using spectral data obtained between 3000 and 300 cm^{-1} are: ν_1, (a'), 1333 cm^{-1}; ν_2(a'), 808 cm^{-1}; ν_3(a'), 530 cm^{-1}; ν_4(a'), 410 cm^{-1}; ν_5(a''),

175. Ketelaar, J. A. A., Haas, C., and van der Elsken, J., *J. Chem. Phys.*, **24**, 624 (1956).
176. Cote, G. L., and Thompson, H. W., *Proc. Roy. Soc. (London)*, **A210**, 206 (1951).
177. Newman, R., and Badger, R. M., *J. Chem. Phys.*, **19**, 1207 (1951).
178. Woltz, P. J. H., Jones, E. A., and Nielsen, A. H., *J. Chem. Phys.*, **20**, 378 (1952).

TABLE 17.   OBSERVED FREQUENCIES (cm^{-1}) OF NOF, NOCl, AND NOBr

Assignment	NOF [a]	NOCl [b]	NOBr [b]
ν_2 (bending)	521	332	265
ν_3 (N—X)	765.86 [c]	592	**542**
ν_1 (N—O)	1844.03 [c]	1799	1801
$2\nu_2$	1037	664	
$\nu_2 + \nu_3$	1290	923	807
$2\nu_3$		1184	
$\nu_1 - \nu_2$		1207	
$2\nu_2 + \nu_3$		1248	
$\nu_1 + \nu_2$	2365	2131	2066
$\nu_1 + \nu_3$	2612	2395	2340
$\nu_1 + \nu_2 + \nu_3$	3087		
$2\nu_1$	3652	3568	3567
$2\nu_1 + \nu_3$	4174	4160	4103
$2\nu_1 + \nu_2$	4441	3898	3831
$3\nu_1$	5417	5303	5303

[a] (178)
[b] Burns, W. G., and Bernstein, H. J., *J. Chem. Phys.*, **18**, 1669 (1950).
[c] Magnuson, D. W., *J. Chem. Phys.*, **20**, 380 (1952).

748 cm^{-1}; and ν_6(a''), 390 cm^{-1}.[179]   The four totally symmetric a' vibrations were ascribed to an S—O stretching mode, an S—F stretching mode, a mode in which all angles increase simultaneously, and a mode in which the F—S—F angle increases while the O—S—F angles decrease.   The two antisymmetric a'' vibrations were attributed to an S—F stretch and a deformation of the SOF$_2$ pyramid.

Infrared spectral data have been used further to elucidate the structure of the nitryl halides, NO$_2$X.   The analysis is consistent with the formula X—NO$_2$ rather than X—O—N—O, the assumed model being a planar structure of C$_{2v}$ symmetry.   The fundamental frequencies of NO$_2$Cl and NO$_2$F are compared with those of the similar nitric acid molecule, NO$_2$OH, in Table 18.   The oxytrichlorides of vanadium and phosphorus have C$_{3v}$ symmetry.   As such, six fundamentals active in both Raman and infrared are allowed.   The spectrum of vanadium oxytrichloride has been

179. O'Loane, J. K., and Wilson, M. K., *J. Chem. Phys.*, **23**, 1313 (1955).

TABLE 18. FUNDAMENTAL FREQUENCIES (cm^{-1}) OF NO_2Cl, NO_2F AND NO_2OH[a]

[After Dodd, Rolfe, and Woodward, *Trans. Faraday Soc.*, **52**, 145 (1956)]

	$\nu_1(a_1)$	$\nu_2(a_1)$	$\nu_3(a_1)$	$\nu_4(b_1)$	$\nu_5(b_1)$	$\nu_6(b_2)$
NO_2OH(IR)	1320	886		1710	583	765
(R)	1300	925	680	1675	610	(767)[c]
NO_2F (IR)	1312	822	460	1793	570	742
NO_2Cl (IR)[b]	1293	794	411	1685	367	651

[a] The OH may be considered as a single unit in this analysis.
[b] These are values observed by Ryason, R., and Wilson, M. K., *J. Chem. Phys.*, **22**, 2000 (1954). However, in this reference the $\nu_3(a_1)$ and $\nu_6(b_2)$ frequencies are interchanged.
[c] From the first harmonic.

observed by Miller and Cousins,[180] and the fundamental frequencies compared with the corresponding data of Delwaulle and François [181] for phosphorus oxytrichloride (Table 19). Other halogen-containing ternary molecules have been studied and specific data regarding these may be obtained by referring to the articles of references 182 through 190.

TABLE 19. FUNDAMENTAL FREQUENCIES (cm^{-1}) OF $VOCl_3$ AND $POCl_3$ (After Miller and Cousins [180])

	Activity	Description	$VOCl_3$	$POCl_3$
a_1	R(p)IR	V=O stretch	1035	1290
		V—Cl stretch	408	486
		V—Cl_3 def.	165	267p?
e	R(dp)IR	V—Cl stretch	504	581
		V—Cl_3 def.	249	337
		Cl_3—V—O rock	129	193

180. Miller, F. A., and Cousins, L. R., *J. Chem. Phys.*, **26**, 329 (1957).
181. Delwaulle, M. L., and François, F., *Compt. rend.*, **220**, 817 (1945).
182. de Lattre, A., *J. Chem. Phys.*, **19**, 1610 (1951), Na_3AlF_6, KPF_6, Na and NH_4 fluoferrates.
183. de Lattre, A., *J. Chem. Phys.*, **20**, 1180 (1952). Complex fluorides.
184. Lagemann, R. T., Jones, E. A., and Woltz, P. J. H., *J. Chem. Phys.*, **20**, 1768 (1952), CF_3OF.

Other Ternary Compounds

A few correlations for identification and analytical purposes have been made for ternary compounds containing key elements other than boron, carbon, or halogen. These may generally be located in some of the works already cited. (See, for example, Herzberg or references 14 and 19–21.) Some of the more recent studies on nitrogen-containing compounds, hydroxides, ferrites, manganites, and titanates will be reviewed here.

Nitrogen compounds. Spectra of nitric acid and its solutions have been observed by Marcus and Fresco.[191] A nitronium ion frequency was observed at 2360 cm^{-1}. The band intensity is enhanced by addition of nitronium fluoborate, sulfuric acid, phosphorus pentoxide, or small amounts of acetic anhydride, and is reduced by sodium nitrate, potassium dihydrogen phosphate, water, and larger amounts of acetic anhydride. Absorption behavior of the nitronium ion in the various media has been used to provide information about the existing equilibria. When the concentration of nitronium ion was large, a combination band was observed near 3745 cm^{-1}. Bands arising from undissociated nitric acid are not observed when a small amount of nitric acid is added to 100% sulfuric acid. Because of the observed behavior in different media, hydrogen-bonded structures were assumed to exist in the nitric acid solutions. The existence of such structure is supported by effects observed in Raman work.

The vibrational frequencies of the nitrite ion (C_{2v} symmetry)

185. Perkins, W. D., and Wilson, M. K., *J. Chem. Phys.*, **20**, 1791 (1952), SO_2F_2.
186. Nielsen, A. H., Burke, T. G., Woltz, P. J. H., and Jones, E. A., *J. Chem. Phys.*, **20**, 596 (1952), F_2CO, $FClCO$, and Cl_2CO.
187. Martz, D. E., and Lagemann, R. T., *J. Chem. Phys.*, **22**, 1193 (1954), $SOCl_2$ and SO_2Cl_2.
188. Pemsler, J. P., and Smith, D. F., *J. Chem. Phys.*, **22**, 1834 (1954), HF . ClF_3 and DF . ClF_3.
189. Katzin, L. I., *J. Am. Chem. Soc.*, **76**, 3089 (1954), Cs_2CoCl_4.
190. Madden, R. P., and Benedict, W. S., *J. Chem. Phys.*, **25**, 594 (1956), ClO_3F.
191. Marcus, R. A., and Fresco, J. M., *J. Chem. Phys.*, **27**, 564 (1957).

have been assigned, using spectral data obtained from microcrystalline samples of $NaNO_2$, KNO_2, and $AgNO_2$ and aqueous solutions of $NaNO_2$. The assignments are: $\nu_1(a_1)$, symmetric stretching – 1345 ± 20 cm^{-1}; $\nu_2(a_1)$, bending – 816 ± 2, 809 ± 2 cm^{-1}; $\nu_3(b_1)$, antisymmetric stretching – 1236 ± 15 cm^{-1}; and $\nu_1 + \nu_3(B_1)$ combination – 2550 ± 30 cm^{-1}.[192]

Ternary compounds containing the carbon-nitrogen linkage have also been investigated in the infrared region. Rotational spectral data and results of electron diffraction and x-ray studies have furnished bond length values for carbon-nitrogen and carbon-oxygen systems. It is known that frequencies due to carbonyl bonds are sensitive to chemical effects. Layton, Kross and Fassel[193] have correlated the bond lengths of a number of such systems with the stretching frequency involved. The stretching frequency of molecules containing the C—N linkage shows a linear dependence on the length of the C—N bond. A plot of C—O bond length versus stretching frequency reveals a slight curvature particularly for frequencies beyond 1700 cm^{-1} and bond lengths below 1.20Å. Data for typical inorganic systems are shown in Table 20.

TABLE 20. BOND LENGTHS AND STRETCHING FREQUENCIES OF SOME INORGANIC C—O AND C—N SYSTEMS

(After Layton, Kross, and Fassel [193])

C—O		C—N	
Bond length, Å	Frequency (cm^{-1})	Bond length, Å	Frequency (cm^{-1})
$Ni(CO_4)$ 1.15 ± 0.03	2045	CNBr 1.158	2187
		CNCl 1.163	2213
COS 1.16 ± 0.05	2050.5		
CO 1.128	2169.8	CNI 1.159	2158
C_3O_2 1.19	$\begin{cases} 2190\ (s) \\ 2258\ (as) \end{cases}$	SCN$^-$ 1.15	2066
CO_2 1.16	2349.3 (as)	(CN_2) 1.16 ± 0.02	2235
		HCN 1.1574	2110

192. Weston, R. E., and Brodasky, T. F., *J. Chem. Phys.*, **27**, 683 (1957).
193. Layton, Jr., Kross, R. D., and Fassel, V. A., *J. Chem. Phys.*, **25**, 135 (1956).

The spectrum of tritium cyanide, TCN, has been obtained in the 400–4000 cm^{-1} region and the fundamental frequencies, ν_1, ν_2, and ν_3, compared with those of HCN and DCN [194] (Table 21).

TABLE 21. COMPARISON OF OBSERVED AND CALCULATED FREQUENCIES (cm^{-1}) FOR HCN, DCN, AND TCN

(After Staats, Morgan, and Goldstein [194])

		ω obs.	Anharmonicity Correction	ω	ω Calculated
HCN[a]	ν_1	2095.5 (Raman)	29.2	2124.7	2125.6
	ν_2	711.7	15.0	726.7	——
	ν_3	3311.7	134.5	3446.2	3448.8
DCN[a]	ν_1	1928	25.4	1953	1955.8
	ν_2	568.9	10.7	579.6	579.5
	ν_3	2629.3	70.9	2700.2	2700.3
TCN	ν_1	1724	27.5[b]	——	1751.9
	ν_2	513	8.4[b]	——	521.4
	ν_3	2460	47.2[b]	——	2507.2

[a] Data of A. E. Douglas and D. Sharma, *J. Chem. Phys.*, **21**, 448 (1953).
[b] Calculated from ω calc. $-\omega$ obs.

The anharmonicity corrections for ν_3 are approximately proportional to the reduced masses computed for the H—CN stretch, treating the molecule as diatomic. The corrections for ν_1 are essentially constant and those for ν_2 vary with ν_2.

Hydroxides. Infrared spectroscopic studies provide information concerning the —OH fundamentals and the combination bands in the adjoining spectral regions. A band at approximately 3333 cm^{-1} was observed in the absorption spectra of $Ca(OH)_2$, $Ni(OH)_2$, $Cd(OH)_2$, $Y(OH)_3$, $La(OH)_2$, $Nd(OH)_3$, β-$Be(OH)_2$, ϵ-$Zn(OH)_2$, γ-$AL(OH)_3$, α- and γ-FeOOH, $B(OH)_3$, and α-AlOOH.[195] Similarly, bands for vanadyl hydroxide, $VO(OH)_2$, have been observed at 3276 cm^{-1} and 3529–66 cm^{-1} and for $Cu(OH)_2$ at 3312

194. Staats, P. A., Morgan, H. W., and Goldstein, J. H., *J. Chem. Phys.*, **25**, 582 (1956).
195. Glemser, O., and Hartert, E., *Z. anorg. u. allgem. Chem.*, **283**, 111 (1956).

cm^{-1} and 3574 cm^{-1}.[196]   The spectra of the hydroxides of alkali metals have been observed by Wickersheim[11] and Phillips and Busing.[197] Hydroxide stretching frequencies for LiOH, LiOH·H$_2$O, and NaOH were reported by the latter authors as 3678 cm^{-1}, 3574 cm^{-1}, and 3637 cm^{-1}, respectively, from infrared measurements; and 3664 cm^{-1}, 3563 cm^{-1}, and 3663 cm^{-1}, respectively, from Raman measurements.

Rather complex absorption patterns have been observed in the —OH stretching region for Ca(OH)$_2$ and Mg(OH)$_2$, both molecules having the same structure.   From neutron diffraction studies, the crystal structure of Ca(OH)$_2$ is known to have, per unit cell, two OH$^-$ ions with bonds parallel to the Z-axis and related by a center of symmetry.   Two fundamental OH stretching modes are expected to appear in the vibrational spectrum, namely an antisymmetric mode which is infrared-active and a symmetric mode which is Raman-active.   It is also anticipated that intensities of the absorption bands should be dependent upon the angle between the incident radiation and the OH bond.   Using single crystals of Ca(OH)$_2$, Busing and Morgan[198] made the following observations: (1) decreased intensity of the low-frequency absorption and increased intensity of the high-frequency absorption at 4164 cm^{-1} occur as predicted when the sample is cooled to liquid nitrogen temperatures; and (2) an unexpected decrease in intensity of the 3720 cm^{-1} band occurs.   An explanation of the details of the spectra could not be proposed from the model assumed.

Ferrites, Manganites, and Titanates

In order to understand the properties of ferromagnetic semiconductors, it is advantageous to have as many relations between structure and electromagnetic response as possible.   The electric and magnetic properties of these materials are dependent on their atomic and ionic configurations in the crystal lattice.   Information about the position and valence of ions can be obtained from

196. Cabannes-Ott, C., *Compt. rend.*, **242**, 2825 (1956).
197. Phillips, B. A., and Busing, W. R., *J. Phys. Chem.*, **61**, 502 (1959).
198. Busing, W. R., and Morgan, H. W., *J. Chem. Phys.*, **28**, 998 (1958).

the vibrational spectra as well as from electronic and magnetic dipole spectra. Recently, vibrational studies of some ferrites, manganites, and titanates have appeared in the literature. In a typical study, the infrared spectra of seven ferrites of the type MFe_2O_4, where M represents a divalent metal ion (specifically Co^{++}, Fe^{++}, Mg^{++}, Ni^{++}, Zn^{++}, Mn^{++}, and $Ni^{++}_{0.3}Zn^{++}_{0.7}$) were analyzed.[199] As in the spectra of most metallic oxides, two absorption bands arising from interatomic vibrations were observed in the region below 1000 cm^{-1}. Force constants were calculated for the bond stretching between metal and oxide ions. The ferrites used in this study were considered as continuously bonded crystals, i.e., the atoms are bonded to all nearest neighbors by equivalent forces, and the frequency distribution of vibrations can be given by a Debye or Born-von Karman treatment of the classical mechanical problem. X-ray diffraction studies of the ferrites indicate a structure equivalent to that of spinel. The ferrites of Co, Fe, and Ni are believed to be predominantly inverse; $ZnFe_2O_4$ is a normal spinel; and some doubt exists as to the configuration of the other ferrites. Theoretical vibrational analysis indicates that only two high-frequency modes, ν_1 and ν_2, and two low-frequency oscillatory modes, ν_3 and ν_4, are infrared-active. Indeed, two high-frequency modes were observed at approximately 570 cm^{-1} and 380 cm^{-1}; the lower-frequency modes were inaccessible in the spectral range covered. Measurements of the integrated vibrational band intensities were compatible with predominantly ionic bonding for the ferrite structures.

The absorption spectra of copper and nickel manganites also show bands in the region $\sim$ 570 cm^{-1} and $\sim$ 460 cm^{-1}. The structures are normal and inverse spinel, respectively.[200] Tables 22A and 22B show the observed spectral frequencies of the ferrites and manganites.

The spectrum of barium titanate in the 5000–300 cm^{-1} region was obtained using the technique of deposition of the finely pulverized material onto salt plates from an isopropyl alcohol suspen-

199. Waldron, R. D., *Phys. Rev.*, 99, 1727 (1955).
200. Dasgupta, S., and Sinha, A. P. B., *Trans. Faraday Soc.*, 53, 909 (1957).

TABLE 22A.   INFRARED SPECTRAL FREQUENCIES (cm^{-1}) OF FERRITES

(After Waldron [199])

	ν_1	ν_2	Other ν's
$CoFe_2O_4$	575	374	shoulder *ca.* 320
$FeFe_2O_4$	570 $\begin{cases} 579^a \\ 610^a \end{cases}$	370–80	
$MgFe_2O_4$	565	406 $\begin{cases} 380 \\ 430{-}40 \end{cases}$	shoulder *ca.* 735
$MnFe_2O_4$	550	392	shoulder *ca.* 645,320
$NiFe_2O_4$	587	396	
$ZnFe_2O_4$	555 $\begin{cases} 575 \\ 540 \end{cases}$	393	shoulder *ca.* 325
$Ni_{0.3}Zn_{0.7}Fe_2O_4$	563	409	

[a] Liquid N$_2$ temperature.   The usual narrowing of bands was not observed at liquid N$_2$ temperature.

sion.[201] Two broad bands were observed, one centered near 550 cm^{-1} and the other starting near 450 cm^{-1} and reaching its maximum below 300 cm^{-1}. Strong absorption near 600 cm^{-1} is common to all titanates. The fact that this band is also found in rutile, TiO_2, suggests a connection with a vibrational mode of the TiO_4 tetrahedra. It has been proposed by Megaw[202] that a change from the cubic form, which exists above the Curie point of 120°C, to the tetragonal is associated with a change in the character of the bonds around the Ti and O atoms. It was expected, therefore, that (1) a change would occur in the spectrum if heated to 150°C and (2) the spectra of the ferroelectric tetragonal $BaTiO_3$ and the hexagonal form which is not ferroelectric would be different. No changes were observed by Mara, Sutherland, and Tyrell[201] when tetragonal $BaTiO_3$ was heated to 150°C, nor was there any apparent difference in the spectra of the two forms (hexagonal and tetragonal) over the 5000–700 cm^{-1} region. A somewhat more detailed study of the infrared absorption of $BaTiO_3$ and

201. Mara, R. T., Sutherland, G. B. B. M., and Tyrell, H. V., *Phys. Rev.*, **96**, 801 (1954).
202. Megaw, H. D., *Acta Cryst.*, **5**, 739 (1952).

TABLE 22B.   INFRARED SPECTRAL FREQUENCIES (cm^{-1}) OF MANGANITES

(After Dasgupta and Sinha [200])

NiO + Mn_2O_3 unheated	942.6 s $\left.{963.4 \atop 921.7}\right\}$ doublet	833.3 m; sh	571.4 m; b	467.1 $\left\{{473 \atop 458}\right.$ vs; b
$MiMn_2O_4$	947.9 ± 26 w; b		578.1 s; sh	465.3 $\left\{{473.0 \atop 457.9}\right.$ vs; b
CuO + Mn_2O_3 unheated	957.8 s $\left.{988.1 \atop 927.6}\right\}$ doublet	845.3 w	554.4 $\left\langle{578 \atop 530.8}\right.$ doublet	466.2 $\left\{{479.4 \atop 457.9}\right.$ vs; b
$CuMn_2O_4$	941.6 ± 17.4 w; b	858.4 vw; shoulder	552.5 $\left\{{578.0 \atop {552.5 \atop 530.8}}\right.$ s; b triplet	465.3 s; sh

sh = sharp   s = strong   vs = very strong
b = broad   w = weak   vw = very weak

related materials was subsequently reported by Last.[203] Thin single crystals and alkali halide disc spectra were observed. Bands attributed to TiO_3 vibrations appeared at 495 cm^{-1} and approximately 340 cm^{-1} in the single crystal spectra of $BaTiO_3$. A third expected vibrational mode, Ba moving against TiO_3, was not observed in the region covered, but on the basis of specific heat data it was estimated that this frequency is approximately 225 cm^{-1}. The band at 495 cm^{-1} was studied over a range of temperatures ($-190°$ to $+175°$ C). Band splitting related to the change of crystal symmetry appeared as the crystal changed from the cubic to tetragonal, orthorhombic, and rhombohedral phases.

The general features of spectra of the perovskite titanates ($SrTiO_3$, $PbTiO_3$, and $CaTiO_3$) and the perovskite niobates ($KNbO_3$ and $NaNbO_3$) were similar to those of $BaTiO_3$. Such differences as were detected were attributed to differences in unit cell size and symmetry. Three ilmenite titanates ($CdTiO_3$, $ZnTiO_3$, and $MgTiO_3$) showed a high frequency band which was broader and less distinct than the corresponding band in the perovskite modifications. Also, the low-frequency band exhibited double structure. The observed band centers are shown in Table 23. Band centers in $BaTiO_3$ shifted to lower frequencies when a matrix of higher refractive index (n, measured at 540 cm^{-1}) was used in the pressed disc technique. For the halides: KBr ($n = 1.48$); AgCl ($n = 1.92$); TlCl ($n = 2.06$); and TlBr ($n = 2.25$), the absorption maxima were 545 and 400 cm^{-1}; 540 and 380 cm^{-1}; 532 and 365 cm^{-1}; and 535 and 360 cm^{-1}, respectively.

COMPOUNDS CONTAINING MORE THAN THREE ELEMENTS

Inorganic substances containing more than three elements may be broadly grouped into two classes, namely: (1) *non-complex compounds* such as certain minerals, salts of heteropoly acids, and simple structures, and (2) *complex compounds,* such as coordination compounds and metal organic structures.

203. Last, J. T., *Phys. Rev.,* **105**, 1740 (1957).

Table 23. Infrared Absorption Band Centers (cm^{-1}) of BaTiO$_3$ and Some Related Materials

(After Last [203])

Single Crystal Spectra	ν_1	Pressed Disc Spectra	ν_1	ν_2
BaTiO$_3$ (cubic)	495	BaTiO$_3$ (tetragonal)	545	400
BaTiO$_3$ (tetragonal)	517;495	BaTiO$_3$ (hexagonal)	555	365
BaTiO$_3$ (orthorhombic)	520;495(sh)	PbTiO$_3$ (tetragonal)	590	405
BaTiO$_3$ (rhombohedral)	632;490	SrTiO$_3$ (cubic)	610	395
PbTiO$_3$ (tetragonal)	610(sh);535	CaTiO$_3$ (orthorhombic)	540;700(sh)	360(b)
		KNbO$_3$ (orthorhombic)	660;550(sh)	375
		NaNbO$_3$ (orthorhombic)	675;510(sh)	375
		CdTiO$_3$ (ilmenite)	575(b)	425;335
		ZnTiO$_3$ (ilmenite)	590(b)	400;315(sh)
		MgTiO$_3$ (ilmenite)	600(b)	475;350

Notation: ν_1 = high frequency stretching
ν_2 = lower frequency bending
(sh) = shoulder
(b) = broad

Non-Complex Compounds. The spectra of a number of minerals were recorded by Hunt, Wisherd, and Bonham.[160] For the purpose of identification, spectra of the ammonium salts of several heteropoly acids were obtained in the 1200–625 cm^{-1} region by Sharpless and Munday.[204] An equation for calculating integrated molar extinction coefficients for the compounds suspended in KBr discs was derived. The KBr disc technique has also been used for obtaining spectra of solid sulfamic acid and the sulfamate ion from 500–4000 cm^{-1} at various temperatures.[205] Assignments of vibrational modes were made for the zwitterion model of the acid $H_3N^+SO_3^-$ with site symmetry in the crystal of C_1. Spectra of the sulfamate ion $H_2NSO_3^-$, observed in H_2NSO_3K and the corresponding deuterated compounds, was interpreted on basis of the C_s model. According to x-ray data,[206] sulfamic acid belongs to the space group V_h^{15}-Pbca with eight molecules per unit cell. According to Halford's tables,[207] this corresponds to C_1 site symmetry. The eighteen fundamental frequencies, their overtones, and combinations are allowed in both infrared and Raman. If, in the crystal, the molecule exists as the zwitterion, $H_3N^+SO_3^-$, the actual site symmetry should not be very different from C_{3v}. On the other hand if the molecular form, NH_2SO_2OH, exists in the crystal, the site symmetry should be very nearly C_s. The zwitterion model would have a simpler spectrum than the molecular model, if one neglects factors such as hydrogen bonding, intermolecular coupling, etc. The zwitterion form should have only eleven fundamentals instead of eighteen. In addition to this, there should appear a broad, intense band in the low frequency N—H stretching region and no hydrogen modes below about 1000 cm^{-1}. The molecular form would be expected to exhibit a sharper, higher frequency N—H stretch, NH_2 deformation bands below 1000 cm^{-1}, an OH stretching mode at a frequency higher than the N—H stretching frequency, and an altered NSO_3 spectrum due to the single-bonded S—OH.

204. Sharpless, N. E., and Munday, J. S., *Anal. Chem.*, **29**, 1619 (1957).
205. Vuagnat, A. M., and Wagner, E. L., *J. Chem. Phys.*, **26**, 77 (1957).
206. Kanda, F. A., and King, A. S., *J. Am. Chem. Soc.*, **73**, 2315 (1951).
207. Halford, R. S., *J. Chem. Phys.*, **14**, 8 (1946).

The observed spectrum suggested the zwitterion configuration. This observation supports the work of Dupuis,[208] who cited evidence for the existence of the zwitterion form of the acid in the solid state.

Two osmium-nitrogen compounds of considerable chemical stability have been studied in the infrared region.[209] The metal-nitrogen stretching frequency in potassium osmiamate, $K[OsO_3N]$, and potassium nitrilopentachloroosmate, $K_2[OsCl_5N]$ was identified by noting the isotopic shift with the N^{15} analogs. For the four compounds, the observed frequencies are: $K[OsO_3N]$ – 1023 cm^{-1} (strong, sharp), 890 cm^{-1} (strong), 858 cm^{-1} (strong); $K[OsO_3N^{15}]$ – 1023 cm^{-1} (strong, sharp), 992 cm^{-1} (strong, sharp), 890 cm^{-1} (strong); $K_2[OsCl_5N]$ – 1073 cm^{-1} (strong, sharp); $K_2[OsCl_5N^{15}]$–1073 cm^{-1}(strong, sharp), 1041 cm^{-1}(strong, sharp). The band at 1023 cm^{-1} for the osmiamate ion and the band at 1073 cm^{-1} for the nitrilopentachloroosmate ion were attributed to the metal-nitrogen vibration. The isotope N^{15} shifts the 1023 cm^{-1} band to 992 cm^{-1} (991 cm^{-1}, calculated value) and similarly the 1073 cm^{-1} band was shifted to 1041 cm^{-1} (1039 cm^{-1}, calculated value). The high frequency of the Os—N vibration implies considerable multiple bond character in accord with the great chemical stability of these compounds. The spectrum confirmed

the structure of the osmiamate ion, as a distorted

tetrahedron in agreement with x-ray data and chemical evidence.

The vibrational spectra of the solid and gaseous borine carbonyls, $B^{11}H_3CO$, $B^{10}H_3CO$, $B^{11}D_3CO$, and $B^{10}D_3CO$ have been reported by Bethke and Wilson.[210] These molecules have point group symmetry C_{3v} and as such there are four fundamentals of species a_1 and four of species e. Table 24 summarizes the observed data.

208. Dupuis, T., *Compt. rend.*, **243**, 1621 (1956); **242**, 2924 (1956).
209. Lewis, J., and Wilkinson, G., *J. Inorg. and Nuclear Chem.*, **6**, 12 (1958).
210. Bethke, G. W., and Wilson, M. K., *J. Chem. Phys.*, **26**, 1119 (1957).

TABLE 24. OBSERVED FREQUENCIES (cm^{-1}) OF BORINE CARBONYL

(After Bethke and Wilson [210])

Species and Activity	Description	Assignment	$B^{10}H_3CO$	$B^{11}H_3CO$	$B^{11}H_3CO$ [a]	$B^{10}D_3CO$	$B^{11}D_3CO$
a_1	B—H stretch	v_1	2385	2379	(2360)*	1694.8	1679.0
IR, ‖	C—O stretch	v_2	2166.0	2164.7	2164	2169.0	2168.5
Raman, polarized	BH_3 bend	v_3	1083.1	1073.4	1105	883	862
	B—C stretch	v_4	707.0	691.4	692	629.5	624.8
e	B—H stretch	v_5	2456	2441	2440	1852	1837
IR, ⊥	BH_3 bend	v_6	1100	1100	1392	801.5	801.3
Raman, depol.	Unsym. bend	v_7	818.8	809.3	809	718.0	708.5
	Sym. bend	v_8	313.7	313.2	(315)*	266.0	266.0

[a] Cowan, R. D., *J. Chem. Phys.* 18, 1101 (1950).
* Estimated.

Molecules of the type $NaXO_2(Ac)_3$, where X is uranium, neptunium, plutonium and americium were examined in the infrared region by Jones.[211] Utilizing the symmetric and antisymmetric stretching frequencies of the O—X—O groups, approximate X—O force constants were calculated and found to decrease in the order $k_{U-O} > k_{Np-O} > k_{Pu-O} > k_{Am-O}$, respective values being 0.705, 0.698, 0.675, and 0.612 megadyne cm^{-1}. The X—O bond distance decreases in the same order. It was suggested that the decrease in bond distance accompanied by the decrease in force constant occurs because the bond, though shortened by contraction of the electron shells of the metal is weakened by interaction with the extra valence shell electrons. The data appear in Table 25.

TABLE 25. VIBRATIONAL FREQUENCIES (cm^{-1}) OF $Na\,XO_2(Ac)_3$ COMPOUNDS

(After Jones [225])

	NaAc[a]	$NaUO_2(Ac)_3$	$NaNpO_2(Ac)_3$	$NaPuO_2(Ac)_3$	$NaAmO_2(Ac)_3$
ν_1 (C—H stretch)	2933	2933	2935	2927	
ν_2 (CH$_3$ def.)	1425	1413	1410	1415	
ν_3 (C—O stretch)	1408	1472	1472	1470	1467
ν_4 (C—C stretch)	924	948	948	948	948
ν_5 (CO$_2$ def.)	645	678	677	677	675
ν_6 torsion about C—C bond					
ν_7 (C—H stretch)	2999	2978	2980	2980	
ν_8 (C—O stretch)	1578	1537	1536	1540	1541
ν_9 (CH$_2$ def.)	1440	(1450)?			
ν_{10} (CH$_3$ rock)	1012	1004	1004	1004	
ν_{11} (CO$_2$ rock)	465				
ν_{12} (C—H stretch)	2999	2978	2980	2980	
ν_{13} (CH$_3$ def.)	1488	(1480)?			
ν_{14} (CH$_3$ rock)	1045	1055	1054	1054	1052
ν_{15} (CO$_2$ rock)	615	612	610	609	
ν_1 (O—X—O)[b]		856	844	818	749
ν_3 (O—X—O)		931	934	930	914
$(\nu_1 + \nu_3)$ (XO$_2$ group)[b]		1781	1770	1739	

[a] Jones, C. H., and McLaren, E. H., *J. Chem. Phys.*, **22**, 1796 (1954).
[b] Observed only on very thick samples.

211. Jones, L. H., *J. Chem. Phys.*, **23**, 2105 (1954).

Complex Compounds

It would be difficult in a work of this nature to include all the investigations which have appeared in the literature on the spectral studies of complex structures. However, some of the typical studies involving the inorganic coordination compounds and the metal-organic complexes will be presented. It is hoped that the reader will supplement the discussion here with ample use of the references recorded in the bibliography of Part III. Typical complexes involving only inorganic moieties are the hexamine metal complexes, $M(NH_3)_6^{+y}X_y$, where M is a metal of valency y and X is a univalent anion. Kobayashi and Fujita[212] observed absorption maxima of the hexammine metal complexes, $[Ni(NH_3)_6]Cl_2$, $[Cr(NH_3)_6]Cl_3$, and $[Co(NH_3)_6]Cl_3$. A strong band observed in the neighborhood of 3000 cm^{-1} was attributed to the N—H stretching mode. The formation of the NH_3-metal bond is associated with a considerable shift of the NH stretching frequency within the NH_3. In coordination compounds, it is expected that the more covalent character of the nitrogen-metal bond will result in a lower frequency for the N—H stretching vibration. The N—H frequencies of the complexes lie between that of pure ammonia and NH_3—H^+, the strongest covalent bond. The shifts of N—H frequencies to longer wavelengths decrease in the order of Co, Cr, Ni, while the complex stability increases in this order. Force constants calculated for the Ni—N, Cr—N, Co—N bonds were 3.62×10^5, 4.38×10^5, and 5.36×10^5 dyne cm^{-1} respectively. The vibrational modes of the NH_3 ligand have been observed and studied in the works of Mizushima *et al.*,[213, 214] Hill and Rosenberg,[215] and Caglioti *et al.*[216]

212. Kobayashi, M., and Fujita, J., *J. Chem. Phys.*, **23**, 1354 (1955).
213. Mizushima, S., Nakagawa, K., and Sweeny, D. M., *J. Chem. Phys.*, **25**, 1006 (1956).
214. Mizushima, S., Nakagawa, I., and Quagliano, J. V., *J. Chem. Phys.*, **23**, 1367 (1955).
215. Hill, D. G., and Rosenberg, F., *J. Chem. Phys.*, **24**, 1219 (1956); *ibid.*, **22**, 148 (1954).
216. Caglioti, V., Silvestroni, P., Sartori, G., and Scrocco, M., *Ricerca sci.*, **26**, 1743 (1956).

It is concluded that the metal-ligand bond is fairly covalent in the complexes $[Co(NH_3)_6]I_3$, $[Co(NH_3)_5Cl]Cl_2$, $[Co(NH_3)_5Br]Br_2$, $[Pd(NH_3)_4]PdCl_4$, and $[Co(NH_3)_5H_2O]Cl_2$.[214] Hexammine cobalt salts of the form, $Co(NH_3)_6X_3$, where X is a halogen and pentammine cobalt salts of the form, $Co(NH_3)_5Z \cdot X_{3+a}$, where Z is a group substituted for one of the ammonia molecules, and is charged or neutral according as a has a negative or zero value, were studied in the region 820 cm^{-1} and 1310 cm^{-1}.[215] As a result of the preliminary work, it was suggested that the salts have bands which probably arise from the vibrations of the octahedral cation, in addition to the usual N—H frequencies. A shift in the 820 cm^{-1} band was noted for change in anion. Two fundamentals are expected to appear in the infrared region for a totally symmetric octahedral molecule. The bands observed in the neighborhood of 820 cm^{-1} and 1310 cm^{-1} were identified with these fundamentals for the hexammine complexes. The bands were still present after exchange of one of the NH$_3$ molecules with a bromide or azide ion or water molecule. With the water-substituted molecule, one would hardly anticipate any appreciable shift because of the small difference in size of the water and NH$_3$ molecule and because the net charge on the complex moiety is unaltered. However, with either the bromide or azide ion one would expect considerable distortion due to the large size difference and the decrease in net charge.

In a later work, Hill and Rosenberg[217] observed over twenty-five complex cobalt salts, finding bands at approximately 3000 cm^{-1}, 1600 cm^{-1}, 1350 cm^{-1}, and 850 cm^{-1}. The spectra obtained for hexammines and pentammines were quite similar; however, there was a marked difference in the spectra of these salts and those of both the hexanitrilo and trisethylenediamine salts. The four absorption bands of the hexa- and pentammine compounds were also observed with metals other than cobalt and were, thus, ascribed to the ammonia ligand.

Although knowledge of the ammonia group is important, vibrations of the NH$_2$ group are also of interest. Mercuric amido chloride, HgNH$_2$Cl, is one of the simplest molecules containing the

217. Hill, D. G., and Rosenberg, F., *J. Chem. Phys.*, **24**, 1219 (1956).

NH$_2$ group.   It is believed to have an infinite chain structure, and although it is not a complex molecule in the general sense of the term it might well be used to gain useful information about the NH$_2$ modes.   Four NH$_2$ deformations (bending, wagging, rocking, twisting) are expected, the twist being inactive in the infrared because of molecular symmetry.   The normal vibrations of the infinite chain of the (HgNH$_2$)$^+$ ion were calculated and found to be in agreement with the observed values.[218]

The differentiation of *cis-trans* isomers by infrared absorption has been studied by Merritt and Wiberley.[219]   Strong absorption bands in the region 1639–1538 cm^{-1} were observed for each of nineteen coordination compounds of cobalt studied.   For complexes containing ethylenediamine, the *trans*-isomer has a peak maximum at a frequency of 21–44 cm^{-1} higher than the *cis*-isomer.   For tetramine complexes, a shift occurs in the 833.3 cm^{-1} region with the *cis*-isomer exhibiting an absorption maximum up to 114 cm^{-1} higher than the *trans*-isomer.

Spectra of complexes containing the cyano group have been observed in mulls, in KBr disks and from single crystals.   Eight octacyano complexes of tungsten and molybdenum were examined in the region 5000–300 cm^{-1} in KBr pellets.[220]   The dehydrated complexes showed two sharply resolved OH stretching vibration bands and a splitting of the C≡N stretching vibration was observed.   When special modifications were devised to dehydrate the samples, the C≡N splitting was less prominent and a strong intensity band observed in the hydrated samples near 400 cm^{-1} was shifted to longer wavelengths.   Jones[221, 222] has calculated bending and stretching force constants for a number of cyanide molecules using the observed vibrational frequencies.   For the

218. Mizushima, S., Nakagawa, I., and Sweeny, D. M., *J. Chem. Phys.*, **25**, 1006 (1956).
219. Merritt, P. E., and Wiberley, S. E., *J. Phys. Chem.*, **59**, 55 (1955).
220. Brame, E. G., Jr., Johnson, F. A., Larsen, E. M., and Meloche, V. W., *J. Inorg. and Nucl. Chem.*, **6**, 99 (1958).
221. Jones, L. H., *J. Chem. Phys.*, **22**, 1135 (1954); **25**, 379 (1956); **27**, 468, 665 (1957).
222. Jones, L. H., and Penneman, R. A., *J. Chem. Phys.*, **22**, 965 (1954); **28**, 169 (1958).

molecules $KAu(CN)_2$, $Hg(CN)_2$ and $KAu(CN)_2$, the results indicate that the cyanides are bound to the metal through the carbon atoms. Using polarized spectra of $KAg(CN)_2$ and $KAu(CN)_2$, Jones showed that the angle of inclination between the linear NC—M—CN groups (where M is Ag or Au) and the c-axis of the crystal is essentially the same for the two compounds. For the analogous angle in $KAg(CN)_2$, a value of 27° was found by x-ray diffraction.[223]

The complex structures of metals with organic ligands have been the subject of much speculation. Several investigators have examined the infrared spectra of metal derivatives of oxalic acid,[224] acetylacetone,[225-228] phthalocyanine,[229] and other organic chelating agents (see bibliography). Most bands of the chelate compounds are difficult to assign because of the complicated structure of the molecule. Consequently, most of the work has been limited to the bands which appear to be relatively sensitive to the metal. The oxalate ion is a simple ligand whose fundamentals may be assigned using the Wilson FG technique. Fujita, Nakamoto, and Kobayashi[224] found that as the metal is changed in the order of Ni^{+2}, Co^{+2}, Cu^{+2}, Fe^{+3}, Cr^{+3}, and Al^{+3} the absorption bands shift in the following manner. The bands arising from the asymmetric O—C—O and C—C—O bending modes and from two of the C—O stretching modes are shifted progressively toward higher frequencies. The bands arising from the two remaining C—O stretching modes and the symmetric C—C—O bending mode appear at lower frequencies. The aluminum complex deviates somewhat but this may be attributed to its different configuration and smaller size (see Table 26).

223. Hoard, J. L., *Z. Krist.*, **84**, 231 (1933).
224. Fujita, J., Nakamoto, K., and Kobayashi, M., *J. Phys. Chem.*, **61**, 1014 (1957).
225. Lecomte, J., *Disc. of the Faraday Soc.*, **9**, 125 (1950).
226. Duval, C. L., Freymann, R., and Lecomte, J., *Bull. soc. chem. France*, 106 (1952).
227. Mecke, R., and Funck, E., *Z. Elektrochem.*, **60**, 1124 (1956).
228. West, R., and Riley, R., *J. Inorg. Nucl. Chem.*, **5**, 295 (1958).
229. Sidorov, A. N., and Terenin, A. N., *Doklady Akad. Nauk USSR*, **104**, 575 (1955).

TABLE 26. INFRARED SPECTRA OF METALLIC OXALATES AND FREE OXALATE ION (Cm^{-1})

(After Fujata, Nakamoto and Kobayashi [224])

Compd.* C_{2v}	Asym. ν(C–O)		Sym. ν(C–O)		ν(C–C)	Asym. δ(O–C–O)	Asym. δ(C–C–O)	Sym. δ(C–C–O)	Sym. δ(O–C–O)
	b_1	a_1	a_1	b_1	a_1	b_1	b_1	a_1	a_1
K_3Alox_3	1718	1656	1404	1296, 1270	905	822, 806	581	431	483[a]
K_3Coox_3	1710	1658	1389	1257	900	824, 810	559	446	476[a]
K_3Crox_3	1714	1650	1390	1259	894	817, 807	543	488	413[a]
K_3Feox_3	1712	1641	1389	1272, 1255	886	804, 795	532	503	
K_2Cuox_2	1675	1637	1415	1280	897	804	538	485	
K_2Coox_2	1625		(1450)	1306		790		507	
K_2Niox_2	1620			1316		772		524	
Ox^{2-}	1664[b]	1630	1485[b], 1450[b]	1335, 1316	898[b]	768	545[b]	518	443[b]
(V_h)	b_{1g}	b_{2u}	a_g	b_{3u}	a_g	b_{3u}	b_{1g}	b_{2u}	a_g

* The symmetry C_{2v} is assigned to the metal-oxalate coordination compound.

[a] Band assignment is not clear.

[b] Raman data by Murata and Kawai, J. Chem. Phys., 25, 589 (1956).

The oxalate ion[230] is considered as planar and the structural parameters are as shown:

The inequality in the angles C—C—O_I and C—C—O_{II} is perhaps due to experimental error in the analysis and the ion has been assigned V_h symmetry. The formation of the M—O bond lengthens the C—O_I bond and strengthens the C—O_{II} bond to an extent dependent on the strength of the metal-oxygen bond. This results in shifts of (C—O_I) and (C—O_{II}) to lower and higher frequencies, respectively. The relation between the strength of the M—O bond and the shifts of the bending modes is somewhat complex, but the M—O bond becomes stronger in the order of the metals, Ni^{+2}, Co^{+2}, Cu^{+2}, Fe^{+3}, Cr^{+3}, Co^{+3}, Al^{+3}. For the divalent ions, this is in the order of the stability constants of the oxalates. For the trivalent ions, stability constant data for the oxalate chelates was not available; however, the order is consistent with the stability constant order of other complexes in which the metals are coordinated by oxygen. Metal complexes involving more complicated ligands than the oxalate ion are constantly being investigated by spectral methods in order to gain more information bearing on the problem of metal-ligand bonding.

A critical review of some of the significant results in the study of transitional metal complexes via infrared spectroscopy has been made by Cotton.[231] This summary treats many inorganic coordination compounds as well as the following organic complexes:

230. Jeffrey, G. A., and Parry, G. S., *J. Am. Chem. Soc.*, **76**, 5283 (1954).
231. Cotton, F. A., "The Infrared Spectra of Transitional Metal Complexes," in Lewis and Wilkins, "Modern Coordination Chemistry," Interscience Publishers Inc., New York, 1956.

metal sandwich compounds, cyclo-pentadienyl metal carbonyls, nitrosyls, alkyls, etc., β-diketones, oxalato and related complexes, alkene and alkyne complexes, complexes of amino acids, urea, ethylenediamine-tetraacetic acid, dimethylglyoxime, and 8-hydroxyquinoline, and complexes of large organic ligands, such as derivatives of tetraphenylporphin.

GLOSSARY

Brief explanatory notes and definitions of many of the terms used in the preceding parts are given below. For more detailed discussions of the concepts, techniques, and notation the following list of general references is recommended.

Bellamy, L. J., "The Infrared Spectra of Complex Molecules," John Wiley & Sons, Inc., New York, 1954, or Methuen and Co., Ltd., London, 1954.

Hershenson, H. M., "Infrared Absorption Spectra-Index for 1945–1957," Academic Press, New York, 1959.

Herzberg, G., "Infrared and Raman Spectra of Polyatomic Molecules," D. Van Nostrand Co., Inc., New York, 1945.

Lewis, J., and Wilkins, R. G., "Modern Coordination Chemistry," Interscience Publishers Inc., New York, 1960. (In Chapter 5, contributing author F. A. Cotton discusses the infrared spectra of transitional metal complexes.)

Lothian, G. F., "Absorption Spectrophotometry," The Macmillan Company, New York, 1958.

"Report on Notation for the Spectra of Polyatomic Molecules," *J. Chem. Phys.*, 23, 1997–2011 (1955).

West, W., "Chemical Applications of Spectroscopy" in A. Weissberger's "Technique of Organic Chemistry," Vol. IX, Interscience Publishers, Inc., New York, 1956. (An excellent section discussing the location of spectra in the literature is given by authors R. N. Jones and C. Sandorfy on pp. 327–331 of this volume.)

Wilson, E. B., Decius, J. C., and Cross, P. C., "Molecular Vibrations," McGraw-Hill Book Co., New York, 1955.

Absorption coefficient (absorbancy index, extinction coefficient, absorptivity). A quantity (index), a, defined by the expression: $a = \dfrac{1}{dc} \log_{10} \dfrac{I_0}{I}$, where d is the length of the absorbing path, c is the concentration of material in any specified units, and $\log I_0/I$ is the absorbence (optical density). When d is expressed in cm. and c in moles per liter, the index is called the molar absorbancy index or molar extinction coefficient, e.

Absorption edge. The limit or discontinuity appearing in the intensity of an absorption spectrum.

Absorptivity. The fraction of the incident radiation absorbed by a substance. The ratio of radiant energy absorbed by a substance to that absorbed by a black body under the same conditions. See also under **absorption coefficient.**

Amorphous. Having no definite form; non-crystalline.

Anharmonic oscillator. An oscillator in which the restoring force does not vary linearly with the displacement of the system from its equilibrium position. The **anharmonicity** may be mechanical or electrical. If electrical, the variation of dipole moment (infrared) or polarizability (Raman) with internuclear distance is non-linear. **Anharmonicity corrections** must be used for exact calculations of band centers and intensities.

Anisotropic. Having different properties for different orientations.

Black body. A body whose absorptivity is unity, i.e., it absorbs all of the radiant energy incident on it for all wavelengths.

Bending modes. Vibrational modes which involve changes in the interbond angles of a molecule. Such modes are associated with lower force constants and thus appear at lower frequencies than do **stretching modes.** Bond-bending vibrations are sometimes called **deformations,** which are described by many authors using such terms as scissors, wag, rock, twist, etc.

Chelate compounds. Compounds which are formed when a metal ion enters into ring formation with a substance containing two or more electron donor groups.

Crystallites. Small, generally imperfectly formed crystals. Component grains of a polycrystalline material.

Crystal systems. Crystals may be classified according to their symmetry into seven major divisions. For the various systems, certain relationships exist among the crystallographic axes—a, b, c—and the axial angles—

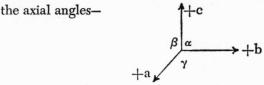

(1) *Triclinic* (no symmetry greater than 1-fold),
$$a \neq b \neq c$$
$$\alpha \neq \beta \neq \gamma \neq 90°$$

(2) *Monoclinic* (one two-fold axis along b and no higher symmetry),

$$a \neq b \neq c$$
$$\alpha = \gamma = 90°, \beta \neq 90°$$

(3) *Orthorhombic, Rhombic* (three two-fold axes along a, b, and c),

$$a \neq b \neq c$$
$$\alpha = \beta = \gamma = 90°$$

(4) *Tetragonal* (one four-fold axis along c),

$$a = b \neq c$$
$$\alpha = \beta = \gamma = 90°$$

(5) *Cubic, Regular, Isometric* (four three-fold axes),

$$a = b = c$$
$$\alpha = \beta = \gamma = 90°$$

(6) *Hexagonal* (one six-fold axis), Three horizontal axes a_1, a_2, a_3 equal and at an angle of 120° to each other, a 4th axis unequal and normal to the plane of a_1, a_2, a_3.

(7) *Trigonal Rhombohedral* (one three-fold axis),

$$a = b = c$$
$$\alpha = \beta = \gamma \neq 90°$$

These seven systems give rise to 32 different **symmetry classes** or **point groups** and 230 **space groups** with which a crystal may be associated. The classification of a crystal into these groups is dependent upon the presence of certain elements of symmetry.

Curie point (temperature). The critical temperature above which ferromagnetic materials lose their spontaneous magnetization. The term is also applicable to ferroelectric materials which often show several Curie points.

$-^d$**x.** A symbol denoting deuterium substitution; the subscript x is a number indicative of the extent of deuteration. E.g., ammonia $-d_2$ and ammonia $-d_3$ refer respectively to the replacement of two and three hydrogens with deuterium atoms.

Deutero–. Prefix denoting the replacement of hydrogen in a compound by its isotope of mass 2, deuterium. Sometimes deuterio–, particularly so used in *Chemical Abstracts*.

Dipole. A unit in which the effective centers of opposite electrical or magnetic charges are separated by a small distance. The **dipole**

moment of such a unit is mathematically the product of one of the charges and the separation distance.

Electromagnetic Spectrum, Subdivisions of Interest in Molecular Structure Studies.

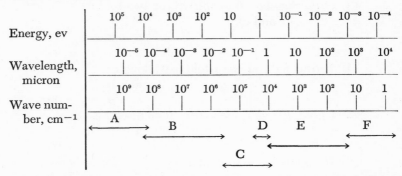

The interactions of the electromagnetic radiation in the regions A, B, C, D, E, and F with matter are as follows:

Region	Effect
A–Gamma rays	Ionization and nuclear transformation
B–X-rays	Electronic transitions within inner orbits
C–Ultraviolet	Electronic transitions involving outer orbits
D–Visible	Electronic transitions involving outer orbits
E–Infrared	Vibrational transitions (also rotational in the far infrared)
F–Microwaves	Rotational transitions

Energy gap.   The energy range between the bottom of the conduction band and the top of the valence band of a semiconductor.   Sometimes referred to as the **forbidden energy gap** or **band,** implying the energy range in which there are no electronic levels.

Ferroelectric.   Pertaining to materials which exhibit spontaneous polarization (dipole moment).

Ferromagnetic.   Pertaining to materials which have permeabilities appreciably greater than 1, exhibiting a permanent magnetic moment.

Ground state.   The lowest energy state of a system.

Hygroscopic.   Term applied to substances which absorb water from the atmosphere.

Intermolecular coupling.   Interaction between molecules.

Isomers.   Substances having the same number and kind of atoms but different structural arrangement of the atoms in the molecule.

Different physical and/or chemical properties are exhibited by the isomeric forms.

Isotropic. Having the same properties in all directions.

Lattice (space lattice). A particular arrangement of structural units (atoms, groups of atoms, or molecules), such that the environments of all points are identical. There are 14 different types of lattices determined by lengths and orientations of the primitive translations which carry the unit cell into its neighbor. For the cubic system, for example, there are three possible lattice types—simple, face-centered, and body-centered.

Matrix. A medium in which a sample is dispersed for the purpose of examining its spectrum. In infrared spectroscopy, matrix materials may be alkali halide powders, as in the pellet technique, or gases, in which the sample is frozen, as in the matrix isolation technique.

Mean free path. The mean (average) distance which is traversed by a particle of a system between successive collisions with other particles.

Mobility. Motion of charged particles subject to force fields. The term is generally applicable to all processes of electrical conduction, whether the charge is carried by holes, electrons, ions, or the like.

Non-polar molecule. A molecule which does not have a dipole moment. Electrons between the bonded atoms are evenly distributed. The bonding is **atomic** or **homopolar.** Such bonding is also often referred to as **covalent.**

Normal modes of vibration. Simple oscillatory motions in which all atoms undergo their maximum displacement at the same time and pass through their equilibrium positions at the same time, i.e., the frequency and phase of the motion for each coordinate of the system are equal. There are $3n-5$ or $3n-6$ ($n =$ number of atoms) genuine normal modes of vibration for molecules, depending on whether the system is linear or not. The five or six non-genuine vibrations are simply translations or rotations of the molecule as a whole.

The lowest frequency normal mode is called the fundamental mode. Modes whose frequencies are integral multiples of the fundamental are called overtones or harmonics. The number ascribed to the harmonic is always identically its frequency divided by that of the fundamental, the $(n + 1)^{th}$ harmonic being the nth overtone.

Two or more normal modes may have the same frequency, in which case they are called **degenerate** vibrations. Under such conditions, it is possible to construct an infinite number of normal modes by superimposing the degenerate modes with different phases. It is, then, no longer required that the atoms move in straight lines although they continue to move with the same frequency. The **degeneracy** is defined as the number of linearly independent modes of a given frequency.

Ortho-para ratio of hydrogen.   In the hydrogen molecule, it is possible to have two different nuclear spin combinations. The molecular form in which the nuclei have antiparallel spins is para-hydrogen; the form in which the spins are parallel is ortho-hydrogen. At room temperature the temperature-dependent ortho-para ratio is 3:1.

Photoconductivity threshold.   The frequency of radiation which is just sufficient to cause increased electric conductivity in a substance when illuminated.

Point groups.   Molecules may be classified into symmetry groups by the number and nature of symmetry elements they possess. In molecular spectroscopy, the 32 possible symmetry groups (point groups) are described most often in the Schoenflies notation; in crystallographic work the Hermann-Mauguin system is used. The Schoenflies notation and associated symmetry elements are:

Symbol	Symmetry Element
C_n (Cyclic)	An n-fold rotation axis
D_n (Dihedral)	An n-fold rotation axis and n two-fold axes $\perp$ to it
S_n	An n-fold rotation-reflection axis
T (Tetrahedral)	Four 3-fold axes directed toward the vertices of a tetrahedron
O (Octahedral)	Three mutually perpendicular 4-fold axes

Subscripts v, h, d, i, s, denote vertical reflection plane containing the symmetry axis, horizontal reflection plane $\perp$ to the axis, dihedral reflection plane bisecting the angle between two 2-fold axes, inversion, and reflection plane respectively. Thus: Molecular symmetry C_{2v} indicates that the molecule possesses a 2-fold rotation axis and two vertical planes of symmetry through the axis.

In crystal studies, numerical superscripts are used to denote the space groups isomorphous with the point group. E.g., D_{4h}^6 and D_{4h}^{17} are both space groups isomorphous with the point group D_{4h}.

Each point group can be reduced into a number of non-equivalent irreducible representations. Vibrational modes are found to belong to one of these representations. The notation used is as follows:

Non-degenerate fundamentals	a, b
Doubly-degenerate fundamentals	e
Triply-degenerate fundamentals	f

For combination bands capital letters are used. For non-degenerate modes the letter a or b is used according as the mode is symmetrical or antisymmetrical with respect to rotation about the principal axis. Subscripts 1, 2 or g, u, and superscripts ' and " are used with both non-degenerate and degenerate modes and are related to the symmetry or asymmetry of the mode with respect to a certain operation of the point group.

Polar molecule. A molecule which possesses a dipole moment. The moment is generally produced by the uneven distribution of electrons between the bonded atoms. The bonding is largely **ionic** or **heteropolar**. Such bonding is also often referred to as **electrovalent**.

Polarizability. When an external electric field produces or alters the dipole moment of a molecule or atom, the process is called polarization. The polarizability of an isotropic molecule is defined by the equation, $\hat{\mu} = \alpha \hat{E}$, where $\hat{\mu}$ is the induced moment and E is the field strength.

Polymerization. Reaction or process by which compounds of higher molecular weight but same percentage composition are formed from simpler compounds. E.g., $n\text{HF} \longrightarrow (\text{HF})_n$.

PQR branches. When a molecule is excited by infrared radiation, vibrational and rotational changes occur concomitantly. Consequently, each vibrational band, when well-resolved, may appear as three branches. As the vibrational quantum number, v, increases, a P, Q, or R branch appears according as the rotational energy is increased, unaffected, or decreased, respectively. The frequencies contained in the three branches diminish in the order $P > Q > R$, the rotational quantum number, J changes by -1, 0, and $+1$ in the same order.

Quadrupole moment. Atoms or molecules which have no dipole moment may have electric moments of higher order. The higher order moments may be thought of as arrangements of dipoles with different orientations. For example, two dipoles combined form a quadrupole, four an octupole. The strength of attraction between atoms or molecules having a quadrupole moment decreases very rapidly as the separation distance increases.

Raman effect. An effect associated with the incoherent scattering of monochromatic light by a substance on which the light is incident. Additional lines appear in the spectrum of the incident light near each of its prominent lines. A necessary condition for a molecule to exhibit the Raman effect is that the molecule experiences a change in polarizability.

Selection rules. A set of rules, derived from quantum mechanics, which govern the possibility of transitions between states of a system. **Forbidden** transitions violate the selection rules while **allowed** transitions are in accord with them. The differences in energy of two vibrational levels between which transitions take place determine the frequencies of infrared absorption bands. Allowed transitions in the infrared depend on the non-vanishing of the integral $\int \psi_a^* M \psi_b \, d\tau$ where ψ_a and ψ_b are wave functions of the upper and lower states respectively and M is the dipole moment operator. When the integral has a non-zero value, the **intensity** of the transition is dependent upon the magitude of that value. A forbidden transition assumes the vanishing of this integral.

Semiconductors. Solids whose electrical resistivity at room temperature lies intermediate between that of conductors and insulators. The electrical charge carrier concentration varies with thermal agitation over some range of temperature. Pure semiconducting substances which are void of impurities are termed **intrinsic,** while those whose electrical properties are dependent on impurities are termed **extrinsic.** Extrinsic semiconductors having an excess of negative charge carriers (electrons) are called n-type semiconductors; those having an excess of positive charge carriers (holes) are called p-type semiconductors.

Skin effect. An effect in which the depth of penetration of electric currents in a conductor decreases with increasing current frequency.

Spectrum. A graphic representation, visual display, or photograph of the intensity distribution of radiant energy with respect to wavelength, frequency, or some related quantity. Various types of spectra may be observed depending on the type of matter-light interaction involved:

Absorption spectrum. Energy is removed from the light beam and reappears as heat or some other form,

Emission spectrum. Energy is released from the substance after it has received proper excitation with heat, bombardment, etc.,

Diffraction spectrum. The incident beam is distributed (spread) by the substance into other beams,

Polarized spectrum. An absorption spectrum obtained with plane-polarized light, i.e., the electric vectors of all components of the incident beam lie in the same plane. Similarly, in emission spectroscopy the substance may be excited with polarized light, followed by determination of the polarization of the emitted light,

Raman spectrum. See Raman effect; a spectrum so obtained.

Reflectance spectrum. The direction of the incident beam is changed as it is impinged upon the surface of the substance.

Stability constant. For the equilibrium reaction, $M + nL \gtrless ML_n$, between a metal ion M and a ligand L, the stability constant β_n for the complex, ML_n, is defined by $\beta_n = [ML_n] / [M] [L]^n$, where the brackets denote concentrations.

Stretching modes. Vibrational modes which involve extensions of bonds between atoms. The mode may be **symmetric** or **antisymmetric** according as the atoms move in-phase or out-of-phase, respectively.

Symmetry elements and operations. Associated with every element of symmetry there is an operation which will transform the molecule (or any geometrical figure) into a configuration that is indistinguishable from the original. Examples of symmetry elements are (1) the identity, (2) center of symmetry, (3) rotation axes, (4) reflection planes and (5) rotation-reflection axes.

Zwitterion. A dipolar ion, i.e., an ion which carries both positive and negative charge. While electrically neutral, the unit has a dipole moment, e.g., the zwitterion form of sulfamic acid, $H_3N^+SO_2O^-$.

PART III

Bibliography of Unclassified References

THIS BIBLIOGRAPHY was constructed largely by searching the section of *Chemical Abstracts* entitled "Electronic Phenomenon and Spectra," for the period January 1952 through December 1958. It is divided chronologically into sections which correspond to the year of publication of the original works. Numbers appearing at the end of an entry refer to the volume and column index of *Chemical Abstracts*. For example, *50–75* indicates that the work was abstracted in column 75 of Volume 50 of *Chemical Abstracts*. Papers are included on the theory, techniques, spectral data, and applications of infrared absorption for a large variety of inorganic materials. Emission, Raman, and reflectance spectra are included only where they appear as part of or in support of an absorption study.

An effort has been made to provide annotations to the bibliography, particularly in the cases of entries whose titles give little information concerning the nature of the work performed. A subject index which was prepared from the material in *Chemical Abstracts*, or the original article is presented at the end of the reference list. Review articles and papers, which for various reasons were unavailable for proper indexing, are included in the index under the heading *General*. A supplementary reference list whose entries appear in the subject index is presented at the end. These references were reported since the original construction of the bibliographic section and therefore are not included in the main body of the bibliography. This supplementary list represents coverage of material appearing in *Chemical Abstracts* or elsewhere through April, 1960. References to published works on metal-organic complexes are not indexed.

1950

1. Bardeen, J., "Theory of Infrared Absorption in Silicon and Germanium," *Phys. Rev.*, **79**, 216. *46–6923*.
2. Herzberg, G., and Reid, C., "Infrared Spectrum and Structure of the HNCO Molecule," *Discussions Faraday Soc.*, **No. 9**, 92. *46–3403*.
   The spectrum of HNCO was examined from 450–8000 cm^{-1} using LiF, NaCl, and KBr prisms and out to 13,220 cm^{-1} using a 21 ft. grating spectrograph.
3. Hornig, D. F., "Infrared Spectra of Crystals at Low Temperatures," *Discussions Faraday Soc.*, **No. 9**, 115. *46–3408*.
   Data and discussion for CO_2 and HCN.
4. Hunt, J. M., Wisherd, M. P., and Bonham, L. C., "Infrared Absorption Spectra of Minerals and Other Inorganic Compounds," *Anal. Chem.*, **22**, 1478.
   Infrared spectra of minerals and other inorganic compounds (64 samples) are obtained for the region 625–5000 cm^{-1}. Spectral positions of the principal absorption bands are tabulated.
5. Lohman, J. B., and Hornig, D. F., "The Infrared Spectrum of Crystalline Hydrogen Sulfide," *Phys. Rev.*, **79**, 235. *46–6924*.
6. Nielsen, H. H., "The Low-Frequency Fundamental Bands in the Spectrum of Arsine," *Discussions Faraday Soc.*, **No. 9**, 85. *46–3405*.
   Discussion of the arsine bands in the region 859–1130 cm^{-1}.
7. Taylor, W. J., Beckett, C. W., Tung, J. Y., Holden, R. B., and Johnston, H. L., "Raman and Infrared Spectra of Pentaborane," *Phys. Rev.*, **79**, 234. *46–6924*.
8. Woltz, P. J. H., Jones, E. A., and Nielsen, A. H., "Some New Measurements on the Infrared and Raman Spectra of Silicon Tetrafluoride," *Phys. Rev.*, **79**, 416. *46–6924*.

1951

9. Bovey, L. F. H., "The Infrared Absorption and Reflection Spectra of the Ammonium Halides," *J. Opt. Soc. Am.*, **41**, 836. *46–343.*

The results of absorption and reflection spectra of NH_4Cl, NH_4F, NH_4Br, and NH_4I at 20° and −150° in the range 1400–3400 cm^{-1} are interpreted in terms of crystal structure.

10. Burke, T. G., and Jones, E. A., "Spectra of Bromine Pentafluoride," *J. Chem. Phys.*, **19**, 1611. *46–4366.*

Spectrum of gaseous BrF_5 was observed from 400–700 cm^{-1} using KBr optics. With supporting data from the Raman spectrum of liquid BrF_5, a tetragonal pyramid structure is suggested.

11. Burke, T. G., and Smith, D. F., "The Infrared and Raman Spectra of Molybdenum Hexafluoride," *Phys. Rev.*, **83**, 485. *47–6754.*

An abstract of a paper presented at the American Physical Society meeting.

12. Callomon, H. J., McKean, D. C., and Thompson, H. W., "Intensities of Vibration Bands. III. Nitrous Oxide," *Proc. Roy. Soc. (London)*, **A208**, 332. *46–5435.*

The absolute band intensity has been determined at 2222 cm^{-1} and has been correlated with the polar properties of the N—N and N—O linkages.

13. Caunt, A. D., Short, L. N., and Woodward, L. A., "Raman and Infrared Spectra of Germanium Tetrafluoride," *Nature (London)*, **168**, 557. *46–10892.*

The most intense infrared absorption band of GeF_4 (gaseous) is located at 800 cm^{-1}.

14. Cotè, G. L., and Thompson, H. W., "Infrared Spectra and the Solid State. III. Potassium Bifluoride," *Proc. Roy. Soc. (London)*, **A210**, 206. *46–10891.*

Spectra are reported for the 1250–5000 cm^{-1} range between 293° and 90°K.

15. Cotè, G. L., and Thompson, H. W., "Infrared Spectra and the Solid State. IV. Fluoborates," *Proc. Roy. Soc. (London)*, **A210**, 217. *46–10891.*

Spectra of ammonium, potassium, and sodium fluoborates are reported for the range 400–5000 cm^{-1}.

16. Dowd, J. J., "Optical Properties of Selenium," *Proc. Phys. Soc. (London)*, **64B**, 783. *46–10896.*

The absorption coefficient of amorphous selenium has been measured in the near infrared region.

17. Duval, Cl., Lecomte, J., and Morandat, J., "The Infrared Absorption Spectra of Metallic Salts Including the XO_2 Group (Chlorites and Nitrites)," *Bull. soc. chim. France*, 745. *46–5436.*

18. Edelson, D., and McAfee, K. B., "The Infrared Spectrum of Sulphur Hexafluoride," *J. Chem. Phys.*, **19**, 1311. *46–3856.*

19. Gebbie, A., and Saker, E. W., "Properties of Amorphous Selenium in the Infrared," *Proc. Phys. Soc. (London)*, **64B**, 360. *46–9423.*

    The infrared transmission of selenium is reported from the visible to 2500 cm^{-1} region.

20. Jones, L. H., Badger, R. M., and Moore, G. E., "The Infrared Spectrum and the Structure of Gaseous Nitrous Acid," *J. Chem. Phys.*, **19**, 1599. *46–5969.*

    The infrared spectrum of nitrous acid indicates the existence of two tautomeric forms believed to be cis and trans. An analysis of the spectral observations is given.

21. deLattre, A., "Infrared Spectrum of Some Complex Hexafluorides," *J. Chem. Phys.*, **19**, 1610. *46–4366.*

    Absorption data is presented for Na_3AlF_6, KPF_6 and sodium and ammonium fluoferrates.

22. Loferski, J. J., and Miller, P. H., Jr., "Infrared Properties of Tellurium," *Phys. Rev.*, **83**, 876. *47–6754.*

    An abstract of a paper presented at the American Physical Society Meeting.

23. Louisfert, J., "Infrared Absorption Spectra of Metallic Carbonates in Powder Form," *Compt. rend.*, **233**, 381. *46–1352.*

    Comparison is made between absorption bands and estimated intensities of natural crystals and synthetic preparations of finely divided metal carbonates.

24. Magnuson, D. W., "Infrared and Microwave Studies of Nitrosyl Fluoride," *Phys. Rev.*, **83**, 485. *47–6754.*

    An abstract of a paper presented at the American Physical Society Meeting.

25. Mathis, R., "The Infrared Spectrum of Hydrogen Sulfide at 1.6μ," *J. phys. radium*, **12**, 764. *46–3405.*

26. Matsumura, O., "Infrared Absorption Bands of Water of Crystallization," *Mem. Faculty Sci. Kyusyu Univ.*, **1B**, 1. *46–4365.*

    Absorption spectra were observed for the following hydrates in the 2857–6667 cm^{-1} region.
    $CdSO_4 \cdot 8/3\ H_2O$, $NiSO_4 \cdot H_2O$, $NiSO_4\ (NH_3)_2\ SO_4 \cdot 6H_2O$, $CuSO_4 \cdot 5H_2O$, $CuSO_4\ (NH_3)_4 \cdot H_2O$, $CuSO_4 \cdot 2H_2O$, $KAl\ (SO_4)_2 \cdot 12H_2O$ and $KNa\ C_4H_4O_6 \cdot 4H_2O$.

27. Milatz, J. M. W., Kluyver, J. C., and Hardebol, J., "Determination of Isotope Ratios, e.g., in Tracer Work, by an Infrared Absorption Method," *J. Chem. Phys.*, **19**, 887–8. *46–341.*

    The C^{13}/C^{12} isotope ratio is determined to within 0.002 units.

28. Murray, R. B., "The Near Infrared Spectrum of Nitrous Oxide with Long Absorbing Paths," *Phys. Rev.*, **83**, 486. *47–6754.*

An abstract of a paper presented at the American Physical Society Meeting.

29. Newman, R., and Badger, R. M., "The Polarized Infrared Spectrum of Potassium Bifluoride at $-185°C$," *J. Chem. Phys.*, 19, 1207.   *46–3406.*

   Polarized infrared spectra of KHF_2 crystals are interpreted at 25°C and $-185°C$ in the 700–5800 cm^{-1} region.

30. Nielsen, A. H., and Jones, E. A., "Analysis of Infrared Spectrum of Chlorine Monofluoride," *J. Chem. Phys.*, 19, 1117.   *47–10348.*

31. Nielsen, A. H., and Lagemann, R. T., "High Dispersion Measurements on the ω_3 of $C^{14}O_2^{16}$ at 4.5μ," *Phys. Rev.*, 83, 245.   *47–6754.*

   An abstract of a paper presented at the American Physical Society Meeting.

32. d'Or, L., and Tarte, P., "Spectroscopic Studies of Nitrous Acid.   The Infrared Spectrum of Gaseous Nitrous Acid," *Bull. soc. roy. sci. Liege*, 20, 478.   *46–7875.*

   Spectral data for ordinary and deuterated nitrous acid were obtained from gaseous mixtures of NO—NO_2—H_2O and NO—NO_2—D_2O. Structural features are discussed.

33. Paul, W., Jones, D. A., and Jones, R. V., "Infrared Transmission of Galena," *Proc. Phys. Soc. (London)*, 64B, 528.   *46–9985.*

   In the 833–5000 cm^{-1} range, reflection, absorption, and transmission data are reported.

34. Penner, S. S., and Weber, D., "Quantitative Infrared Intensity Measurements.   I.   Carbon Monoxide Pressurized with Infrared-inactive Gases," *J. Chem. Phys.*, 19, 807.   *46–341.*

   Measurements of infrared intensity of CO pressurized with H_2, He, A, O_2 and N_2 have been made for systems having total pressures up to 700 lbs./sq.in.   Values of integrated absorption for the fundamental of CO is reported as 237 cm^{-2} atm^{-1}, and for the first overtone as 1.64 cm^{-2} atm^{-1}.

35. Penner, S. S., and Weber, S., "Quantitative Infrared Measurements.   II.   Studies on the First Overtone of Unpressurized Carbon Monoxide," *J. Chem. Phys.*, 19, 817.   *46–341.*

   Cells of varying lengths and at different gas pressures were used to measure quantitatively the absorption of unpressurized CO for the first overtone.   A value of 1.69 cm^{-2} atm^{-1} was reported.

36. Penner, S. S., and Weber, D., "Quantitative Line-Width Measurements in the Infrared.   I.   Carbon Monoxide Pressurized with Infrared-Inactive Gases," *J. Chem. Phys.*, 19, 1351.   *46–2401.*

   Quantitative infrared-intensity measurements on CO pressurized with gases are reported.   For pressures up to 100 lbs./sq.in. correlations are made between pressure, absorption and optical density.

37. Penner, S. S., and Weber, D., "Quantitative Linewidth Measurements in

the Infrared. II. Unpressurized Carbon Monoxide," *J. Chem. Phys.*, 19, 1361. *46–2401*.

38. Richardson, W. S., "The Infrared Spectra of $DC^{12}N$ and $DC^{13}N$," *J. Chem. Phys.*, 19, 1213.

    A tabulation is presented for the fundamental infrared frequencies of $DC^{12}N$, $DC^{13}N$, $HC^{12}N$ and $HC^{13}N$.

39. Robinson, D. Z., "The Experimental Determination of the Intensities of Infrared Absorption Bands. IV. Measurements of the Stretching Vibrations of OCS and CS_2," *J. Chem. Phys.*, 19, 881. *46–342*.

40. Rossini, F. D., "American Petroleum Institute Spectral Data and Standard Samples," *Applied Spectroscopy*, 6, No. 1, 3. *46–2899*.

    A report of the available catalogs of spectral data and other materials on infrared, ultraviolet, Raman, and mass spectral data.

41. Shelton, R. D., and Nielsen, A. H., "Infrared Study of the Polymer Bands of Hydrogen Fluoride Vapor," *J. Chem. Phys.*, 19, 1312. *46–3856*.

    LiF, CaF, and NaCl optics were used in examining the HF polymer bands from 425–3000 cm^{-1}. Temperatures ranged from 32–88° C and pressures from atmospheric to vacuum.

42. Simon, I., "Optical Constants of Germanium, Silicon, and Pyrite in the Infrared," *J. Opt. Soc. Amer.*, 41, 730.

    Reflection method is applied to investigate optical properties of semiconductors. Data are reported for the region 600–2400 cm^{-1}.

43. Smith, R. A., "Electric and Optical Properties of Certain Sulfides, Selenides, Tellurides," *Semiconducting Materials*, 198. *49–15455*.

    The electrical and optical properties of sulfides, selenides, and tellurides of Pb and Bi are given along with various hypotheses to explain the experimental results.

44. Taylor, J. H., "Two New Absorption Bands of N_2O," *J. Chem. Phys.*, 19, 1314. *46–35*.

45. Thompson, H. W., and Williams, R. L., "Vibration-Rotation Bands of Nitrous Oxide," *Proc. Roy. Soc. (London)*, A208, 326. *46–5435*.

    A re-investigation of the absorption spectrum of nitrous oxide gas near 2222 cm^{-1} has been reported. The results are discussed analytically.

46. Vincent-Geisse, J., "Variation in the Fine Structure of an Infrared Absorption Spectrum Observed With a Slit of Variable Width," *Compt. rend.*, 233, 1179. *46–10889*.

47. Welsh, H. L., Crawford, M. F., MacDonald, J. C. F., and Chisolm, D. A., "Induced Infrared Absorptions of Hydrogen, Nitrogen, and Oxygen in the First Overtone Regions," *Phys. Rev.*, 83, 1264. *46–340*.

1952

48. Allen, H. C., Jr., and Cross, P. C., "The Asymmetric Rotor. X. The Hydrogen Sulfide Spectrum in the 5150 cm^{-1} region," *J. Chem. Phys.*, **20**, 1709. *47–4739.*

49. Bass, A. M., and Benedict, W. S., "A New Infrared Band System of FeO," *Astrophys. J.*, **116**, 652. *47–3694.*

50. Benedict, W. S., Claassen, H. H., and Shaw, J. H., "Absorption Spectrum of Water Vapor Between 4.5 and 13 Microns," *J. Research Natl. Bur. Standards*, **49**, 91 (Research Paper No. 2347). *47–966.*

    The absorption spectrum has been measured with a 3600 line/inch replica echelette grating as dispersing element.   The absorbing path lengths and concentrations of water vapor were varied.

51. Boyd, D. R. J., and Thompson, H. W., "The Fundamental Vibration Band of Hydrogen Iodide," *Spectrochim. Acta*, **5**, 308.   *47–8515.*

    Greater resolving power has been used in re-examining the HI fundamental vibration band (near 2222 cm^{-1}).   New values have been obtained for the molecular rotational constants.

52. Briggs, H. B., "Infrared Absorption in High-Purity Germanium," *J. Opt. Soc. Amer.*, **42**, 686.   *48–10425.*

    Spectral curves for single crystals of Ge and for thin films of Ge on glass are presented for the range 400–5000 cm^{-1}.

53. Briggs, H. B., and Fletcher, R. C., "New Infrared Absorption Bands in p-Type Germanium," *Phys. Rev.*, **87**, 1130.   *47–11969.*

    Bands were found at 2941 and 2128 cm^{-1} in p-type germanium. The absorption is proportional to the concentration of free holes.

54. Burke, T. G., Smith, D. F., and Nielsen, A. H., "The Molecular Structure of MoF$_6$, WF$_6$, and UF$_6$ from Infrared and Raman Spectra," *J. Chem. Phys.*, **20**, 447.   *46–7432.*

    The region 250–5000 cm^{-1} was examined for MoF$_6$ and WF$_6$ spectra; 588–5000 cm^{-1} for UF$_6$ spectrum.   An interpretation of the observed spectra is given.

55. Caunt, A. D., Short, L. N., and Woodward, C. A., "Raman and Infrared Spectra of Germanium Tetrafluoride," *Trans. Faraday Soc.*, **48**, 873. *47–4743.*

56. Chatterjee, S. D., Ghosh, N. N., and Naha, A. M., "Near-infrared Absorption by Solutions of Inorganic Substances," *J. Chem. Phys.*, **20**, 344. *46–8963.*

    Description of an infra-red colorimeter for the range 9091–12,500 cm^{-1} is given.

    Absorption data are given for aqueous and ammoniacal solutions of CuSO$_4$, NiSO$_4$, also for aqueous solutions of CuCl$_2$, Cu(NO$_3$)$_2$, metal sulfates, and metal NH$_4$ sulfates of Cu, Ni, and Fe(II), and several other inorganic molecules.

57. Chisolm, D. A., MacDonald, J. C. F., Crawford, M. M., Welsh, H. C., "Induced Infrared Absorption in Hydrogen and Hydrogen-foreign Gas Mixtures at Pressures up to 1500 Atmospheres," *Phys. Rev.* **88**, 957. *47–3120.*

58. Clark, M. A., and Cashman, R. J., "Transmission and Spectral Response of Lead Sulfide and Lead Telluride," *Phys. Rev.,* **85**, 1043. *46–5973.*

Transmissions of PbS, 0.48 mm crystal, at 2000–5000 cm^{-1} and of PbTe, 0.11 mm crystal at 1667–5000 cm^{-1} have been observed at 23°–72°, and −194°. Comparison is made at each temperature between the transmittance and the spectral response of photocells made of the same compound.

59. Cohn, H., "Infrared Spectrum of Crystalline Potassium Perchlorate. Reassignment of the Lower Fundamental Frequencies of the Perchlorate Ion," *J. Chem. Soc.,* 4282. *47–4739.*

A Nujol paste was used to measure infrared transmission of potassium perchlorate. The lower fundamental frequencies of the perchlorate ion were reassigned.

60. Coulon, R., "The Infrared Spectrum of Gaseous Hydrofluoric Acid Between 1400 cm^{-1} and 700 cm^{-1}," *J. phys. radium,* **13**, 371. *47–403.*

Three absorption bands are reported. The intensity of the band occurring at 1025 cm^{-1} increases with pressure to the extent that polymeric formation in HF is assumed without doubt.

61. Dayal, B., "The Vibration Spectrum of Rutile," *Proc. Indian Acad. Sci.,* **32A**, 304. *47–7896.*

62. Duval, C., and Lecomte, J., "Infrared Absorption Spectra of Ions of the Type BO_2^- and BO_3^{-3}," *Bull. soc. chim. France,* 101. *47–42.*

Spectral data for the 625–2000 cm^{-1} region have been obtained for samples of Mg, Ca, Ni, Mn, Sr, and Ba orthoborates and for Na, Pb, and Ba metaborates.

63. Duval, C., and Lecomte, J., "Some Solid-State Reactions Studied by Infrared Absorption Spectra," *Compt. rend.,* **234**, 2445. *46–10890.*

Infrared spectroscopy techniques have been applied to powdered solids to determine whether a chemical reaction has occurred after mixing.

64. Eberhardt, W. H., and Burke, T. G., "An Absorption Band of Nitrosyl Chloride at 30μ," *J. Chem. Phys.,* **20**, 529. *46–8964.*

The spectrum of NOCl has been examined from 250–10,000 cm^{-1}.

65. Edelson, D., "The Infrared Spectrum of Disulfur Decafluoride," *J. Am. Chem. Soc.,* **74**, 262. *47–1492.*

66. Fabricand, B. P., Carlson, R. O., Lee, C. A., and Rabi, I. I., "The Rotational Spectrum of Potassium Chloride," *Phys. Rev.,* **86**, 607. *47–6757.*

An abstract of a paper presented at the American Physical Society meeting.

67. Florinskaya, V. A., and Pechenkina, R. S., "Reflection and Transmission

Spectra of Different Modifications of Silica in the Infrared Region," *Doklady Akad. Nauk S.S.S.R.*, **85**, 1265. *47–1491*.

Spectra of quartz crystals, cut parallel and perpendicular to the optical axis, fused quartz, quenched crystalline quartz, pure artificial cristobalite, and pure artificial tridymite were recorded up to 714 cm^{-1}.

68. Giguére, P. A., and Liu, I. D., "Infrared Spectrum, Molecular Structure, and Thermodynamic Functions of Hydroxylamine," *Can. J. Chem.*, **30**, 948. *47–7320*.

The absorption spectra were obtained in the region 400–6667 cm^{-1} for the gaseous and solid states. An analysis was made and a structure suggested.

69. Giguére, P. A., and Liu, I. D., "The Infrared Spectrum of Hydrazine," *J. Chem. Phys.*, **20**, 136. *46–6488*.

Spectral data is given for the absorption of hydrazine from 400–6667 cm^{-1}. The spectrum of the liquid and of the solid at −70°C were measured.

70. Granier-Mayence, J., "Absorption Spectra at Low Temperature. Study of Gaseous Nitrous Oxide and of Gaseous and Liquid Nitric Oxide," *Ann. Phys.*, **7**, 453. *47–3115*.

71. Gross, E. F., and Karryev, N. A., "Absorption of Light in a Crystal of Cuprous Oxide in the Infrared and the Visible," *Doklady Akad. Nauk S.S.S.R.*, **84**, 261. *46–8963*.

Absorption spectrum of Cu_2O is reported in the region 714–1429 cm^{-1}.

72. Gruen, D. M., "Interpretation of the Visible and Near-Infrared Spectra of NpO_2^+ and PuO_2^{++} Ions," *J. Chem. Phys.*, **20**, 1818. *47–1487*.

73. Gutowsky, H. S., and Liehr, A. D., "Infrared Spectra of Phosphorus Trifluoride, Phosphorus Oxyfluoride, and Phosphorus Pentafluoride," *J. Chem. Phys.*, **20**, 1652. *46–10896*.

Spectra were determined at room temperature using NaCl and KBr optics.

74. Hansler, R. C., Bell, E. E., and Oetjen, "Infrared Rotational Spectrum of Hydrogen Sulfide," *Phys. Rev.*, **88**, 174. *48–8024*.

An abstract of a paper presented at the American Physical Society meeting.

75. Harris, L., and Beasley, J. K., "The Infrared Properties of Gold-Smoke Deposits," *J. Opt. Soc. Am.*, **42**, 134. *46–4365*.

Porous structures of colloidal-gold particles are examined under infrared radiation. An interpretation of the optical properties is given.

76. Howard, J. N., and Chapman, R. M., "The Pressure Dependence of the Absorption by Entire Bands of Water Vapor in the Near Infrared," *J. Opt. Soc. Am.*, **42**, 423. *46–7430*.

Absorption has been determined as a function of total pressure, water vapor density, and optical path length in the region from 1429–10,000 cm^{-1}.

77. Howard, J. N., and Chapman, R. M., "Near-Infrared Absorption by Entire Bands of Carbon Dioxide," *J. Opt. Soc. Am.*, **42**, 856. *49–7977.*

78. Hyde, C. E., and Hornig, D. F., "The Measurement of Bond Moments and Derivatives in HCN and DCN from Infrared Intensities," *J. Chem. Phys.*, **20**, 647. *46–10890.*

    The absolute infrared absorption intensities of the fundamentals for HCN and DCN have been measured.

79. Jolly, W. L., "Absorption Spectroscopy in Liquid Ammonia," *U. S. Atomic Energy Comm., Nat'l. Sci. Foundation, Wash., D.C. UCRL–2008*, 3. *47–11993.*

    Spectral curves are given for:
    1) Solid NH_4I, KI, and NaI in liquid NH_3,
    2) H_2O, aqueous NH_3, and liquid NH_3 in the region 7143–16667 cm^{-1},
    3) $CuSO_4$ in H_2O and aqueous NH_3 and $Cu(NO_3)_2$ in liquid NH_3 from 833–25,000 cm^{-1},
    4) $KMnO_4$ in H_2O and liquid NH_3, and
    5) Solutions of Na in liquid NH_3 from 4000–10,000 cm^{-1}.

80. Jones, D. A., Jones, R. V., and Stevenson, R. W. H., "Infrared Transmission Limits of Single Crystals of Some Fluorides," *Proc. Phys. Soc. (London)*, **65B**, 906. *47–3120.*

    Measurements from 769–2000 cm^{-1} were made for LiF, synthetic CuF_2, natural CaF_2, CdF_2, SrF_2, PbF_2, and BaF_2.

81. Keller, W. D., Spotts, J. H., and Biggs, D. L., "Infrared Spectra of Some Rock-Forming Minerals," *Am. J. Sci.*, **250**, 453. *46–7875.*

    Infrared absorption data for 54 samples of carbonate, sulfate, phosphate, and silicate minerals are given.

82. Lagemann, R. T., Jones, E. A., and Woltz, P. J. H., "The Infrared and Raman Spectra of CF_3OF," *J. Chem. Phys.*, **20**, 1768. *47–4740.*

    The region 400–5000 cm^{-1} was investigated for the CF_3OF spectrum. Assignments were made for nine of the twelve fundamental vibration frequencies.

83. deLattre, A., "Infrared Spectrum of Some Complex Fluorides," *J. Chem. Phys.*, **20**, 1180. *46–8964.*

    Bands for K, Cu, Zn, and Ni fluosilicates are reported at 488 ± 6 and 735 ± 6 cm^{-1}. A new band for KBF_4 is reported at 523 cm^{-1}. Bands for anhydrous and hydrated aluminum fluorides and $KAHF_4$ are discussed.

84. deLattre, A., "Infrared Spectrum of Sulphur Hexafluoride in the Lithium Fluoride Region," *J. Chem. Phys.*, **20**, 520. *46–8964.*

85. Lord, R. C., "Far-Infrared Transmission of Silicon and Germanium," *Phys. Rev.*, **85**, 140. *46–4365.*

The transmission bands observed with 2mm thick samples of Si and Ge between 250–833 cm^{-1} are discussed.

86. Lord, R. C., McDonald, R. S., and Miller, F. A., "Notes on the Practice of Infrared Spectroscopy," *J. Opt. Soc. Am.*, **42**, 149.   *46–4913.*

    Techniques for spectroscopy in the infrared are described in detail.

87. Louisfert, J., and Pobeguin, T., "Differentiation of Calcium Carbonates by Means of Infrared Absorption Spectra," *Compt. rend.*, **235**, 287. *47–2040.*

    Various forms of CaCO$_3$ were subjected to infrared spectral analysis. A quantitative method is described as being more sensitive than the usual X-ray diffraction methods.

88. Magnuson, Dale W., "The Infrared Spectrum of Nitrosyl Fluoride.   II. Rotational Analysis of ν_1 and ν_3," *J. Chem. Phys.*, **20**, 380.   *47–6754.*

89. McCubbin, T. K., "The Spectra of HCl, NH$_3$, H$_2$O, and H$_2$S from 100–700 Microns," *J. Chem. Phys.*, **20**, 668.   *46–10890.*

90. Mecke, R., "Infrared Spectroscopy and the Character of Chemical Binding," *J. Chem. Phys.*, **20**, 1935.   *47–4739.*

    A method is developed for obtaining bond moments in the ground state by extrapolation of values calculated for the transition moments of the bond.   Other mathematical expressions are given.

91. Miller, F. A., and Wilkins, C. H., "Infrared Spectra and Characteristic Frequencies of Inorganic Ions," *Anal. Chem.*, **24**, 1253.   *46–10892.*

    The infrared spectral curves of 159 inorganic salts are given.   They include metaborates, tetraborates, boron nitride, carbonates, bicarbonates, nitrites, nitrates, phosphates, orthoarsenates, sulfites, sulfates, bisulfates, thiosulfates, chromates, metravanadates, cyanides, cyanates, thiocyanates, metasilicates, silicofluorides, silica-gel, oxides, selenites, selerates, chlorates, perchlorates, bromates, iodates, periodates, dichromates, molybdates, tungstates, permanganates, ferrocyanides, chlorides, and cobaltinitrites.

92. Moore, G. E., and Badger, R. M., "The Infrared Spectra and Structure of the Chloramines and Nitrogen Trichloride," *J. Am. Chem. Soc.*, **74**, 6076.   *47–3697.*

    Spectra of gaseous NH$_2$Cl, NHDCl, NHCl$_2$, and NCl$_3$ were obtained in the region 400–7140 cm^{-1}.

93. Moss, T. S., "Optical Properties of Tellurium in the Infrared," *Proc. Phys. Soc. (London)*, **65B**, 62.   *46–10896.*

    Absorption constant of tellurium layers is given for the near infrared region.

94. Newman, R., and Badger, R. M., "Infrared Spectra of Cyanuric Acid and Deuterocyanuric Acid," *J. Am. Chem. Soc.*, **74**, 3545.   *46–10891.*

    Spectra of sublimed films of (HNCO)$_3$ and (DNCO)$_3$ along with the polarized spectra of (101) single crystals of the acid are reported.

95. Newman, R., "Polarized Infrared Spectrum of Sodium Nitrite," *J. Chem. Phys.*, **20**, 444. *46–7430.*

96. Nielsen, A. H., Burke, T. G., Woltz, P. J. H., and Jones, E. A., "The Infrared and Raman Spectra of F_2CO, $FClCO$, and Cl_2CO," *J. Chem. Phys.*, **20**, 596. *46–10891.*

97. Nielsen, A. H., and Woltz, P. J. H., "The Infrared Spectrum of ClO_2," *J. Chem. Phys.*, **20**, 1878. *47–4739.*

   Interpretation is made of the ClO_2 spectrum in the 250–5000 cm^{-1} region.

98. Oberly, J. J., and Weiner, G., "Infrared Reflection Spectra of Phosphates and Arsenates," *J. Chem. Phys.*, **20**, 740. *46–9423.*

   Reflection spectra for KH_2PO_4, KH_2AsO_4, $NH_4H_2PO_4$, and $NH_4H_2AsO_4$ are given for the 400–10,000 cm^{-1} region at room temperature. Spectra for $NH_4H_2PO_4$ and $NH_4H_2AsO_4$ are also given at liquid $-N_2$ temperatures for the 667–5000 cm^{-1} region.

99. Osberg, W. E., and Hornig, D. F., "The Vibrational Spectra of Molecules and Complex Ions in Crystals. VI. Carbon Dioxide," *J. Chem. Phys.*, **20**, 1345. *47–9773.*

   A discussion of the discrepancy between the predicted and observed infrared spectrum of crystalline CO_2 is given.

100. Perkins, W. D., and Wilson, M. K., "The Infrared Spectrum of Sulfuryl Fluoride," *J. Chem. Phys.*, **20**, 1791. *47–4740.*

   The spectrum of SO_2F_2 was obtained for the region 240 cm^{-1} to 4000 cm^{-1}. Assignments were made and a partial calculation of force constant presented.

101. Perkins, W. D., and Wilson, M. K., "The Vibrational Spectrum of Dinitrogen Tetroxide," *Phys. Rev.*, **85**, 755.

   An abstract of a paper presented at the American Physical Society meeting.

102. Plyler, E. K., and Acquista, N., "Infrared Properties of Cesium Bromide Prisms," *J. Research Nat'l. Bur. Standards*, **49**, 61 (Research Paper No. 2343). *47–969.*

103. Plyler, E. K., and Ball, J. J., "Filters for the Infrared Region," *J. Opt. Soc. Am.*, **42**, 266. *46–5972.*

   Transmission of deposited films of Te, Bi, Sb, and Mg oxides were measured. Filters have been made for the region 250–1000 cm^{-1}.

104. Plyler, E. K., Benedict, W. S., and Silverman, S., "Precise Measurements in the Infrared Spectrum of Carbon Monoxide," *J. Chem. Phys.*, **20**, 175. *46–6487.*

   Absorption and emission measurements have been made and an analysis of results given.

105. Ramanathan, K. G., "Infrared Absorption by Metals at Low Temperatures," *Proc. Phys. Soc. (London)*, **65A**, 532. *46–10896.*

Absorptions were measured at liquid He temperature for copper, tin, lead, aluminum, and various alloys.

106. Ramdas, A. K., "The Infrared Absorption Spectrum of Potassium Chlorate Crystals. I," *Proc. Indian Acad. Sci.*, **35A**, 249. *46–10892.*

The spectrum of a single $KClO_3$ crystal is reported for the 667–5000 cm^{-1} region.

107. Ramdas, A. K., "The Infrared Spectrum of Potassium Chlorate Crystals. II," *Proc. Indian Acad. Sci.*, **36A**, 55. *47–2040.*

Infrared spectrum of a single $KClO_3$ crystal was obtained from 455–10,000 cm^{-1}.

108. Sands, J. D., and Turner, G. S., "Development in Solid Phase Infrared Spectroscopy," *Anal. Chem.*, **24**, 791. *46–7432.*

Infrared absorption spectra of solids is made faster, more accurate, and convenient by laminating or impregnating the solid under study between or into sheets of materials which transmit in the infrared, e.g., AgCl, mica, polyethylene. Spectral curves are given for mica and polyethylene.

109. Sokolov, A. V., and Cherepanov, V. I., "Optical Properties of Metallic Alloys in the Infrared Spectral Region," *Zh. Eksper. Theor. Fiz.*, **22**, 493 (No. 4).

110. Stedman, D. F., "Disproportionation in Deuterated Ammonia," *J. Chem. Phys.*, **20**, 718. *46–10890.*

Infrared absorption spectra of ammonia containing equimolar proportions of deuterium and hydrogen seem to indicate a disproportionation.

111. Taylor, J. H., Benedict, W. S., and Strong, J., "Infrared Spectra of Water and CO_2 at 500°," *J. Chem. Phys.*, **20**, 1884. *47–4739.*

Spectra were obtained in the region 400–5000 cm^{-1} varying pressure, temperature, and concentration.

112. Thompson, H. W., Williams, R. C., and Callomon, H. J., "The Fundamental Vibration Band of Hydrogen Bromide," *Spectrochim. Acta,* **5**, 313. *47–8515.*

The HBr band near 2500 cm^{-1} has been examined under high resolution. A satisfactory interpretation has been made for the lines of both isotropic species $H^{79}Br$ and $H^{81}Br$.

113. Tourin, R. H., "Infrared Emission and Absorption of Thermally Excited Carbon Dioxide," *J. Chem. Phys.*, **20**, 1651. *46–10890.*

Emission and absorption of CO_2 up to 1100°C are given.

114. Vincent-Geisse, J., "Measurement of Intensity of the Infrared Absorption Rays of a Gas," *Compt. rend.*, **234**, 2435. *46–9985.*

A method for measuring the intensity of an absorption band when the slit width is large compared to the band is proposed. Measurements of the fundamental band of CO by means of a fluorite prism assembly will be undertaken.

115. Webber, D. S., and Baker, A. N., Jr., "Structure of the 3μ Band of NaBr·2H$_2$O," *Phys. Rev.*, **85**, 755.

An abstract of a paper presented at the American Physical Society meeting.

116. Weber, D., Holm, R. J., and Penner, S. S., "Integrated Absorption for Vibration-Rotation Bands of Carbon Dioxide," *J. Chem. Phys.*, **20**, 1820. *47–1491.*

117. Wilson, M. K., and Polo, S. R., "Infrared Spectra of NF$_3$ and PF$_3$," *J. Chem. Phys.*, **20**, 1716.

Spectra for NF$_3$ and PF$_3$ are reported in the range 250 cm^{-1}–5000 cm^{-1}.

118. Woltz, P. J. H., Jones, E. A., and Nielsen, A. H., "The Infrared Spectrum of Nitrosyl Fluoride," *J. Chem. Phys.*, **20**, 378. *46–7430.*

Twelve absorption bands have been observed and identified in the prism spectrum of NOF between 260 and 5000 cm^{-1}.

119. Woltz, P. J. H., and Nielsen, A. H., "The Infrared Spectra of Carbon Tetrafluoride and Germanium Tetrafluoride," *J. Chem. Phys.*, **20**, 307. *46–7431.*

Infrared spectrum of GeF$_4$ has been obtained from 260–5000 cm^{-1}. A scarcity of bands as compared with spectra of CF$_4$ and SiF$_4$ was observed.

120. Yaroslavskiĭ, N. G., and Karyakin, A. V., "Changes of the Infrared OH Absorption Band of Microporous Glass on Low-Temperature Absorption of Oxygen and Nitrogen," *Doklady Akad. Nauk S.S.S.R.*, **85**, 1103. *47–967.*

121. Yoneda, H., Kida, S., and Kobayashi, M., "Absorption Spectra of Cobaltic Complex Salts in the Very Near Infrared Region," *J. Chem. Soc. Japan, Pure Chem. Sect.*, **73**, 518. *47–2599.*

Spectra of aqueous solution of cobaltic complex salts were measured in the range 714–16,667 cm^{-1}.

1953

122. Acquista, N., and Plyler, E. K., "Infrared Measurements with a Cesium Iodide Prism," *J. Opt. Soc. Amer.*, **43**, 977. *48–1156.*

A 35° cesium iodide prism has been used to observe radiations at wavelengths as long as 54μ. The transmittances of CsBr, TlBr–I, CsI, and films of polystyrene and polyethylene are reported.

123. Adel, A., "Absorption Line Width in the Infrared Spectrum of Atmospheric CO$_2$," *Phys. Rev.*, **90**, 1024. *47–9774.*

124. Adel, A., "Absorption Line Width in the Infrared Spectrum of the Ammonia Molecule," *J. Opt. Soc. Amer.*, **43**, 1053. *48–1150.*

125. Andreev, S. N., and Balicheva, T. G., "Infrared Absorption Spectrum of Liquid Water in the 3200–3600 cm^{-1} Region," *Doklady Akad. Nauk*

S.S.S.R., **90**, 149 (Engl. translation issued as U.S. Atomic Energy Comm., *NSF–tr–66*). *48–6829.*

126. Ard, J. S., "Mull and Solvent Media for Infrared Use," *Anal. Chem.*, **25**, 1743. *48–3143.*

Hexachlorobutadiene and tetrachloroethylene are proposed as supplemental mull and solvent media to paraffin oil and CS_2, respectively.

127. Barchewitz, P., Grenier-Besson, M., and Amat, G., "The Vibration Spectrum of Nitrous Oxide," *Compt. rend.*, **237**, 1322. *48–3793.*

128. Barrow, G. M., "The Infrared Spectra of Oriented Rhombic Sulfur Crystals with Polarized Radiation," *J. Chem. Phys.*, **21**, 219. *47–3697.*

129. Benesch, W., and Elder, T., "Relative Optical Collision Diameters from the Pressure Broadening of Individual Infrared Absorption Lines," *Phys. Rev.*, **91**, 308. *47–11001.*

The broadening of isolated vibration-rotation lines of HCl and CH_4 by He, Ne, A, Kr, Xe, SF_6, O, H, N, CO, CO_2, N_2O, SO_2, and HCl is studied. Collision diameters are compared with previously reported values.

130. Bethell, D. E., and Sheppard, N., "The Infrared Spectrum of Nitric Acid Monohydrate," *J. chim. phys.*, **50**, C72. *48–4974.*

131. Bethell, D. E., and Sheppard, N., "The Infrared Spectrum of the H_3O^+ Ion in Acid Hydrates," *J. Chem. Phys.*, **21**, 1421. *47–11983.*

Spectra of $HClO_4$ and HNO_3 and their monohydrates were taken between flat AgCl plates.

132. Borzyak, P. G., "Optical Absorption and the Photoeffect for a Semiconducting Antimony-Cesium Photocathode at Low Temperatures," *Trudy Inst. Fiz., Akad. Nauk Ukr. S.S.R.* **4**, 28. *49–5114.*

133. Briggs, H. B., and Fletcher, R. C., "Absorption of Infrared Light by Free Carriers in Germanium," *Phys. Rev.*, **91**, 1342. *47–11969.*

Infrared absorption of carriers, injected in Ge across a p-n junction at room temperature, was found to be proportional to the concentration of carriers.

134. Brown, J. K., "Recent Advances in Infrared Spectroscopy," *B.C.U.R.A. Mon. Bull.*, **17**, 449. *48–8027.*

A review.

135. Burstein, E., Bell, E. E., Davisson, J. W., and Lax, M., "Optical Investigations of Impurity Levels in Silicon," *J. Phys. Chem.*, **57**, 849. *48–1138.*

Infrared measurements were carried out for a number of p-type silicon samples, inclduing B-doped single crystals in the 260–5000 cm^{-1} range.

136. Cannon, C. G., "Infrared Spectra of Coals and Coal Products," *Nature*, **171**, 308. *47–5255.*

Infrared spectra for 18 samples of coals and other similar products are summarized and compared.

137. Chevet, A., "Preliminary Investigations of the Infrared Spectra of Silica Gels," *J. phys. radium*, **14**, 493. *48–1153*.

The spectra of two commercial silica gels were obtained in the region 1667–3333 cm^{-1} to determine the manner of modification of the OH bands after maintaining the gels for 6 hours at temperatures ranging from 100°–1200°.

138. Chulanovskii, V. M., "Infrared Absorption Spectrum of the OH Group in Water and in Some Water Solutions," *Doklady Akad. Nauk S.S.S.R.*, **93**, 25. *49–12127*.

The absorption spectra are given for pure water and solutions of water in organic solvents.

139. Coulon, R., Oskengorn, B., Robin, St., and Vodar, B., "Infrared Absorption of N_2 and O_2 Induced by Intermolecular Forces," *J. phys. radium*, **14**, 63. *48–1147*.

140. Dash, W. C., "Optical Absorption and Photoconduction in the Visible and Near Infrared in Single Crystals of BaO," *Phys. Rev.*, **92**, 68. *48–1139*.

141. Decius, J. C., and Pearson, D. P., "The Infrared Absorption of Crystalline and Liquid Hydrazine Monochloride and Monobromide," *J. Am. Chem. Soc.*, **75**, 2436. *47–9776*.

Absorption spectra of N_2H_5Cl, N_2D_5Cl, N_2H_5Br, and N_2D_5Br in the crystalline state were obtained in the 400–3333 cm^{-1} region.

142. Douglas, A. E., and Sharma, D., "Rotation-Vibration Spectra of Diatomic and Simple Polyatomic Molecules with Long Absorbing Paths. IX. The Spectra of the HCN and DCN Molecules from 2.5–0.5μ," *J. Chem. Phys.*, **21**, 448. *47–5798*.

143. Duval, Cl., and Lecomte, J., "Some Solid State Reactions Studied by Infrared Absorption," *Bull. soc. chim. France*, 203–6. *46–10890*, *47–6257*.

144. Evstigneev, V. B., "The Use of Heavy Water as a Solvent for Spectroscopic Investigations in the Near-Infrared Region," *Doklady Akad. Nauk S.S.S.R.*, **89**, 105.

145. Ferriso, C. C., and Hornig, D. F., "The Infrared Spectrum of the Oxonium Ion," *J. Am. Chem. Soc.*, **75**, 4113. *48–1153*.

Films of oxonium chloride and oxonium bromide were examined in the infrared region at −195°. Spectral results indicate a symmetrical pyramidal configuration for $OH_3{}^+$.

146. Florinskaya, V. A., and Pechenkina, R. S., "Reflection and Transmission Spectra of Potassium Silicate Glasses in the Infrared," *Doklady Akad. Nauk S.S.S.R.*, **91**, 59. *48–8050*.

147. Gaunt, J., "Infrared Spectra and Molecular Structure of Some Group VI Hexafluorides," *Trans. Faraday Soc.*, **49**, 1122. *48–6829*.

The spectra of SF_6, SeF_6, TeF_6, MoF_6, WF_6, and UF_6 are investigated between 400 and 5000 cm^{-1}.

148. Genzel, L., and Muser, H., "Photoelectric and Optical Properties of a Particular Type of PbS Layer," Z. *Physik*, **134**, 419–24. *47–9758*.

Long wavelength limit and photoeffect of the PbS layers examined occur at 1.8μ.

149. Gibson, A. F., "Injected Absorption in Germanium," *Proc. Phys. Soc. (London)*, **66B**, 588. *47–9757*.

150. Glusker, D. L., Thompson, H. W., and Mulliken, R. S., "Infrared Spectra of Solutions of Iodine," *J. Chem. Phys.*, **21**, 1407. *47–11988*.

Infrared absorption spectra of various organic solvents were obtained before and after addition of iodine. Solvent interaction effects are discussed.

151. Goodwin, A. G., "The How and Why of Spectroscopy," *Australian J. Instr. Technol.*, **9**, 59. *48–4957*.

A review of techniques and uses of spectroscopy, including infrared.

152. Haccuria, M., "Infrared Spectra of Amorphous Silica, Tridymite, Cristobalite, Quartz and Vitreous Silica," *Bull. soc. chim. Belges*, **62**, 428. *48–4316*.

Infrared spectral curves were obtained for the region 416–5000 cm^{-1}.

153. Hadvi, D., "Infrared Spectroscopy," *Nova Proizvodnja*, **3**, 162. *48–1133*.

A review describing the principles of infrared spectroscopy and its scientific and industrial applications.

154. Hansler, R. L., and Oetjen, R. A., "The Infrared Spectra of HCl, DCl, HBr, and NH$_3$ in the Region from 40–140 Microns," *J. Chem. Phys.*, **21**, 1340. *47–11983*.

155. Harris, L., and Loeb, A. L., "Conductance and Relaxation Time of Electrons in Gold Blacks from Transmission and Reflection Measurements in the Far Infrared," *J. Opt. Soc. Amer.*, **43**, 1114. *48–1155*.

156. Hawkins, J. A., and Wilson, M. K., "The Infrared and Raman Spectra of SiH$_2$Cl$_2$," *J. Chem. Phys.*, **21**, 360. *47–4198*.

157. Hawkins, J. A., Polo, S. R., Wilson, M. K., "Note on the Vibrational Spectra of SiHCl$_3$, SiH$_2$Cl$_2$, and SiH$_2$Br$_2$," *J. Chem. Phys.*, **21**, 1122. *47–9149*.

158. Haynie, W. H., and Nielsen, H. H., "The Fundamental Absorption Bands in the Infrared Spectrum of Stibine and Deuterated Stibine," *J. Chem. Phys.*, **21**, 1839. *48–1151*.

159. Herzberg, G., and Herzberg, L., "Rotation-Vibration Spectra of Diatomic and Simple Polyatomic Molecules with Long Absorbing Paths. XI. The Spectrum of Carbon Dioxide Below 1.25μ," *J. Opt. Soc. Amer.*, **43**, 1037. *48–1150*.

160. Hunt, J. M., and Turner, D. S., "Determination of Mineral Constituents of Rocks by Infrared Spectroscopy," *Anal. Chem.*, **25**, 1169.

The spectra of natural sediments (muds), quartz, orthoclase, colomite, and other minerals were obtained in the region 625–5000 cm^{-1}.

161. Innes, K. K., Cross, P. C., and Bair, E. J., "The Asymmetric Rotor. XI. Hydrogen Sulfide Absorption in the Regions 8700 cm^{-1} and 11000 cm^{-1}," *J. Chem. Phys.*, **21**, 545. *47–5799*.

162. Jones, L. H., "Polarized Infrared Spectrum of KAu(CN)$_2$," *J. Chem. Phys.*, **21**, 1891. *48–1153*.

  The absorption spectrum was examined in the range 400–4000 cm^{-1}.

163. Jones, L. H., and Penneman, R. A., "Infrared Spectra and Structure of Uranyl and Transuranium (V) and (VI) Ions in Aqueous Perchloric Acid Solutions," *J. Chem. Phys.*, **21**, 542. *47–5797*.

164. Kaiser, W., Collins, R. J., and Fan, H. Y., "Infrared Absorption in p-Type Germanium," *Phys. Rev.*, **91**, 1380. *47–11970*.

  Absorption measured at 5, 77, 201, 300, 382, and 453°K. The absorption coefficient is proportional to the hole concentration.

165. Kaiser, W., Collins, R. C., and Fan, H. Y., "Infrared Absorption of p-Germanium," *Naturwissenschaften*, **40**, 497. *48–8047*.

  The infrared spectrum of p-Ge was measured from 285–6667 cm^{-1} at room temperature. The samples used ranged from 0.04–10 ohm cm. specific resistance. Indium or gallium acceptors were used.

166. Karyakin, A. V., Nikitin, V. A., and Ivanov, K. I., "Infrared Spectra of Peroxides," *Zhur. Fiz. Khim.*, **27**, 1856. *49–5126*.

167. Kendall, D. N., "Identification of Polymorphic Forms of Crystals by Infrared Spectroscopy," *Anal. Chem.*, **25**, 382–9. *47–6256*.

168. Kluyver, J. C., and Milatz, J. M., "An Infrared Isotope Analyzer," *Physica*, **19**, 401. *48–450*.

  A method for determining the isotope ratios in tracer experiments is described. The method is based on the shift in the infrared absorption bands of isotopic molecules. An application to the measurement of C^{13}/C^{12} in CO$_2$ is discussed.

169. Lecomte, J., "The Infrared Spectrum of Water in Solids. I. General Introduction and Formulation of the Question," *J. chim. phys.*, **50**, C53. *48–4977*.

170. Lecomte, J., and Duval, C., "The Infrared Spectrum of Water in Solids. II. Experimental Determinations," *J. chim. phys.*, **50**, C64. *48–4977*.

  Three groups of products are observed when Cu is precipitated by certain bases.

  Absorption maxima and intensities are given for a number of hydrated and deuterated calcium sulfates, for manganese sulfate mono- and hepta-hydrate, and for a number of other compounds, including brucite, goethite, topaz, beryl, Na tartrate, and oxalates.

171. Lecomte, J., Ceccaldi, M., and Roth, E., "The Isotopic Determination of Water by Measuring the Absorption in the Infrared," *J. chim. phys.*, **50**, 166. *47–9149*.

172. Lippincott, E. R., and Tobin, M. C., "The Vibrational Spectra and

Structure of Nitrogen Tetrasulfide," *J. Chem. Phys.*, **21**, 1559. *47–11975.*

Spectra are obtained for N_4S_4 and $N_4S_4H_4$ in the infrared region.

173. Loferski, J. J., "Infrared Optical Properties of Tellurium Crystals," *Univ. Microfilms (Ann Arbor, Mich.) Pub. No. 4942; Dissertation Abstr.*, **13**, 246. *47–6766.*

174. Mara, R. T., and Sutherland, G. B. B. M., "The Infrared Spectrum of Brucite ($Mg(OH)_2$)," *J. Opt. Soc. Amer.*, **43**, 1100. *48–1154.*

The spectra of single crystals of brucite were examined between 3333 and 5000 cm^{-1}.

175. McConaghie, V. M., and Nielsen, H. H., "The Fundamental Absorption Bands in the Infrared Spectrum of Phosphine," *J. Chem. Phys.*, **21**, 1836. *48–1151.*

176. Mills, I. M., Thompson, H. W., and Williams, R. C., "The Fundamental Vibration-Rotation Band of Hydrogen Chloride," *Proc. Roy. Soc. (London)*, **A218**, 29. *47–9769.*

The HCl band near 2899 cm^{-1} was measured under high resolution; new rotational constants were deduced.

177. Momin, A. U., "The Infrared Spectrum of Magnesium Oxide Between 1 and 21 Microns," *Proc. Indian Acad. Sci.*, **37A**, 254–9. *47–6766.*

178. Monfils, A., "The Infrared Spectrum and the Structure of the Molecule SiH_3Cl," *Compt. rend.*, **236**, 795. *47–6254.*

Revised data for infrared bands of SiH_3Cl are recorded.

179. Moore, G. E., "The Spectrum of Nitrogen Dioxide in the 1.4–3.4μ Region and the Vibrational and Rotational Constants of the Nitrogen Dioxide Molecule," *J. Opt. Soc. Amer.*, **43**, 1045. *48–1150.*

180. Newman, R., "Optical Studies of Injected Carriers. I. Infrared Absorption in Germanium," *Phys. Rev.*, **91**, 1311. *47–11969.*

181. Nielsen, H. H., "The Infrared Spectra and the Molecular Structure of Pyramidal Molecules," *J. Chem. Phys.*, **21**, 142. *47–3696.*

Mathematical.

182. d'Or, L., and Tarte, P., "The Infrared Spectra and the Structure of Nitrous Acid Anhydride," *Bull. soc. roy. sci. Liege*, **22**, 276. *48–3793.*

183. Paul, W., and Jones, R. V., "Absorption Spectra of Lead Sulfide at Different Temperatures," *Proc. Phys. Soc. (London)*, **66B**, 194. *47–9146.*

The spectrum of PbS was measured in the 1000–10,000 cm^{-1} region. A change in the absorption edge and photoconductive limit was noted with temperature change.

184. Ramdas, A. K., "Infrared Absorption Spectrum of Silicon Carbide," *Proc. Indian Acad. Sci.*, **37A**, 571. *47–11983.*

Crystals of SiC were examined by transmission in the 500–10,000 cm^{-1} region.

185. Ramdas, A. K., "Infrared Spectra of Sodium Chlorate and Potassium Chlorate Crystals," *Proc. Indian Acad. Sci.*, **37A**, 451. *47–8515.*

The spectra were measured for sodium and potassium chlorate in the 475–10,000 cm^{-1} region. Absorption maxima were observed and assignments were made.

186. Ramdas, A. K., "The Infrared Absorption Spectra of Sodium Nitrate and Calcite," *Proc. Indian Acad. Sci.*, **37A**, 441–50. *47–8515*.

The spectra were measured for sodium nitrate and calcite in the 475–10,000 cm^{-1} region. Using these data and that of other workers, assignments were made.

187. Rank, D. H., and Cronemeyer, D. C., "The Infrared Absorption Characteristics of Thermiated Germanium," *Phys. Rev.*, **90**, 202. *47–9148*.

188. Shelton, R. D., Nielsen, A. H., and Fletcher, W. H., "The Infrared Spectrum and Molecular Constants of Sulfur Dioxide," *J. Chem. Phys.*, **21**, 2178. *48–4317*.

189. Simeral, Wm. G., "The Infrared Absorption Spectra of Diamond, Silicon, and Germanium," *Dissertation Abstracts*, **13**, 840. *48–1793*.

190. Tanenbaum, M., and Briggs, H. B., "Optical Properties of Indium Antimonide," *Phys. Rev.*, **91**, 1561. *48–448*.

The spectrum of crystalline indium antimonide was obtained in the infrared region. The limit of absorption occurs near 3.2μ. Effects of various doping elements on the absorption limit are reported.

191. Teranishi, R., and Decius, J. C., "Infrared Absorption of Solid N_2O_5," *J. Chem. Phys.*, **21**, 1116. *47–9149*.

Solid N_2O_5 spectrum was obtained using a technique of subliming the solid onto AgCl and KBr windows of the spectrograph maintained at liquid nitrogen temperatures.

192. Thompson, H. W., and Williams, R. L., "Vibration Bands and Molecular Rotational Constants of Nitrous Oxide," *Proc. Roy. Soc. (London)*, **A220**, 435. *48–5648*.

193. Tyler, J. E., and Ehrhardt, S. A., "Infrared Spectra of Evaporated Films," *Anal. Chem.*, **25**, 390–4. *47–6256*.

194. Uchida, Y., and Fukuda, K., "The Infrared Vibration Spectrum and the Structure of Hydrogen Peroxide," *Bull. Inst. Chem. Research, Kyoto Univ.*, **27**, 1. *48–6807*.

A review.

195. Vernier, P., "Optical and Photoelectric Properties of Microcrystalline Layers of Lead Sulfide in the Visible and Infrared," *J. phys. radium*, **14**, 175. *48–7422*.

196. Waldron, R. D., and Hornig, D. F., "Infrared Spectra and Structure of Crystalline Ammonia Hydrates," *J. Am. Chem. Soc.*, **75**, 6079. *48–3142*.

$NH_3 \cdot H_2O$ and 2 $NH_3 \cdot H_2O$ were subjected to spectral analysis. The structures are discussed.

197. Wearmouth, W. G., "Infrared Spectroscopy," *Lab. Practice*, **2**, 297, 373, 422. *48–5635*.

A review.

198. Wilson, M. K., and Palo, S. R., "Erratum: The Infrared Spectra of NF_3 and PF_3," *J. Chem. Phys.*, **21**, 1426. *47–11002.*

1954

199. Allen, H. C., and Plyler, E. K., "Infrared Spectrum of Hydrogen Sulfide in the 6290 cm^{-1} Region," *J. Research Natl. Bur. Standards*, **52**, 205 (Research Paper No. 2490). *48–8652.*
200. Allen, H. C., and Plyler, E. K., "Infrared Spectrum of Hydrogen Sulfide. II. The 5100 cm^{-1} Region," *J. Chem. Phys.*, **22**, 1104. *48–12554.*
201. Amat, G., Barchewitz, P., and Grenier-Besson, M. L., "The $2v_3$ Band of Nitrous Oxide at 2.26μ," *J. phys. radium*, **15**, 563. *49–5126.*
202. Andersen, F. A., and Bak, B., "Infrared Absorption Spectra of SiD_3Cl, SiH_3F, and SiD_3F," *Acta. Chem. Scand.*, **8**, 738. *48–13427.*

   The spectral curves are obtained from 667–3000 cm^{-1}. Calculations are made and a compilation of stretching and deformation force constants for CH_4, CH_3F, CH_3Cl, SiH_4, SiH_3F, and SiH_3Cl is presented.
203. Avery, D. G., Goodwin, D. W., Lawson, W. D., and Moss, T. S., "Optical and Photoelectrical Properties of Indium Antimonide," *Proc. Phys. Soc. (London)*, **67B**, 761. *49–1423.*

   Measurements of the reflection and transmission of InSb between -183 and $226°$ have been made from 714–14290 cm^{-1}.
204. Bappu, M. K. V., "Spectroscopic Study of Amethyst Quartz in the Ultraviolet and Infrared Regions," *Indian J. Phys.*, **27**, 385; *Sci. Abstr.*, **57A**, 701. *51–7852.*
205. Biondi, M. A., "Optical and Infrared Absorption of Copper at 4.2°K," *Phys. Rev.*, **96**, 534. *49–2866.*

   The infrared absorption of copper is reported for the region 2500–20,000 cm^{-1} at 4.2°K.
206. Blunt, R. F., Hosler, W. R., and Frederikse, H. P. R., "Electrical and Optical Properties of Intermetallic Compounds. II. Gallium Antimonide," *Phys. Rev.*, **96**, 576. *49–2861.*
207. Blunt, R. F., Frederikse, H. P. R., Becker, J. H., and Hosler, W. R., "Electrical and Optical Properties of Intermetallic Compounds. III. Aluminum Antimonide," *Phys. Rev.*, **96**, 578. *49–2861.*
208. Breckenridge, R. G., Blunt, R. F., Hosler, W. R., Frederikse, H. P. R., Becker, J. H., and Oshinsky, W., "Electrical and Optical Properties of Intermetallic Compounds. I. Indium Antimonide," *Phys. Rev.*, **96**, 571. *49–2860.*
209. Brügel, W., "Introduction to Infrared Spectroscopy," *Wiss. Forschungsber., Naturw. Reihe*, **62**, 1. *48–11177.*

   A review containing 595 references. It includes theory, application and methods of study, structure and analysis.
210. Burch, D. E., Howard, J. N., and Williams, D., "The Effect of Foreign-

Gas Broadening on the Total Absorption by the 6.3μ Band of Water Vapor," *Phys. Rev.*, 94, 1424. *49–10043*.

An abstract of a paper presented at the American Physical Society meeting.

211. Burstein, E., "Anomalous Optical Absorption Limit in InSb," *Phys. Rev.*, 93, 632. *48–6836*.

212. Caldwell, R. S., and Fan, H. Y., "Infrared Absorption of Tellurium," *Phys. Rev.*, 94, 1427. *49–10043*.

An abstract of a paper presented at The American Physical Society meeting.

213. Callen, H. B., "Electronic Structure, Infrared Absorption, and Hall Effect in Tellurium," *J. Chem. Phys.*, 22, 518. *48–7421*.

214. Callomon, H. J., and Thompson, H. W., "Vibration-Rotation Bands and Molecular Constants of Carbonyl Sulfide," *Proc. Roy. Soc. (London)*, A222, 431. *48–6255*.

The bands of $C^{12}O^{16}S^{33}$ near 2000 cm^{-1} were examined.

215. Chisolm, D. A., and Welsh, H. L., "Induced Infrared Absorption in Hydrogen and Hydrogen-Foreign Gas Mixtures at Pressures up to 1500 Atmospheres," *Can. J. Phys.*, 32, 291. *48–8042*.

216. Christensen, M. T., and Thompson, H. W., "Rotational Constants of Nitrous Oxide," *Trans. Faraday Soc.*, 50, 1027. *49–5126*.

217. Clauson-Kaas, N., Nedenskov, P., Bak, B., and Rastrup-Andersen, J., "Note on the Potassium Bromide Disk Technique for Measurements of Infrared Spectra," *Acta. Chem. Scand.*, 8, 1088. *49–4408*.

218. Collins, R. J., and Fan, H. Y., "Infrared Lattice Absorption Bands in Germanium, Silicon, and Diamond," *Phys. Rev.*, 93, 674. *48–6815*.

219. Corbridge, D. E. C., and Lowe, E. J., "The Infrared Spectra of Some Inorganic Phosphorus Compounds," *J. Chem. Soc.*, 493. *48–6829*.

Absorption spectra of more than 90 inorganic phosphorus compounds are reported for the 650–4000 cm^{-1} range. Some assignments are made.

220. Corbridge, D. E. C., and Lowe, E. J., "The Infrared Spectra of Some Inorganic Phosphorus Compounds. II. Some Salts of Phosphorus Oxy-Acids," *J. Chem. Soc.*, 4555. *49–2870*.

The spectra of over sixty phosphorous compounds are presented for the range 650–4000 cm^{-1}. Correlations are made for the assignments to various structural groups.

221. Coulon, R., Oksengorn, B., and Vodar, B., "The Perturbation of the Fundamental Infrared Band of Hydrogen Fluoride by Various Gases Compressed up to 1200 Atmospheres," *Compt. rend.*, 239, 964. *49–2870*.

222. Coulon, R., Galatry, L., Oksengorn, B., Robin, S., and Vodar, B., "Perturbation of the Fundamental Infrared Absorption Banks of Hydrogen Chloride and Carbon Monoxide by Various Gases Under Pressures up to 1000 Atmospheres," *J. phys. radium*, 15, 58. *48–6248*.

Perturbation of the bands of HCl and CO by He, H_2, A, O, and N, increase in that order.

223. Cunnell, F. A., Edmond, J. T., and Richards, J. L., "Measurements on Some Semiconducting Compounds with the Zinc-Blende Structure," *Proc. Phys. Soc. (London)*, **67B**, 848. *49–1423*.

The infrared transmission of specimens of AlSb, GaSb, InAs, InP, and GaAs has been measured.

224. Dalby, F. W., Nielsen, H. H., and Dickey, F. P., "The Absorption Spectra of Water Vapor in the 2.7μ and 6.0μ Regions," *Phys. Rev.*, **94**, 1423. *49–10043*.

An abstract of a paper presented at the American Physical Society Meeting.

225. Dewulf, G., "Glasses Transparent in the Infrared," *Rev. opt.*, **33**, 513. *49–13757*.

Curves of the infrared transmission of various glasses are given.

226. Douglas, A. E., and Møller, C. K., "The Near-Infrared Spectrum and the Internuclear Distances of Nitrous Oxide," *J. Chem. Phys.*, **22**, 275. *48–5648*.

227. Duval, C., and Lecomte, J., "Infrared Absorption Spectra of Metallic Salts Containing the Group XO_4, in the Region of Their Deformation Vibrations," *Compt. rend.*, **239**, 249. *49–5126*.

Data are given on the absorption spectra of anhydrous salts containing the anion XO_4^{-n} and various cations between 290 and 650 cm^{-1}. In this work X is Si, P, Cl, S, V, Cr, Mn, As, Se, Mo, W, or Re and n is 1, 2, or 3.

228. Duval, C., and Lecomte, J., "Remarks on the Infrared Spectra of Metallic Salts Containing Groups of the XO_2-Type Ion," *J. Opt. Soc. Amer.*, **44**, 261. *48–6828*.

A study of the infrared spectra, 700–1500 cm^{-1}, of metal salts of metaborate and orthoborate indicate that the BO_2-ion does not exist, the ion is in the polymerized form $(BO_2)_n$.

229. Duval, C., and Lecomte, J., "Application of Infrared Absorption Spectra for Detecting and Following Reactions in the Solid State," *Proc. Intern. Symposium Reactivity of Solids, Gothenburg.* Part 1, 509 (1952). *48–11926*.

230. Eischens, R. P., Pliskin, W. A., and Francis, S. A., "Infrared Spectra of Chemisorbed Carbon Monoxide," *J. Chem. Phys.*, **22**, 1986. *49–722*.

231. Elsey, R. D., and Haszeldine, R. N., "The Potassium Bromide Technique in Infrared Spectroscopy," *Chemistry and Industry*, 1177. *49–2869*.

The KBr pellet technique is compared extensively with the Nujol-mull technique.

232. Emschwiller, G., "Infrared Spectra of Ferrocyanides and of Ferricyanides and the Constitution of Prussian Blue," *Compt. rend.*, **238**, 1414. *48–8049*.

233. Fahrenfort, J., "Infrared Spectrum of Carbon Dioxide Under Pressure," *Chem. Weekblad,* **50,** 501. *49–56.*

The spectrum of CO_2 has been measured up to pressures of 60 atmospheres.

234. Fan, H. Y., and Becker, M., "Infrared Optical Properties of Silicon and Germanium," *Semiconducting Materials (Proc. Conf. Univ. Reading (England),* 132. *48–13425.*

235. Fleischmann, R., "Procedure for the Optical Isotope Analysis of Certain Compounds," *Z. Physik,* **137,** 516.

An infrared gas analyzer has been used to record the concentration ratio of Cl isotopes in HCl gas and of other gases with similar absorption properties.

236. Foëx, M., "The Infrared Transparency of Silica Glasses Prepared in the Solar Oven Under Varying Atmosphere," *Bull. soc. chim. France,* 767. *48–12554.*

A strong infrared absorption band in the spectrum of silica-glass at 3636 cm^{-1} has been attributed to small amounts of water vapor. Absorption studies have been made under varying humidity and gas content.

237. Ford, M. A., and Wilkinson, G. R., "Pressed Alkali Halide Disks with Reference to Use in Spectroscopy," *J. Sci. Instr.,* **31,** 338. *49–3666.*

238. Frederickson, L. D., "Characterization of Hydrated Aluminas by Infrared Spectroscopy. Application to Study of Bauxite Ores," *Anal. Chem.,* **26** (12), 1883. *49–3728.*

239. Gamo, I., "The Fundamental Vibrations of Phosphine," *Compt. rend.,* **239,** 1478. *49–4406.*

240. Garino-Canina, V., "Absorption Band of Vitreous Silica at 2.72μ," *Compt. rend.,* **239,** 705. *49–2867.*

241. Giguere, P. A., and Harvey, K. B., "The Nonexistence of Discrete O_3^{-2} Ions in K_2O_3," *J. Am. Chem. Soc.,* **76,** 5891. *49–10060.*

The spectrum of K_2O_3 in the rock-salt infrared region has been examined. No absorption bands attributable to O_3^{-2} ions were observed.

242. Gruen, D. M., and Fred, M., "Absorption Spectra of Uranium (IV) Fluorides," *J. Am. Chem. Soc.,* **76,** 3850. *48–13420.*

The spectra of UF_4, $NaUF_5$, KUF_5, δ-Na_2UF_6 and α-Na_2UF_6 were measured from 7000 Å by the KBr pellet technique.

243. Gutowsky, H. S., and Stejskal, E. O., "The Infrared Spectrum of Disilane," *J. Chem. Phys.,* **22,** 939. *48–11927.*

The infrared spectrum of Si_2H_6 gas was observed in the region 350–4000 cm^{-1}.

244. Hacskaylo, M., "Prep. of Compounds for Infrared Spectrometry," *Anal. Chem.,* **26** (9), 1410. *49–1431.*

245. Hadni, A., "Spectra of Some Simple Molecules in the Far Infrared," *J. phys. radium,* **15,** 417. *48–11925.*

Simple molecules (e.g., CS_2 and NH_3) were examined in the region from 167–555 cm^{-1}.

246. Haendler, H. M., Bukata, S. W., Millard, B., Goodman, E. I., and Littman, J., "Infrared Spectral Studies of BrF$_3$ and BrF$_5$," *J. Chem. Phys.*, **22**, 1939. *49–1431.*

247. Hall, L. H., Bardeen, J., and Blatt, F. J., "Infrared Absorption Spectrum of Germanium," *Phys. Rev.*, **95**, 559. *48–11178.*

248. Hass, G., and Salzberg, C. D., "Optical Properties of Silicon Monoxide in the Wavelength Region from 0.24 to 14.0μ," *J. Opt. Soc. Amer.*, **44**, 181. *48–6251.*

249. Hawkins, N. J., Mattraw, H. C., and Carpenter, D. R., "The Infrared Spectrum of Uranium Hexafluoride at Elevated Temperatures," *U. S. Atomic Energy Comm.*, **KAPL–1041**, 7. *49–4407.*

The absorption spectrum of UF$_6$ is recorded for the 434–5000 cm^{-1} range at 100° and room-temperature.

250. Herman, M. A., "Infrared Spectrometry," *Mededel. Vlaam. Chem. Ver.*, **16**, 207. *49–2190.*

A review.

251. Hiebert, G. L., "Infrared Spectrum of Crystalline Solutions and the Structure of the Hydrogen Halides," *Dissertation Abstr.*, **14**, 2210. *49–4405.*

252. Hill, D. G., and Rosenberg, A. F., "Infrared Absorption Spectra of Complex Cobalt Salts," *J. Chem. Phys.*, **22**, 148. *48–4316.*

Bands were observed in the region 820–1310 cm^{-1} for the following compounds:

$Co(NH_3)_6 Cl_3$, $Co(NH_3)_6 Br_3$, $Co(NH_3)_6 I_3$,
$Co(NH_3)_5 H_2 OCl_3$, $Co(NH_3)_5 H_2 O Br_3$, $Co(NH_3)_5 H_2 OI_3$,
$Co(NH_3)_5 N_3 Cl_2$, $CO(NH_3)_5 N_3 Br_2$, $Co(NH_3)_5 N_3 I_2$,
$Co(NH_3)_5 FCl_2$, $Co(NH_3)_5 FBr_2$, $Co(NH_3)_5 FI_2$, $Co(NH_3)_5 Cl Cl_2$,
$Co(NH_3)_5 BrCl_2$, and $Co(NH_3)_5 Br Br_2$.

253. Holstein, T., "Optical and Infrared Volume Absorptivity of Metals," *Phys. Rev.*, **96**, 535. *49–2866.*

254. Hrostowski, H. J., Wheatley, G. H., and Flood, W. F., "Anomalous Optical Behavior of InSb and InAs," *Phys. Rev.*, **95**, 1683. *48–13437.*

The infrared spectra from 1250–10,000 cm^{-1} are presented for InSb and 4 Te-doped samples of InSb. The discrepancies between theory and experimental findings are discussed.

255. Hrostowski, H. J., and Pimentel, G. C., "The Infrared Spectra of Stable Pentaborane and Deuteriated Pentaborane," *J. Am. Chem. Soc.*, **76**, 998. *48–7434.*

256. Hunt, J. M., and Turner, D. S., "Determination of Mineral Constituents of Rocks by Infrared Spectroscopy," *Anal. Chem.*, **25** (8), 1169.

Quantitative analyses have been made for minerals (such as quartz, kaolinite, orthoclase, calcite, and dolomite) to within 10 per cent.

257. Jaumann, J., and Kessler, R., "The Role of Free Carriers in the Short-wave Infrared Absorption of Germanium," Z. *Naturforsch.*, **9a**, 476. *48–12553*.

   The infrared absorption of Ge (p and n types) was measured up to 300° below wavelengths of 8μ. The samples ranged from 42–0.018 ohm cm specific resistivity.

258. Johannesen, R. B., *et al.*, "Application of Infrared Spectroscopy to the Determination of Impurities in Titanium Tetrachloride," *J. Res. Nat. Bur. Stand.*, **53** (4), 197.

259. Johnston, R. W., and Cronemeyer, D. C., "Infrared Absorption of NiO," *Phys. Rev.*, **93**, 634. *48–6252*.

   The transmission of varying thicknesses of NiO was recorded for the region 714–10,000 cm^{-1}.

260. Jones, L. H., and Penneman, R. A., "Infrared Absorption Studies of Aqueous Complex Ions. I. Cyanide Complexes of Ag(I) and Au(I) in Aqueous Solution and Adsorbed on Anion Resin," *J. Chem. Phys.*, **22**, 965. *48–11926*.

261. Jones, L. H., "Polarized Infrared Spectrum of KAu(CN)$_2$: Revision and Refinement," *J. Chem. Phys.*, **22**, 1135. *48–12554*.

262. Jones, L. H., "The Infrared Spectra and Structure of LiOH, LiOH·H$_2$O, and the Deuterium Species. Fundamental Frequency of OH−," *J. Chem. Phys.*, **22**, 217. *48–4975*.

263. Jones, L. H., and Penneman, R. A., "Infrared Absorption Spectra of Aqueous HF$_2$$^{-1}$, DF$_2$$^{-1}$, and HF," *J. Chem. Phys.*, **22**, 781. *48–11925*.

264. Josien, M. L., and Sourisseau, G., "The Study of Some Complexes of Hydrochloric Acid by Infrared Spectroscopy," *Compt. rend.*, **238**, 2525. *49–722*.

265. Kaiser, W., and Fan, H. Y., "Infrared Absorption, Photoconductivity and Impurity States in Germanium," *Phys. Rev.*, **93**, 977. *48–6830*.

266. Kaiser, W., and Fan, H. Y., "Infrared Properties of Indium Antimonide," *Phys. Rev.*, **94**, 1431. *49–10043*.

   An abstract of a paper presented at the American Physical Society meeting.

267. Katzin, L. I., "The Absorption Spectrum of Cs$_2$CoCl$_4$ at Liquid-Nitrogen Temperatures," *J. Am. Chem. Soc.*, **76**, 3089. *48–11188*.

   The spectrum of Cs$_2$CoCl$_4$ dispersed in KBr was determined at room temperatures and at liquid-nitrogen temperature.

268. Keller, F. L., and Nielsen, A. H., "The Infrared Spectrum and Molecular Constants of DBr," *J. Chem. Phys.*, **22**, 294. *48–6248*.

269. Ketelaar, J. A. A., Haas, C., and Fahrenfort, J., "Relation Between the Infrared Spectra and Raman Spectra of Crystals. Variation of Frequency with Incidence in the Infrared Spectra of NaNO$_3$," *Physica*, **20**, 1259. *49–14484*.

270. Ketelaar, J. A. A., "The Infrared Spectra of KH$_2$PO$_4$ and KD$_2$PO$_4$," *Acta Cryst.*, **7**, 691. *50–5413*.

An abstract of a paper presented at the third General Assembly of the International Union of Crystallography.

271. King, G. W., Blanton, E. H., and Frawley, J., "Spectroscopy from the Point of View of Communication Theory. IV. Automatic Recording of Infrared Spectra of Punched Cards," *J. Opt. Soc. Amer.*, **44** (5), 397.

272. Kiyama, R., Minomura, S., and Ozawa, K., "Infrared Absorption in Gaseous Ammonia at (Various) Pressures," *Rev. Phys. Chem. Japan*, **24**, 56. *49–7978*.

Measurements at 19° from 1300–6500 cm^{-1} are reported for gaseous ammonia at pressures up to 5 Kg./sq. cm.

273. Kolesova, V. A., "Problem of the Interpretation of Vibration Spectra of the Silicates and the Silicate Glasses," *Zhur. Eksptl. i Teoret. Fiz.*, **26**, 124. *50–59*.

Particular discussion is made of the vibrations ascribed to the SiO$_4$ group in the region 1250–833 cm^{-1}, 833–769 cm^{-1}, 588–500 cm^{-1}, and beyond 476 cm^{-1}.

274. Kluyver, J. C., and Blokhuis, E. W. M., "The Infrared Isotope Analyzer. II," *Physica*, **20**, 427. *49–5125*.

An analyzer permitting the determination of the C^{13}/C^{12} ratio in CO$_2$ and the N^{15}/N^{14} ratio in N$_2$O is described.

275. Kuratani, K., "The Application of Infrared Absorption to Chemistry," *Kagaku no Ryôiki (J. Japan Chem.) Extra Ed.*, No. 7, 41. *48–13401*.

A review.

276. Lecomte, J., "Spectrophotometry in the Infrared; Its Importance in Physics and Chemistry," *Rev. opt.*, **33**, 553. *49–13757*.

277. Lejeune, R., and Duyckaerts, G., "Note on the Infrared Spectra of Powders," *Spectrochim. Acta*, **6** (3), 194.

278. Loferski, J. J., "Infrared Optical Properties of Single Crystals of Tellurium," *Phys. Rev.*, **93**, 707. *48–6830*.

279. Long, D. A., Murfin, F. S., and Williams, R. C., "The Raman and Infrared Spectra of Carbon Suboxide," *Proc. Roy. Soc. (London)*, A**223**, 251. *48–8047*.

A redetermination and re-evaluation of previously reported data on the spectrum of carbon suboxide have been made.

280. Lord, R. C., and Steese, C. M., "The Infrared Spectra of Monochlorogermane and Monochlorogermane-d$_3$," *J. Chem. Phys.*, **22**, 542. *48–7435*.

281. Mara, R. T., Sutherland, G. B. B. M., and Tyrell, H. V., "Infrared Spectrum of Barium Titanate," *Phys. Rev.*, **96**, 801. *49–2869*.

The absorption of BaTiO$_3$ was measured in the infrared region 303–5000 cm^{-1}. Hexagonal and tetragonal BaTiO$_3$ gave identical spectra from 667–5000 cm^{-1}. The spectrum of SrTiO$_3$ is also given.

282. Martz, D. E., and Lagemann, R. T., "Infrared Spectra of Thionyl Chloride and Sulfuryl Chloride," *J. Chem. Phys.*, **22**, 1193. *48–13427.*

The spectral region investigated was 400–5000 cm^{-1}. The symmetry of the molecules is discussed.

283. Mathieu, L. C., "Vibrational Spectrum of the Hydrogen in Potassium Acid Carbonate," *J. phys. radium*, **15**, 531. *50–9878.*

The polarized infrared absorption and Raman spectra were obtained for solid $KHCO_3$ and vibrational assignments are made.

284. Maybury, R. H., Katz, J. J., and Gordon, S., "Cell for the Measurement of Infrared Spectra in Liquid Hydrogen Fluoride," *Rev. Sci. Instr.*, **25**, 1133. *49–12134.*

A cell adapted for use in the 400–10,000 cm^{-1} range for high-vacuum or high-pressure determination of spectra of substances in liquid HF or SO_2 is described.

285. McCarty, L. V., Smith, G. C., and McDonald, R. S., "Infrared Absorptiometry for Quantitative Determination of Boron Hydrides in Presence of Pentaborane," *Anal. Chem.*, **26** (6), 1027. *48–11972.*

286. Miller, R. L., "The Infrared Spectrum and the Force Field of Crystalline Hydrogen Peroxide and Their Relation to the Ice Problem," *Dissertation Abstracts*, **14**, 2213. *49–4405.*

287. Morita, N., "Optical Constants of Boron in Visible and Near Infrared," *J. Sci. Research Inst. (Tokyo)*, **48**, 8. *48–11194.*

288. Narayanan, P. S., Sundaramma, K., and Krishman, R. S., "Infrared Studies of L(–)allohydroxyproline and Rutile," *J. Indian Inst. Sci.*, **36**, 137. *49–724.*

The infrared spectra were obtained for the region 833–10,000 cm^{-1}.

289. Newman, R., "Optical Studies of Injected Carriers. III. Infrared Absorption in Germanium at Low Temperatures," *Phys. Rev.*, **96**, 1188. *49–3660.*

The infrared absorption of carriers injected into germanium is given at 82°K, 201°K, and 302°K.

290. Nielsen, A. H., and Lagemann, R. T., "The Infrared Spectrum and Molecular Constants of $C^{14}O_2$," *J. Chem. Phys.*, **22**, 36. *48–4974.*

291. Nielsen, A. H., "Infrared Spectrum of σ_2 for $B^{10}F_3$ and $B^{11}F_3$," *J. Chem. Phys.*, **22**, 659. *48–8652.*

The spectra of σ_2 for $B^{10}F_3$ and $B^{11}F_3$ were determined and discussed for the region 650–750 cm^{-1}.

292. Nightingale, R. E., Downie, A. R., Rotenberg, D. L., Crawford, B. L., Ogg, R. A., "The Preparation of Infrared Spectra of the Oxides of Nitrogen," *J. Phys. Chem.*, **58**, 1047. *49–2870.*

The spectra of the nitrogen oxides, NO, NO_2—N_2O_4, and N_2O_5, were obtained in the 650–2000 cm^{-1} region. Methods of preparation, analysis, and identification of bands are reported.

293. Noland, J. A., "Optical Absorption of Single-Crystal Strontium Titanate," *Phys. Rev.*, 94, 724. *48–8652.*
    The absorption of $SrTiO_3$ is reported for the region 666–28,570 cm^{-1}.

294. Oswald, F., "The Optical Properties of Indium Phosphide in the Infrared," *Z. Naturforsch,* 9a, 181. *48–11926.*
    The region 657–12,500 cm^{-1} was used for transmission and reflectivity measurements of indium phosphide.

295. Oswald, F., and Schade, R., "Determination of Optical Constants of the Type $A^{III}B^{IV}$ Semiconductors in the Infrared," *Z. Naturforsch,* 9a, 611. *49–51.*
    Transmission data are given for $A^{III}B^{IV}$ type semiconductors in the region 657–12,500 cm^{-1}. Absorption constants are derived for AlSb, GaAs, GaSb, InP, InSb, and InAs.

296. Pemsler, J. P., and Smith, D. F., "An Infrared Band of a Molecular Complex Between Hydrogen Fluoride and Chlorine Trifluoride," *J. Chem. Phys.*, 22, 1834. *49–2189.*
    A band, located at 3891 cm^{-1}, has been associated with the complex $HF \cdot ClF_3$.

297. Polo, S. R., and Wilson, M. K., "The Spectrum of $SO^{16}O^{18}$ and the Potential Constants of SO_2," *J. Chem. Phys.*, 22, 900. *48–11926.*

298. Primas, H., and Günthard, H., "The Theory of the Shape of Absorption Bands of Suspended Materials and Its Application to the Nujol Method in Infrared Spectroscopy," *Helv. Chim. Acta*, 37, 360. *48–7433.*

299. Pross, A. W., "Estimation of Impurities in Liquid Chlorine by Infrared Absorption Spectrophotometry," *Nature*, 174, 467.

300. Pross, A. W., "Estimation of Impurities in Liquid Chlorine by Infrared Absorption Spectroscopy," *Canadian J. Chem.*, 32 (10), 956.

301. Ramdas, A. K., "Infrared Absorption Spectrum of Barite," *Proc. Indian Acad. Sci.*, 39A, 81. *48–8652.*
    The infrared absorption spectrum of barite crystals was determined in the 400–10,000 cm^{-1} range.

302. Rix, H. D., "The Infrared and Raman Spectra of Carbon Suboxide," *J. Chem. Phys.*, 22, 429. *48–7434.*
    Gaseous carbon suboxide was investigated from 500–4545 cm^{-1} in the infrared; the Raman spectrum was photographed in the liquid phase. An analysis of the two spectra is given.

303. Ryason, R., and Wilson, M. K., "Vibrational Spectrum and Structure of Nitryl Chloride," *J. Chem. Phys.*, 22, 2000. *49–4406.*
    The infrared spectrum of gaseous NO_2Cl and the Raman spectrum of liquid NO_2Cl are consistent with the structure of $ClN(\cdot O)_2$.

304. Saier, E. L., and Pozefsky, A., "Quantitative Determination of Nitric Oxide and Nitrous Oxide by Infra-Red Absorption," *Anal. Chem.*, 26 (6), 1079. *48–11976.*

305. Schulz, L. G., "An Experimental Confirmation of the Drude Free-Electron Theory of the Optical Properties of Metals for Silver, Gold, and Copper in the Near Infrared," *J. Opt. Soc. Amer.*, 44, 540. *48–11194.*

Transmission measurements were made between 3333 and 10,000 cm^{-1}.

306. Setton, R., Lecomte, J., and Hackspill, L., "Infrared Absorption Spectra of the Compounds $(COCs)_2$," *Compt. rend.*, 238, 2472. *49–723.*

The infrared spectra of two isomeric forms of $(COCs)_2$ were measured under controlled conditions. The results, discussed on basis of these spectra, suggest that the nature of the CO bond is intermediate between single and double.

307. Shelton, R. D., Nielsen, A. H., and Fletcher, W. H., "The Infrared Spectrum and Molecular Constants of Sulfur Dioxide," *J. Chem. Phys.*, 22, 1791. *49–718.*

308. Sverdlov, L. M., and Zaitseva, I. N., "Vibrational Spectra and the Diborane Structure," *Izvest. Akad. Nauk S.S.S.R., Ser. Fiz.*, 18, 672. *50–7592.*

309. Teranishi, R., and Decius, J. C., "The Infrared Spectrum of Crystalline Nitrogen Pentoxide," *J. Chem. Phys.*, 22, 896. *48–11926.*

310. Toribara, T. Y., and DiStefano, V., "Infrared Identification in Paper Chromatography," *Anal. Chem.*, 26 (9), 1519. *49–2556.*

The freeze-drying technique for sample preparation is described.

311. Tourin, R. H., "Infrared Spectra of Thermally Excited Gases," *Natl. Bur. Standards (U.S.) Circ.*, 523, 87.

Results obtained on CO_2 in both emission and absorption.

312. Vincent-Geisse, J., "Measurements of Intensity and Band Widths in the Infrared Region of Gases or Vapors," *Compt. rend.*, 239, 251. *49–5125.*

Values are given for CO, CH_4, N_2O, and NO.

313. Vincent-Geisse, J., "Measurements of Intensity and Line Width in the Infrared. Application to Carbon Monoxide," *J. phys. radium*, 15, 539. *50–9875.*

314. Williams, R. C., "Intensities of the Infrared Bands of Carbon Suboxide," *J. Chem. Phys.*, 22, 345. *48–5648.*

315. Yoshinaga, H., Fujita, S., Yamada, Y., Mitsuishi, A., Kubota, B., and Minami, S., "Recent Infrared Instrumentation and Its Applications," *Oyo Butsuri*, 23, 51, 97. *48–10421.*

A review.

1955

316. "Abstracts of Papers Presented at the American Physical Society Meeting," *Phys. Rev.*, 98, 223.

A series of paper abstracts, including papers on infrared absorption spectra.

317. Aigrain, P., and des Cloizeaux, J., "Optic Absorption Limit and Effective Mass of Electrons in Indium Antimonide," *Compt. rend.*, **241**, 859. *50–6181.*

318. Allen, H. C., Tidwell, E. D., and Plyler, E. K., "Vibrational Energy of Deuterium Cyanide," *J. Chem. Phys.*, **23**, 1356. *49–12960.*

   The spectrum was obtained for the region 1900–8000 cm^{-1}. Calculations were made for the vibrational energy.

319. Allin, E. J., Hare, W. F. J., and MacDonald, R. E., "Infrared Absorption Spectra of Liquid and Solid Hydrogen," *Phys. Rev.*, **98**, 554. *49–10740.*

   Gaseous hydrogen at 3400 atmospheres and 298°K, liquid hydrogen at 18.0°K, and solid hydrogen at 11.0°K were examined in the infrared regions 3700–5500 cm^{-1}.

320. Appel, J., "Electric and Optical Properties of Silver Telluride," *Z. Naturforsch.*, **10a**, 530. *51–3282.*

321. Barrow, G. M., "The Infrared Spectrum of Sulfur Dichloride," *J. Phys. Chem.*, **59**, 987. *50–676.*

   Absorption maxima are given for the vapor state of sulfur dichloride. Assignments are made for the liquid.

322. Beachell, H. C., and Levy, E. J., "Near Infrared Spectrum of Liquid Diborane," *J. Chem. Phys.*, **23**, 2168. *50–3083.*

   The spectrum was observed and analyzed for the 4500–10,500 cm^{-1} region.

323. Bethell, D. E., and Sheppard, N., "Infrared Spectrum and Structure of Boric Acid," *Trans. Faraday Soc.*, **51**, 9. *49–11417.*

   Polycrystalline mulls and a single crystal of B(OD)$_3$ were examined between 3600 and 500 cm^{-1}.

324. Blades, H., and Hodgins, J. W., "Absorption Spectra of Metals in Solution," *Can. J. Chem.*, **33**, 411. *49–10056.*

   Spectral data are presented for solutions of Li, Na, K, and Ca in ammonia and organic amines for the region 4000 and 33,333 cm^{-1}.

325. Blount, E. R., and Abbate, M. J., "Infrared Microspectroscopy. IV. A Double Beam Infrared Microspectrometer," *J. Opt. Soc. Amer.*, **45** (12), 1028. *50–2298.*

326. Blunt, R. F., Frederikse, H. P. R., and Hosler, W. R., "Electrical and Optical Properties of Intermetallic Compounds. IV. Magnesium Stannide," *Phys. Rev.*, **100**, 663. *50–3069.*

327. Bonhomme, J., "Quantitative Analysis with the Infrared Absorption Spectra of Powders. II. Experimental Study," *Spectrochim. Acta*, **7**, 32. *49–7980.*

   Graded samples of calcite and Dowex of known particle size were investigated in KBr pellets. The results of spectral analysis are discussed in connection with theoretical formulas.

328. Bonhomme, J., and Duyckaerts, G., "The Importance of Grain Size in the Infrared Spectrometry of Powders," *Compt. rend. 27e congr. intern.*

chim. ind., Brussels (1954), **1**; *Industrie chim. belge,* **20**, Spec. No., 145. *50–8325.*

A study was made on the influence of particle size on the absorption spectrum of KBr pellets of $CaCO_3$, Dowex, and K_4 $(Fe(CN)_6)$.

329. Bonino, G. B., and Fabbri, G., "The Infrared Absorption Spectrum of Potassium Ferrocyanide," *Atti accad. nazl. Lincei, Rend., Classe sci. fis., mat. e nat.,* **19**, 386. *50–12651.*

Crystalline K_4Fe $(CN)_6$ and its trihydrate are examined from 416–3333 cm^{-1}.

330. Boyd, D. R. J., "Infrared Spectrum of Trideuterio-silane and the Structure of the Silane Molecule," *J. Chem. Phys.,* **23**, 922. *49–13780.*

331. Braithwaite, J. G. N., "Infrared Filters Using Evaporated Layers of Lead Sulfide, Lead Selenide, and Lead Telluride," *J. Sci. Instr.,* **32**, 10. *49–7389.*

Optical properties of the filter materials have been studied and found to be similar to those of the single crystals.

332. Busing, W. R., "Infrared Spectra and Structure of NaOH and NaOD," *J. Chem. Phys.,* **23**, 933. *49–13780.*

333. Corbridge, D. E. C., and Lowe, E. J., "Quantitative Infrared Analysis of Condensed Phosphates," *Anal. Chem.,* **27** (9), 1383. *49–2870.*

334. Coulon, R., Robin, J., and Vodar, B., "Infrared Spectrum of Mixtures of the Compressed Gases, Hydrogen Chloride and Hydrogen, and the Appearance of a Frequency of Combination Between Hydrogen Chloride and Hydrogen," *Compt. rend.,* **240**, 956. *49–10741.*

The spectra of mixtures of the compressed gases up to total pressures of 845 atmospheres were obtained between 6000 and 9000 cm^{-1}.

335. Crosby, G. A., "Infrared Spectra of HDS and H_2O_2; Analysis of 6140 cm^{-1} Band of HDS," *Dissertation Abstr.,* **15**, 198. *49–7384.*

336. Crosby, G. A., Bair, E. J., and Cross, P. C., "Analysis of the 6140 cm^{-1} band of HDS," *J. Chem. Phys.,* **23**, 1660. *50–676.*

337. Cumming, C., "The v_3 Infrared Band of Ammonia," *Can. J. Phys.,* **33**, 635. *50–676.*

338. Davis, P. W., "Far Infrared Spectra of Several Pyramidal Trihalides," *Dissertation Abstr.,* **15**, 1086. *49–12961.*

339. Dash, W. C., and Newman, R., "Intrinsic Optical Absorption in Single-Crystal Germaniam and Silicon at 77°K and 300°K," *Phys. Rev.,* **99**, 1151. *49–15477.*

340. Decius, J. C., "Coupling of the Out-of-Plane Bending Mode in Nitrates and Carbonates of the Aragonite Structure," *J. Chem. Phys.,* **23**, 1290. *49–13780.*

The infrared spectra of samples of KNO_3 and $BaCO_3$ in Nujol mulls were obtained between 800 and 885 cm^{-1}.

341. Dickey, F. P., and Hoffman, J. M., "Vibration-rotation Band v_2 of Heavy Water Vapor," *J. Chem. Phys.,* **23**, 1718. *50–676.*

342. Dingle, R. B., "Theory of the Infrared Absorption by Carriers in Semi-conductors," *Phys. Rev.*, **99**, 1901. *50–2280.*

343. Dixon, R. N., and Sheppard, N., "The Vibration-rotation Spectrum of Silyl Iodide," *J. Chem. Phys.*, **23**, 215. *49–4406.*
    The spectrum of silyl iodide is reported for the 500–5000 cm⁻¹ region.

344. D'or, L., Haccuria, M., and Machiroux, R., "Infrared Absorption Spectra of Silica in Its Different Forms and of the Hexagonal Variety of Germanium Dioxide," *Compt. rend. 27ᵉ congr. intern. chim. ind., Brussels* (1954), **3**; *Industrie chim. belge*, **20**, Spec. No., 150. *50–11820.*
    Bands are located for powdered quartz, tridymite, cristobalite, fused silica, and amorphous silica.

345. Dows, D. A., and Pimentel, G. C., "Infrared Spectra of Gaseous and Solid Hydrazoic Acid and Deuterohydrazoic Acid; The Thermodynamic Properties of Hydrazoic Acid," *J. Chem. Phys.*, **23**, 1258. *49–14484.*

346. Dows, D. A., Pimentel, G. C., and Whittle, E., "Infrared Spectra of Intermediate Species in the Formation of Ammonium Azide from Hydrazoic Acid," *J. Chem. Phys.*, **23**, 1606. *50–676.*

347. Dows, D. A., Whittle, E., and Pimentel, G. C., "Infrared Emission and Absorption in an Ammonia-Oxygen Diffusion Flame," *J. Chem. Phys.*, **23**, 499. *49–10059.*
    Absorption and emission spectra were detected in the range 600–4000 cm⁻¹.

348. Dows, D. A., Whittle, E., and Pimentel, G. C., "Infrared Spectrum of Solid Ammonium Azide: A Vibrational Assignment," *J. Chem. Phys.*, **23**, 1475. *49–15486.*

349. Drouard, E., "Infrared Study of the Water in the Li₂SO₄·H₂O Crystal," *Compt. rend.*, **240**, 1700. *49–10744.*
    Crystals of Li₂SO₄·H₂O were examined in the 3000–3600 cm⁻¹ region.   A rough calculation of the directions of the OH bonds is made.

350. Duyckaerts, G., "Quantitative Analysis with the Infrared Absorption Spectra of Powders.   I.   Theoretical Investigation of the Question," *Spectrochim. Acta*, **7**, 25. *49–7980.*
    A theoretical discussion of the KBr-powder pellet technique.

351. Dupuis, T., "A New Method for the Gravimetric Determination of Tungsten; Infrared Absorption Spectra of Tungstates Prepared at Different pH Values," *Mikrochim. Acta*, **4**, 851.

352. Duval, C., "Applications of Infrared Absorption Spectra Carried Out on a Drop of Aqueous Solution," *Compt. rend.*, **240**, 1646. *49–12966.*
    Spectra may be obtained on 0.01 ml. drops of aqueous solutions, using thallium bromide-iodide cell walls.

353. Duval, C., and Lecomte, J., "Infrared Absorption Spectra of Metallic Phosphites and Hypophosphites; Their Interpretation," *Compt. rend.*, **240**, 66. *49–5965.*

The absorption bands were observed between 300 and 3700 cm^{-1} and correlation is made with Raman spectra.

354. Edwards, J. O., Morrison, G. C., Ross, V. F., and Schultz, J. W., "The Structure of the Aqueous Borate Ion," *J. Am. Chem. Soc.*, **77**, 166. *49–4405*.

355. Farmer, V. C., "Pressed-disk Technique in Infrared Spectroscopy," *Chemistry and Industry*, 586. *49–12966*.
The effect of adsorption of solids onto particles of the alkali metal halide used to prepare the disk is discussed.

356. Feĭgel'son, E. M., "The Absorptive Properties of Water Vapor and Carbon Dioxide in the Atmosphere," *Izvest. Akad. Nauk S.S.S.R., Ser. Geofiz.*, 69. *50–3082*.
The wavelength region 588–2000 cm^{-1} was investigated.

357. Ferriso, C. C., and Hornig, D. F., "Infrared Spectra of Oxonium Halides and the Structure of the Oxonium Ion," *J. Chem. Phys.*, **23**, 1464. *49–15487*.
Spectra are obtained for OH_3F, OH_3Cl, OH_3Br, OH_3I, and OD_3Cl at $-195°$. The expected symmetrical pyramidal structure is confirmed.

358. Florence, J. M., Glaze, F. W., and Black, M. N., "Infrared Transmittance of Some Calcium Aluminate and Germanate Glasses," *J. Research Natl. Bur. Standards*, **55**, 231 (Research Paper 2625). *50–16394*.

359. Friedel, R. A., Wender, I., Shufler, S. L., and Sternberg, H. W., "Spectra and Structures of Cobalt Carbonyls," *J. Am. Chem. Soc.*, **77**, 3951. *49–15487*.

360. Gaunt, J., "Infrared Spectrum of Tellurium Hexafluoride from 25 to 40μ," *Trans. Faraday Soc.*, **51**, 893. *50–2293*.
A strong absorption band of TeF_6 was observed with the aid of a cesium bromide prism. The band is centered at 325 cm^{-1}.

361. Giese, A. T., and French, C. S., "The Analysis of Overlapping Spectral Absorption Bands by Derivative Spectrophotometry," *Applied Spectroscopy*, **9** (2), 78. *50–62*.

362. Haas, M., "Infrared Spectrum of Gypsum, $CaSO_4·2H_2O$," *Dissertation Abstr.*, **15**, 2245. *50–3082*.

363. Hadži, D., and Novak, A., "Infrared Spectra of Graphitic Oxide," *Trans. Faraday Soc.*, **51**, 1614. *50–11820*.
Spectra of graphitic oxide (prepared by method of Brodie: Annalen *114*, 6 (1860)) was examined from 667–2000 cm^{-1} as translucent film, and as paraffin oil and perfluorokerosene mulls.

364. Hadži, D., and Novak, A., "Infrared Spectra and Structure of Graphitic Oxide," *Bull. sci., Conseil acad. RPF Yougoslavie*, **2**, 48. *49–12961*.

365. Hall, J. F., and Ferguson, W. F. C., "Optical Properties of Cadmium Sulfide and Zinc Sulfide from 0.6–14 Microns," *J. Opt. Soc. Amer.*, **45**, 714. *49–15478*.
Evaporated films of CdS and ZnS were examined in the infrared region

714–16,667 cm^{-1}. Formulas are given for the approximation of the index of refraction and absorption from the reflectance and transmission when the absorption is small.

366. Halperin, A., and Garlick, G. F. J., "The Absorption Spectrum of Excited Crystals of Cadmium Sulfide," *Proc. Phys. Soc. (London)*, **68B**, 758.

Absorption bands of CdS crystals extend out to 1.4μ with maximum intensity at 0.78μ.

367. Harbeke, G., and Lautz, G., "Optical Investigations on the Semiconductor Properties of Arsenic and Zn$_3$As$_2$ Layers," *Abhandl. braunschweig. wiss. Ges.*, **7**, 36. *51–70.*

Transmission, reflection, and refractive index are reported for the 3704–20,000 cm^{-1}.

368. Hare, W. F. J., Allin, E. J., and Welsh, H. L., "Infrared Absorption of Liquid and Solid Hydrogen with Various Ortho-para Ratios," *Phys. Rev.*, **99**, 1887. *50–675.*

The absorption of solid hydrogen which contained 25, 50, 75 and 100% para-hydrogen was measured from 4000–5500 cm^{-1} at 13.6 ± 0.2°K.

369. Harris, L., "Preparation and Infrared Properties of Aluminum Oxide Films," *J. Opt. Soc. Amer.*, **45**, 27. *49–5964.*

Transmission measurements show that aluminum oxide films show absorption beyond 11μ in thicknesses on the order of 250A°.

370. Hawkins, N. J., Mattraw, H. C., and Sabol, W. W., "Infrared Spectrum of Plutonium Hexafluoride," *J. Chem. Phys.*, **23**, 2191. *50–2293.*

371. Herington, E. F. G., and Kynaston, W., "Infrared Spectra of Compounds Containing the Pentacyanoferrate Group," *J. Chem. Soc.*, 3555. *50–59.*

Spectra of Na$_3$(Fe(CN)$_5$NH)$_3$·6H$_2$O, Na$_2$(Fe(CN)$_5$NH$_3$)·H$_2$O, Na$_3$(Fe(CN)$_5$H$_2$O)·H$_2$O and Na$_2$(Fe(CN)$_5$H$_2$O) were obtained and a discussion of the main absorption bands given.

372. Hornig, D. F., and Osberg, W. E., "Infrared Spectrum and the Structure of the Low-Temperature Phases of Crystalline Hydrogen Chloride, Hydrogen Bromide, and Hydrogen Iodide," *J. Chem. Phys.*, **23**, 662. *49–10741.*

373. Janz, G. J., and Fitzgerald, W. E., "A Low Temperature Infrared Cell Assembly," *Applied Spectroscopy*, **9** (4), 178. *50–3089.*

A cell is described which is usable at temperatures down to −115°C.

374. Jones, L. H., "Infrared Spectrum of Ni(CO)$_4$ Vapor," *J. Chem. Phys.*, **23**, 2448. *50–3083.*

The spectrum of Ni(CO)$_4$ over the 270–10,000 cm^{-1} range was reported.

375. Josien, M. L., and Sourisseau, G., "The Infrared Spectrum of Hydrochloric Acid in Solution. Formation of Organic Complexes," *Bull. soc. chim. France*, 178. *49–7977.*

The spectra of HCl in 25 organic solvents or solvent pairs were observed at 15° from 2300–2900 cm^{-1}.

376. Josien, M. L., Sourisseau, G., and Castinel, C., "Infrared Spectra of Hydrobromic and Hydriodic Acids in Solution. Formation of Organic Complexes," *Bull. soc. chim. France*, 1539. *50–4640.*

377. Kahn, A. H., "Theory of the Infrared Absorption of Carriers in Germanium and Silicon," *Phys. Rev.*, **97**, 1647. *49–7982.*

378. Kaiser, W., and Fan, H. Y., "Infrared Absorption of Indium Antimonide," *Phys. Rev.*, **98**, 966. *49–11417.*

   The infrared spectra of samples of InSb were measured between 5 and 500°K over the range 285–3333 cm^{-1}. A wide range of carrier concentrations was employed.

379. Kawai, K., and Shimizu, K., "Potential Constants for Some Nitrosyl Halides," *Science and Ind. (Japan)*, **29**, 9. *49–13781.*

   A set of potential constants was calculated from published values of infrared absorption spectra for FNO, ClNO, and BrNO using the Wilson FG matrix method.

380. Kaye, W., "Near-Infrared Spectroscopy. II. Instrumentation and Technique. A Review," *Spectrochim. Acta*, **7** (4), 181. *50–680.*

381. Ketelaar, J. A. A., Colpa, J. P., and Hooge, F. N., "Pure Rotational Absorption Spectrum of Hydrogen," *J. Chem. Phys.*, **23**, 413. *49–5962.*

   The absorption of compressed hydrogen was observed from 667–1250 cm^{-1} at pressures up to 114 atmospheres; optical path length 100 cm.

382. Kiyama, R., and Ozawa, K., "Measurement of Infrared Absorption Intensity for Stretching Vibration of Carbon Disulfide Molecules," *Rev. Phys. Chem. Japan*, **25**, 38. *49–15486.*

383. Klemperer, Wm., "Infrared Spectrum of LiH," *J. Chem. Phys.*, **23**, 2452. *50–3082.*

384. Klimovskaya, L. K., and Turkevich, V. V., "The Absorption Spectra Caused by Copper Ions," *Dopovidi ta Povidomlennya Lviv. Univ.*, **2**, No. 5, 77. *52–2531.*

   The region 200–1200 mμ was investigated for Cu^{++} salts and minerals. Two maxima were found in the absorption curves, one of which lies in the infrared region.

385. Kobayashi, M., and Fujita, J., "Infrared Absorption Spectra of Hexammine Metal Complexes," *J. Chem. Phys.*, **23**, 1354. *49–12960.*

   Absorption in the infrared is reported for Ni(NH$_3$)$_6$ Cl$_2$, Cr(NH$_3$)$_6$ Cl$_3$ and Co(NH$_3$)$_6$ Cl$_3$.

386. Krishnamachari, S. L. N. G., "Force Constants for Substituted Germanes. I. GeH$_3$Cl and GeD$_3$Cl," *Indian J. Phys.*, **29**, 147. *51–7860.*

387. Krishnamachari, S. L. N. G., "Force Constants for Substituted Germanes. II. GeCl$_3$H and GeCl$_4$," *Indian J. Phys.*, **29**, 384. *51–7860.*

388. Kuentzel, L. E., "Calcium carbonate as an Internal Standard for Quantitative Infrared Analysis," *Anal. Chem.*, **27** (2), 301.

389. Lacroix, R., "Structure from the Absorption Spectra of Nickel Salts in Solution," *Arch. sci. (Geneva)*, **8**, 317.   *50–9870*.

    Spectral data have been obtained for $Ni(H_2O)_6^{++}$ and assignments made.

390. Lakshmi, K., and Shaw, J. H., "Absorption Bands of Nitrous Oxide Near 4.5μ," *J. Chem. Phys.*, **23**, 1887.   *50–2287*.

391. Lax, M., and Burstein, E., "Infrared Lattice Absorption in Ionic and Homopolar Crystals," *Phys. Rev.*, **97**, 39.   *49–5125*.

    An analysis is made of the infrared absorption in alkali halides, MgO, diamond, silicon, and germanium.

392. Lecomte, J., Boulle, A., and Lang-Dupont, M., "Infrared Study of the Dehydration and Rehydration of $CaHPO_4$," *Compt. rend.*, **241**, 1927. *50–9878*.

393. Lipson, H. G., Burstein, E., and Smith, P. L., "Optical Properties of Plastically Deformed Germanium," *Phys. Rev.*, **99**, 444.   *49–15459*.

394. Longworth, R., and Morawetz, H., "Measurement of the Infrared Spectra of Solids at Varying Temperatures by the Pressed Alkali Halide Disc Technique," *Chem. and Ind.*, **46**, 1470.   *50–9876*.

395. MacDiarmio, A. G., and Maddock, A. G., "Structure of Silyl Isothiocyanate," *J. Inorg. Nucl. Chem.*, **1**, 411.   *50–3897*.

396. Macfarlane, G. G., and Roberts, V., "Infrared Absorption of Germanium Near the Lattice Edge," *Phys. Rev.*, **97**, 1714.   *49–7982*.

397. Macfarlane, G. G., and Roberts, V., "Infrared Absorption of Silicon Near the Lattice Edge," *Phys. Rev.*, **98**, 1865.   *49–12128*.

398. Magee, C. B., "Molecular Spectroscopy—Infrared Spectra of Cobalt Hydrocarbonyl and Cobalt Carbonyl Nitrosyl and a Raman Tube for Gases at Relatively Low Pressures," *Dissertation Abstr.*, **15**, 991.   *49–12961*.

399. Malm, J. G., Weinstock, B., and Claasen, H. H., "Infrared Spectra of Neptunium Hexafluoride and Plutonium Hexafluoride," *J. Chem. Phys.*, **23**, 2192.   *50–2293*.

400. Margolin, I. A., and Rumyantseo, N. P., "Osnovy Infrakrasnoi tekhniki" (Principles of Infrared Practices).   Moscow: Voen. Izdatel. (1955), 262 pp.   *50–13620*.

401. "Materials of the IXth All-Union Conference on Spectroscopy," *Izvest. Akad. Nauk S.S.S.R., Ser. Fiz.*, **19**, 5ff.   *50–3885*.

    A series of articles on instrumentation, spectral determination, problems of spectral analysis, etc.

402. Mathieu, J. P., Couture-Mathieu, L., and Poulet, H., "Vibrational Spectra of Piezoelectric Crystals.   V.   Lithium Potassium Sulfate," *J. phys. radium*, **16**, 781.   *50–11822*.

403. Mattraw, H. C., "A Heated Infrared Cell," *Applied Spectroscopy*, **9** (4), 177.   *50–3089*.

    A cell which is usable up to 125°C is described.

404. Mattraw, H. C., Hawkins, N. J., Carpenter, D. R., and Sabol, W. W.,

"Infrared Spectrum of Iridium Hexafluoride," *J. Chem. Phys.*, **23**, 985. *49–10744.*

405. Matutano, J. R. B., and Otero, C., "The Infrared Spectrum of Sulfur Monofluoride," *Anales real soc. españ. fis. y quím. (Madrid)*, **51B**, 223. *49–15486.*

 The spectrum of S_2F_2 was measured from 2000–400 cm^{-1} and assignments were made.

406. Maybury, R. H., Gordon, S., and Katz, J. J., "Infrared Spectra of Liquid Anhydrous Hydrogen Fluoride, Liquid Sulfur Dioxide, and Hydrogen Fluoride-Sulfur Dioxide Solutions," *J. Chem. Phys.*, **23**, 1277. *49–13781.*

 The absorption spectra are obtained for the region 400–10,000 cm^{-1}.

407. Mayo, D. W., Opitz, H. E., and Peake, J. S., "Vibrational Spectra of SiH_3Br and SiH_2Br_2," *J. Chem. Phys.*, **23**, 1344. *49–12962.*

408. Merritt, P. E., and Wiberley, S. E., "Infrared Absorption Spectra of Cistrans Isomers of Coordination Compounds of Cobalt (III)," *J. Phys. Chem.*, **59**, 55. *49–3661.*

409. Mizushima, S., Nakagawa, I., and Quagliano, J. V., "Infrared Absorption Spectra of Inorganic Coordination Complexes. III. Deformation Frequencies of the NH Ligand," *J. Chem. Phys.*, **23**, 1367. *49–13780.*

 Degenerate, symmetrical, and rocking frequencies were observed for the complexes: $[Co(NH_3)_6]I_3$, $[Co(NH_3)_5Cl]Cl_2$, $[Co(NH_3)_5Br]$ Br_2, $[Pd(NH_3)_4Pd]Cl_4$, and $[Co(NH_3)_5H_2O]Cl_2$.

410. Newman, R., "Optical Properties of Indium-doped Silicon," *Phys. Rev.*, **99**, 465. *49–15461.*

411. Nichols, N. L., Hause, C. D., and Noble, R. H., "Near-infrared Spectrum of Nitric Oxide," *J. Chem. Phys.*, **23**, 57. *49–5126.*

412. Nikitine, S., Reiss, R., and Perny, G., "The Absorption Bands of the Green Series of Cu_2O at Low Temperatures," *Compt. rend.*, **240**, 505. *50–4636.*

 The spectrum of Cu_2O was obtained for the region 400–667 cm^{-1} at temperatures from 4.2–196°K.

413. O'Loane, J. K., and Wilson, M. K., "Infrared Spectrum of SOF_2," *J. Chem. Phys.*, **23**, 1313. *49–14485.*

 Assignments are made for the fundamentals of SOF_2, using spectral data obtained between 300 and 3000 cm^{-1}.

414. Ordway, G. L., Cross, P. C., and Bair, E. J., "Asymmetric Rotor, XII. The Infrared Spectrum of Hydrogen Sulfide from 7480–7880 cm^{-1}," *J. Chem. Phys.*, **23**, 541. *49–10741.*

415. Pace, E. L., and Pierce, L., "Infrared and Raman Spectra of Nitrogen Trifluoride," *J. Chem. Phys.*, **23**, 1248. *49–13781.*

416. Palik, E. D., "The Pure Rotational Spectra of DBr, HI, and DI in the Spectral Region Between 45 and 170 Microns," *J. Chem. Phys.*, **23**, 217. *49–4403.*

417. Palik, E. D., "Pure Rotational Spectrum of Hydrogen Selenide Between 50 and 250 cm⁻¹," *J. Chem. Phys.*, **23**, 980. *49–10741*.

418. Palik, E. D., "Rotational Spectra of Hydrogen Selenide, Partially Deuterated Ammonia, and Other Molecules in the Far Infrared Spectral Region," *Dissertation Abstr.*, **15**, 2247. *50–3083*.

419. Pliskin, W. A., and Eischens, R. P., "The Effect of Using the Pressed Salt Technique to Obtain the Spectrum of Chemisorbed Ammonia," *J. Phys. Chem.*, **59**, 1156. *50–2293*.

420. Plyler, E. K., and Acquista, N., "Small-grating Spectrometer for the Far Infrared Region," *J. Chem. Phys.*, **23** (4), 752. *49–10064*.

421. Plyler, E. K., Blaine, L. R., and Tidwell, E. D., "Infrared Absorption and Emission Spectra of Carbon Monoxide in the Region from 4 to 6μ," *J. Research Natl. Bur. Standards,* **55**, 183 (Research Paper 2617). *50–16385*.

422. Porlezza, C., and Rama, S., "Absorbing Power of Crystalline and Melted Quartz in the Infrared Zone of Spectrum," *Atti soc. toscana sci. nat. (Pisa) Ser. A*, **62**, 496. *50–16387*.

423. Porlezza, C., and Rama, S., "Experimental Observations on the Spectroscopic Behavior of Melted Quartz Between 1.0 and 4.5μ," *Atti soc. toscana sci. nat. (Pisa)*, Ser. A, **62**, 500. *50–16387*.

424. Premaswarup, D., "Vibrational Analysis of the Tantalum Oxide Bands," *Indian J. Phys.*, **29**, 109. *49–12957, 51–7850*.

425. Reding, F. P., and Hornig, D. F., "Vibrational Spectra of Molecules and Complex Ions in Crystals. VIII. The Infrared Spectrum of a Mixed Crystal of Ammonia-d_1 and Ammonia-d_2," *J. Chem. Phys.*, **23**, 1053. *49–12961*.

   A mixed crystal of NH_3, NDH_2, ND_2H, and ND_3 was examined in the infrared at −190°.

426. Reitzel, J., "Infrared Spectra of Silica from 400 to 600 cm⁻¹," *J. Chem. Phys.*, **23**, 2407. *50–3897*.

427. Roberts, V., and Quarrington, J. E., "Accurate Measurements of Absorption in InSb and GaSb," *J. Electronics*, **1**, 152.

428. Rundle, R. E., Nakamoto, K., and Richardson, J. W., "Concerning Hydrogen Positions in Aquo Complexes, $CuCl_2 \cdot 2H_2O$," *J. Chem. Phys.*, **23**, 2450. *50–3088*.

   A polarized infrared spectrum of single $CuCl_2 \cdot 2H_2O$ crystals has been investigated.

429. Silas, R. S., "Infrared Investigation of Some Substituted Ammonium Compounds," *Dissertation Abstr.*, **15**, 1509. *50–1467*.

430. Someren, E. H. S. van, and Lachman, F., "Spectrochemical Abstracts, 1946–1951," London: Hilger and Watts, 1955. 179 pp. *50–4651*.

431. Spitzer, W. G., and Fan, H. Y., "Infrared Absorption in Indium Antimonide," *Phys. Rev.*, **99**, 1893. *50–675*.

   The infrared transmission of InSb is reported at ca. 5, 78, 210, and

297°K for the region 66–2000 cm^{-1}.   Reflection data is also presented.

432. Strauss, F. B., and Thompson, A. E., "Duplication of Infrared Spectra on a Reduced Scale," *Chem. & Ind.*, 44, 1402.   *50–5336.*

433. Svatos, G. F., Curran, C., and Quagliano, J. V., "Infrared Absorption Spectra of Inorganic Coordination Complexes.   V.   The N—H Stretching Vibration in Coordination Compounds," *J. Am. Chem. Soc.*, 77, 6159.   *50–3086.*

434. Tabe, H., "Infrared Spectra and Characteristic Frequencies of Basic Aluminum Sulfates and Aluminum Hydroxides," *J. Pharm. Soc. Japan*, 75, 1304.   *50–2295.*

435. Terenin, A. N., Yaroslavskiĭ, N. G., Karyakin, A. V., and Sidorova, A. I., "Spectroscopy in the Infrared of Molecules Adsorbed on Porous Glass," *Mikrochim. Acta*, 467.   *49–11419.*

 Organic and inorganic molecules adsorbed on porous glass are examined in the infrared region.

436. Waldron, R. D., "Infrared Spectra of Ferrites," *Phys. Rev.*, 99, 1727.   *50–2295.*

 Spectra in the region 280–2500 cm^{-1} are given and analyzed for $CoFe_2O_4$, $FeFe_2O_4$, $MgFe_2O_4$, $MnFe_2O_4$, $NiFe_2O_4$, $ZnFe_2O_4$ and $Ni_{0.3}Zn_{0.7}Fe_2O_4$.

437. Wardzynski, W., "The Influence of Ultraviolet Irradiation on the Absorption in the Infrared Region of Potassium Bromide and Potassium Iodide Crystals with Anionic Impurities," *Bull. acad. polon. sci., Classe III*, 3, 169.   *49–14481.*

 The absorption of KBr and KI crystals to which ≤ 0.01 mol. % of impurity anion was added was measured in the infrared.   The effect of ultraviolet irradiation and thermal treatment on the observed spectra is discussed.

438. Wright, N., "Infrared Analysis—A Progress Report on an Advancing Method," *Applied Spectroscopy*, 9 (3), 105.

439. Yates, D. J. C., Sheppard, N., and Angell, C. L., "Infrared Spectrum of Ammonia Adsorbed on Porous Silica," *J. Chem. Phys.*, 23, 1980.   *50–2292.*

440. Zaitsev, G. A., and Neporent, B. S., "Anisotropy of the Absorption of Gypsum Crystals in the Infrared," *Zhur. Eksptl. i Teoret. Fiz.*, 29, 857.   *50–5404.*

 The absorption spectrum of gypsum has been investigated in the 909–5000 cm^{-1} range.   Reflection data were also obtained.

1956

441. Adams, R. M., and Katz, J. J., "New Variable-thickness Infrared Cell and the Infrared Spectra of HF, DF, H_2O, and D_2O," *J. Opt. Soc. Am.*, 46, 895.   *51–78.*

442. Allen, H. C., and Plyler, E. K., "Infrared Spectrum of Hydrogen Sulfide," *J. Chem. Phys.*, **25**, 1132.   *51–5553*.
    This investigation was carried out in the 1250 cm^{-1} region.

443. Allen, H. C., Blaine, L. R., Plyler, E. K., and Cross, P. C., "Infrared Spectrum of Hydrogen Sulfide from 2200 to 2800 cm^{-1}," *J. Chem. Phys.*, **24**, 35.   *50–4639*.

444. Allen, H. C., Plyler, E. K., and Blaine, L. R., "Infrared Spectrum and Rotational Constants of Carbon Disulfide," *J. Am. Chem. Soc.*, **78**, 4843.   *51–1731*.

445. Allen, H. C., Tidwell, E. D., and Plyler, E. K., "Infrared Spectra of Hydrogen Cyanide and Deuterium Cyanide," *J. Chem. Phys.*, **25**, 302.   *50–16387*.
    Twenty-two bands of HCN and eighteen bands of DCN were measured in the region 1900–8000 cm^{-1}.

446. Arends, C. B., "Infrared Studies on Isotopic Carbon Dioxide," *Dissertation Abstr.*, **16**, 461.   *50–10533*.

447. Arends, C. B., and Eggers, D. F., Jr., "Simple Aid to Infrared Intensity Measurements," *Rev. Sci. Instrum.*, **27** (11), 939.   *51–17455*.

448. Barrow, G. M., Krueger, R. H., and Basolo, F., "Vibrational Assignments for Metal Ammines," *J. Inorg. Nuclear Chem.*, **2**, 340.   *50–14365*.

449. Beattie, I. R., and Tyrrell, H. J. V., "The Spectra of Some Solid Cobaltic Nitroammines and Certain Other Cobaltic Complexes in the 2–15μ Region," *J. Chem. Soc.*, 2849.   *51–856*.
    The spectra of compounds containing the grouping [Co(NO$_2$)$_n$ (NH$_3$)$_{6-n}$] which bears a charge of (3–n) and of related compounds have been examined using the KBr-pellet technique.

450. Benedict, W. S., Gailar, N., and Plyler, E. K., "Rotation-vibration Spectra of Deuterated Water Vapor," *J. Chem. Phys.*, **24**, 1139.   *50–12652*.

451. Berglund-Larsson, U., "Determination of Small Amounts of Deuterium Oxide in H$_2$O by Infrared Spectroscopy," *Acta Chem. Scand.*, **10**, 701.

452. Bethke, G. W., "Convenient Calibration Curve for Prism Infrared Spectrometers," *J. Opt. Soc. Amer.*, **46** (7), 560.

453. Bicelli, L., "Infrared Absorption Spectra of Salts of Sulfamic Acid.   I. Salts of Lead, Cadmium, and Silver," *Ann. chim.* (Rome), **46**, 661.   *51–4142*.
    Spectra of Pb(SO$_3$NH$_2$)$_2$.2H$_2$O, Cd(SO$_3$NH$_2$)$_2$, and Ag(SO$_3$NH$_2$)$_2$ were observed and discussed for the region 667–5000 cm^{-1}.

454. Biondi, M. A., "Optical Absorption of Copper and Silver at 4.2°K," *Phys. Rev.*, **102**, 964.   *50–14358*.
    The absorption of Cu and Ag have been measured at 4.2°K for the region 0.3–3.3μ in the infrared.

455. Blount, E., Callaway, J., Cohen, M., Dumke, W., and Phillips, J., "Infrared Absorption of Indium Antimonide," *Phys. Rev.*, **101**, 563.   *50–6906*.

456. Bonino, G. B., and Fabbri, G., "Resolution of the Infrared Spectral Band Attributed to the CN Groups of Crystalline Potassium Ferrocyanide in Aqueous Solution," *Atti acad. nazl. Lincei, Rend., Classe Sci. fis., mat. e nat.*, **20**, 414. *50–16386*.

457. Bonino, G. B., and Fabbri, G., "Infrared Absorption Spectrum of Potassium Molybdenum Octacyanide," *Atti accad. nazl. Lincei, Rend., Classe sci., fis., mat. e nat.*, **20**, 566. *52–9763*.

458. Bonino, G. B., and Salvetti, O., "Symmetry and Infrared Absorption of Anhydrous and Hydrated Potassium Ferrocyanide," *Atti. accad. nazl., Lincei, Rend., Classe sci. fis., mat. e nat.*, **20**, 150. *50–14364*.

459. Bonino, G. B., and Salvetti, O., "Infrared Absorption Spectrum of Crystalline Potassium Ferrocyanide," *Ricerca sci.*, **26**, 3627. *51–7147*.

   Four bands in the 400–600 cm^{-1} region and 9 bands in the 2000–2100 cm^{-1} region have been ascribed to the symmetry deformation $O_h \rightarrow D_{4h} \rightarrow V_n$.

460. Borgen, O., and Krogh-Moe, J. "Infrared Spectra of Some Modifications of Arsenic Trioxide and Antimony Trioxide," *Acta Chem. Scand.*, **10**, 265. *50–12651*.

   Spectra of cubic and monoclinic As_2O_3 and Sb_2O_3 were obtained from 667–5000 cm^{-1}.

461. Breckenridge, R. C., Russell, B. R., and Hahn, E. E. (Editors), "Photoconductivity Conference." John Wiley & Sons, Inc., New York, N.Y. *51–5529*.

   This collection contains several articles on optical properties of semiconductors.

462. Bryant, F. J., "Gravimetric, Volumetric, and Absorptiometric Analysis," *Research*, **9**, 50.

   A review.

463. Bues, W., and Gehrke, H. W., "Vibrational Spectra of Metals, Glasses, and Crystals of Sodium Di-, Tri-, and Tetra Phosphates," *Z. anorg. u. allgem. chem.*, **288**, 291. *51–7147*.

   A description is given of the possible vibrations in phosphate anions as observed in spectra of $Na_4P_2O_7$, $Na_5P_3O_{10}$ glass, and $Na_6P_4O_{13}$ glass. Assignments are made.

464. Bues, W., and Gehrke, H. W., "Vibrational Spectra of Molten, Glassy, and Crystalline Highly Polymeric Phosphates," *Z. anorg. u. allgem. chem.*, **288**, 307. *51–7859*.

465. Burke, T. G., "Infrared Spectra of Selenium Hexafluoride and Tellurium Hexafluoride," *J. Chem. Phys.*, **25**, 791. *51–858*.

466. Cabannes-Ott, C., "Infrared Spectroscopy of the Hydrated Oxides of Copper, Cadmium, and Magnesium," *Compt. rend.*, **242**, 355. *50–7592*.

467. Cabannes-Ott, C., "Infrared Study, Between 300 and 4000 cm^{-1}, of Copper and Vanadyl Hydroxides," *Compt. rend.*, **242**, 2825. *50–16386*.

468. Caglioti, V., Silvestroni, P., Sartori, G., and Scrocco, M., "Infrared Investigations of Ammine Complexes of Transition Metals," *Ricerca Sci.*, **26**, 1743.   *50–16388.*

The frequencies of the absorption lines near 3000, 1500, and 1300 cm^{-1} have been measured for various ammine complexes including the bivalent hexammine complexes of Fe, Cd, Mn, Zn, CO, Ni, and Cu, the bivalent tetrammine complexes of Cd and Cu, and the trivalent hexammine complexes of Cr, Fe, and Co.

469. Chatt, J., and Duncanson, L. A., "Use of the Infrared Spectrum to Distinguish Bridging from Terminal Thiocyanato Sulfur Groups on Coordination Compounds," *Nature*, **178**, 997.   *51–84.*

470. Cho, C. W., Allin, E. J., and Welsh, H. C., "Structure of the Infrared 'Atmospheric' Bands in Liquid Oxygen," *J. Chem. Phys.*, **25**, 371.

471. Cotton, F. A., Liehr, A. O., and Wilkinson, G., "Spectra and Structures of Metal-Carbon Monoxide Compounds. II. Manganese and Rhenium Decacarbonyls," *J. Inorg. Nuclear Chem.*, **2**, 141.   *50–9870.*

Infrared absorption data have been obtained in the 450–3000 cm^{-1} region.

472. Dagg, I. R., and Thompson, H. W., "Infrared Bonds and Rotational Constants of HCN and DCN," *Trans. Faraday Soc.*, **52**, 455.   *50–15233.*

473. Dalby, F. W., "Infrared Spectrum of Water Vapor," *Dissertation Abstr.*, **16**, 769.   *50–10533.*

474. Dalby, F. W., and Nielsen, H. H., "Infrared Spectrum of Water Vapor. I.   The 6.26μ Region," *J. Chem. Phys.*, **25**, 934.   *51–4144.*

475. Dodd, R. E., Rolfe, J. A., and Woodward, L. A., "Infrared and Raman Spectra of Nitryl Fluoride," *Trans. Faraday Soc.*, **52**, 145.   *50–14365.*

The spectrum of gaseous nitryl fluoride was studied between 5000 and 400 cm^{-1}.   Assignments of the fundamentals are:

$\nu_1(a_1)$ 1312 cm^{-1} $\nu_3(a_1)$ 460 cm^{-1} $\nu_5(b_1)$ 570 cm^{-1}

$\nu_2(a_1)$ 822 cm^{-1} $\nu_4(b_1)$ 1793 cm^{-1} $\nu_6(b_2)$ 742 cm^{-1}

476. Dodd, R. E., Woodward, L. A., and Roberts, H. L., "Raman and Infrared Spectra of Sulfur Tetrafluoride," *Trans. Faraday Soc.*, **52**, 1052.   *51–5553.*

The infrared spectrum of gaseous SF_4 at room temperature was measured from 400–5000 cm^{-1}.   The Raman spectrum of the liquid at $-60°$ was also reported.

477. Dows, D. A., and Hexter, R. M., "Infrared Spectra of Gaseous and Solid Digermane," *J. Chem. Phys.*, **24**, 1029.   *50–11113.*

The region 400–4000 cm^{-1} was studied.   The spectra obtained were analyzed and assignments made.

478. Dows, D. A., and Hexter, R. M., "Infrared Spectrum of Digermane; ν_5 and ν_7 Bands," *J. Chem. Phys.*, **24**, 1117.   *50–11113.*

479. Doyle, W. P., "Absorption Spectrum of Solid Arsenic Trisulfide," *Proc. Phys. Soc. (London)*, **69B**, 865.   *51–14419.*

480. Dupuis, T., "Attempt to Interpret the Infrared Spectra of Salts of the Type XO_3Y_1, in Particular of the Sulfamates," *Compt. rend.*, **242**, 2924. *50–15236*.

The spectra of approximately ten sulfamates ($SO_3M_1NH_2$) for the region 300–1600 cm^{-1} have been compared with those of sulfates, thiosulfates, and selenosulfates.

481. Dupuis, T., "The Infrared Absorption Spectra of Sulfamic Acid, Heavy Sulfamic Acid, and Their Salts," *Compt. rend.*, **243**, 1621. *51–4821*.

The spectra were measured in the 700–3500 cm^{-1} region. Evidence is noted for the existence of two forms in the solid, NH_2SO_2OH and $^+NH_3SO_3^-$.

482. Dupuis, T., "Study of Infrared Absorption Spectra of Ordinary Amido-Sulfonic Acid, Heavy Amido-Sulfonic Acid, and Their Salts," *C. R. Acad. Sc. (Paris)*, **243** (21), 1621.

483. Edgell, W. F., Magee, C., and Gallup, G., "The Infrared Spectrum of Cobalt Carbonyl Hydride," *J. Am. Chem. Soc.*, **87**, 4185. *51–857*.

The spectrum of $HCo(CO)_4$ is reported for the region 303–5000 cm^{-1}.

484. Eischens, R. P., Francis, S. A., and Pliskin, W. A., "The Effect of Surface Coverage on the Spectra of Chemisorbed Carbon Monoxide," *J. Phys. Chem.*, **60**, 194. *50–6918*.

485. Elsayed, M. F. A., and Sheline, R. K., "The Infrared Spectrum and Structure of Hexacyanodi-Nickelate (I) Ion, $[Ni_2(CN)_6]^{-4}$," *J. Am. Chem. Soc.*, **78**, 702. *50–8326*.

486. Fan, H. Y., Spitzer, W., and Collins, R. J., "Infrared Absorption in n-Type Germanium," *Phys. Rev.*, **101**, 566. *50–6906*.

Results are reported for the absorption of various carrier and impurity concentrations in samples of n-type germanium at 78–450°K from 263–2000 cm^{-1}.

487. Freitag, W. O., and Nixon, E. R., "Infrared Spectra of Gaseous and Crystalline Cyanogen Halides," *J. Chem. Phys.*, **24**, 109. *50–4640*.

Spectral information is reported for ClCN and BrCN gas, ClCN, BrCN, and ICN crystals for the LiF, NaCl, KBr, and CsBr regions.

488. Fujita, J., Nakamoto, K., and Kobayashi, M., "Infrared Spectra of Metallic Complexes. I. The Effect of Coordination on the Infrared Spectra of Ammine, Rhodanato, and Azido Complexes," *J. Am. Chem. Soc.*, **78**, 3295. *50–16392*.

489. Fujita, J., Nakamoto, K., and Kobayashi, M., "Infrared Spectra of Metallic Complexes. II. The Absorption Bands of Coordinated Water in Aquo Complexes," *J. Am. Chem. Soc.*, **78**, 3963. *51–856*.

Spectral studies were made in the rock salt region. The absorption bands of coordinated water in Ni^{+2}, Cu^{+2}, and Cr^{+3} aquo complexes were observed and discussed.

490. Galatry, L., and Vodar, B., "The Rotational Spectrum of a System of

Two Diatomic Molecules in Electrostatic Interaction," *Compt. rend.*, **242**, 1871.   *50–9875.*

491. Garcia, S. G., Beutelspacher, H., and Flaig, W., "Infrared Spectrography of Clays and Structurally Analogous Minerals," *Anales real soc. españ. fis. y quim. (Madrid)*, **52B**, 369.

Spectra for kaolinite, dickite, halloysite, montmorillonite, nontronite, attapulgite, illite, vermicullite, muscovite, biotite, talc, pyrophyllite, and chrysolite have been recorded for the 833–1250 cm^{-1}.

492. Gaunt, J., "The Analysis of Heavy Water by Infrared Spectrometry," *Spectrochim. Acta*, 8 (2), 57.   51–135.

493. Genzel, L., "Spectral Studies in the 1mm. Wave Length Region.   IV. Vacuum Spectrometer.   Rotation Spectra of H_2S and NH_3," Z. *Physik*, **144**, 311.   *50–16396.*

The rotational spectra have been recorded for the 80–1000μ region.

494. Giguère, P. A., and Falk, M., "Infrared Spectrum of Solid Sulfur Dioxide," *Can. J. Chem.*, **34**, 1833.   *51–5554.*

Spectral data are recorded for the 500–5000 cm^{-1} range.   The following assignments are made:

a band at 1144 cm^{-1}, symmetrical stretching;

a doublet at 1310–22, asymmetrical stretching;

a doublet at 528–35, bending.

An overtone at 2287 and a combination band at 2455 are also reported.

495. Giguère, P. A., and Harvey, K. B., "The Infrared Absorption of Water and Heavy Water in Condensed States," *Can. J. Chem.*, **34**, 798.   *50–12652.*

The spectra of thin films of H_2O and D_2O have been measured at temperatures between 20° to −180° for the infrared region, 2–30μ.

496. Glemser, O., and Hartert, E., "Hydrogen Bonding in Crystallized Hydroxides," Z. *anorg. u. allgem. Chem.*, **283**, 111.   *50–9878.*

The absorption spectra of $Ca(OH)_2$, $Mg(OH)_2$, $Ni(OH)_2$, $Cd(OH)_2$, $Y(OH)_3$, $La(OH)_3$, $Nd(OH)_3$, β-$Be(OH)_2$, ϵ-$Zn(OH)_2$, v-$Al(OH)_3$, a−and γ-FeOOH, $B(OH)_3$, and a−AlOOH (deposited from iso-propyl alcohol suspensions) were obtained and analyzed.   A band at ∼ 3μ was observed in all cases.

497. Glover, R. E., and Tinkham, "Transmission of Super-conducting Films at Millimeter-Microwave and Far-Infrared Frequencies," *Phys. Rev.*, **104**, 844.   *51–5538.*

For Sn and Pb superconducting/normal state transmission ratios were measured from 20–100 cm^{-1}.

498. Graddon, D. P., "The Absorption Spectra of Complex Oxalates," *J. Inorg. Nucl. Chem.*, **3**, 308.   *51–4139.*

For the most part the spectral data are given for the ultraviolet region. However, some supporting data are presented for the infrared region.

499. Grechushnikov, B. N., and Feofilov, P. P., "Vibration Structure in the Absorption Spectrum of Ruby," *Soviet Phys., JETP,* **2,** 330. *50–11820.*

500. Guy, J., and Chaigneau, M., "Infrared Spectrum of B(CN)₃," *Bull. soc. chim. France,* 257. *50–9876.*

Characteristic bands of $B(CN)_3$ have been located at 4500, 3200, 1700, 1500, 1265, 875, 850, and 793 cm⁻¹.

501. Haas, C., "Vibration Spectra of Crystals," *Spectrochim. Acta,* **8,** 19. *50–13609.*

Experiments have been conducted on crystals of zinc blende, quartz, and sodium nitrate.

502. Haase, H., "Infrarot Bibliographie," The Hague: M. Nijhoff. 80 pp.

503. Haeusler, C., "Study of the Ammonia Band at 4μ," *Compt. rend.,* **242,** 1153. *50–9875.*

504. Harrick, N. J., "Use of Infrared Absorption to Determine Carrier Distribution in Germanium and Surface Recombination Velocity," *Phys. Rev.,* **101,** 491. *50–4626.*

505. Harrick, N. J., "Use of Infrared Absorption in Germanium to Determine Carrier Distributions for Injection and Extraction," *Phys. Rev.,* **103,** 1173. *50–4626.*

506. Hartert, E., and Glemser, O., "Infrared Spectroscopic Determination of Metal-Oxygen Distances in Hydroxides, Basic Salts, and Salt Hydrates," *Z. Elektrochem.,* **60,** 746. *51–857.*

507. Hartmann, H., and Schlafer, H. C., "Intercombination Spectra of Transition Metal Complex Ions," *Rec. trav. chim.,* **75,** 648. *52–9746.*

508. Hass, M., and Sutherland, G. B. B. M., "The Infrared Spectrum and Crystal Structure of Gypsum," *Proc. Roy. Soc. (London),* **A236,** 427. *51–81.*

Single crystals of gypsum have been observed in the infrared from 450–3800 cm⁻¹.

509. Hawkins, N. J., and Sabol, W. W., "OsO₄: Infrared Spectrum of the Vapor and Comments on the OVFF (orbital valency force field) Constants," *J. Chem. Phys.,* **25,** 775. *51–857.*

Studies were made of OsO_4 under its own vapor pressure at temperatures up to ca. 130°, in the region 250–5000 cm⁻¹.

510. Hidalgo, A., and Serratosa, J. M., "Application of Infrared Absorption Spectra to the Study of Clay Minerals," *Ion,* **16,** 645. *51–2396.*

A review.

511. Hidalgo, A., and Serratosa, J. M., "Infrared Absorption Spectra of Clay Minerals in the 600–350 cm⁻¹ Region," *Anales real soc. espan. fis. y quim. (Madrid),* **52B,** 101. *50–10532.*

512. Hidalgo, A., Serratosa, J. M., and Jubrias, M., "Infrared Absorption Spectra of Clay Minerals Submitted to Thermal Treatment," *Anales edafol. y fisiol. Vegetal (Madrid),* **15,** 607. *52–1762.*

513. Hill, D. G., and Rosenberg, F., "Infrared Absorption Spectra of Complex Cobalt Compounds," *J. Chem. Phys.*, **24**, 1219.   *50–12651*.
The spectra of over 25 complex cobalt salts were obtained and analyzed for the 667–5000 cm^{-1}.

514. Hisatsune, I. C., and Crawford, B., "The Molecular Complex NO_4," *J. Chem. Phys.*, **24**, 1257.   *50–11113*.

515. Houziaux, C., "Infrared Absorption Spectra of Some Natural Glasses Between 2 and 24 Microns," *Geochim. et Cosmochim. Acta*, **9**, 298. *51–6337*.
Spectral data and analysis are reported for 5 tektites and 2 obsidians.

516. Houziaux, L., "Absorption Spectra of Some Silicate Glasses in Infrared Between 2 and 24 Microns," *Silicates inds.*, **21**, 491.   *51–6337*.
Reflection and absorption spectra have been investigated.   Different maxima are found in the two methods and no direct relation between intensities was apparent.

517. Jones, L. H., "Determination of Accurate Water Vapor Calibration Points for Prism Spectrometers in the Region 1330–2100 cm^{-1}," *J. Chem. Phys.*, **24**, 1250.   *50–12651*.

518. Jones, L. H., "Polarized Infrared Spectrum of $KAg(CN)_2$," *J. Chem. Phys.*, **25**, 379.   *50–16387*.

519. Jones, L. H., "Infrared Spectrum and Structure of the Thiocyanate Ion," *J. Chem. Phys.*, **25**, 1069.   *51–4821*.
The absorption spectra of aqueous and solid KNCS were observed and analyzed between 280 and 10,000 cm^{-1}.

520. Jones, L. H., and Chamberlain, M. M., "Formation of Mixed Crystals in the Use of the Alkali-halide Disk Technique for Preparing Samples of $KAu(CN)_2$ for Infrared Spectra," *J. Chem. Phys.*, **25**, 365.   *50–15236*.

521. Jones, L. H., and Robinson, E. S., "Infrared Spectra and Molecular Constants of Gaseous Tritium Bromide and Tritium Chloride," *J. Chem. Phys.*, **24**, 1246.   *50–12651*.

522. Josien, M. L., and Saumagne, P., "Infrared Spectrum in the 2500 cm^{-1} Region of Hydrogen Sulfide Solutions.   Formation of Molecular Complexes," *Bull. soc. chim. France*, 937.   *50–13610*.

523. Kaiser, W., Keck, P. H., and Lange, C. F., "Infrared Absorption and Oxygen Content in Silicon and Germanium," *Phys. Rev.*, **101**, 1264. *50–6906*.

524. Kaplan, L. D., Migeotte, M. V., and Neven, L., "9.6μ-Band of Telluric Ozone and Its Rotational Analysis," *J. Chem. Phys.*, **24**, 1183.   *50–12652*.

525. Kaufman, J. J., and Koski, W. S., "Infrared Study of the Exchange of Deuterium Between Decaborane and Diborane," *J. Am. Chem. Soc.*, **78**, 5774.   *51–3291*.

526. Keller, F. L., and Nielsen, A. H., "Grating Measurements on v_2 of Nitrogen Dioxide at 200°," *J. Chem. Phys.*, **24**, 636.   *50–8326*.

527. Kessler, R., "Free Defect Electrons in the Infrared Absorption in Germanium," Z. *Naturforsch,* 11a, 763. *51–3281.*

528. Ketelaar, J. A. A., Haas, C., and Elsken, J. Vander, "Infrared Absorption Spectra of Bifluorides in Alkali Halide Disks. The Formation of Mixed Crystals," *J. Chem. Phys.,* 24, 624. *50–8326.*

Identical spectra are obtained for $NaHF_2$, KHF_2, and NH_4HF_2 in KCl, while different spectra are obtained in Nujol mulls. The behavior is explained on basis of mixed crystal formation in the KCl technique.

529. Khalilov, A. K., "Rotation-vibration Spectra of Molecules in the Infrared Region," *Trudy Inst. Fiz. i Mat., Akad. Nauk Azerbaidzhan. S.S.R., Ser. Fiz.,* 8, 55. *52–7854.*

The region 27–13160 cm^{-1} has been observed for CO_2, CH_4, and H_2O.

530. Klemperer, W., "Infrared Spectrum of Gaseous Aluminum Chloride," *J. Chem. Phys.,* 24, 353. *50–7593.*

Spectra of gaseous Al_2Cl_6 and $AlCl_3$ were observed from 325–1200 cm^{-1}.

531. Klemperer, W., and Lindeman, L., "Infrared Spectrum of Mercuric Chloride and Bromide," *J. Chem. Phys.,* 25, 397. *51–857.*

532. Kuipers, G. A., Smith, D. F., and Nielsen, A. H., "Infrared Spectrum of Hydrogen Fluoride," *J. Chem. Phys.,* 25, 275. *50–16377.*

New data was obtained for the HF molecule between 416 and 667 cm^{-1}. Five lines of the pure rotational spectrum of HF were observed. Molecular constants were re-evaluated.

533. Kuipers, G. A., "The Spectrum of Monomeric Hydrogen Fluoride: Molecular Constants, Line Shapes, Intensities, and Breadths," *U.S. Atomic Energy Comm.,* K-1290, 147 pp. *50–16377.*

534. Lakshmi, K., Rao, K. N., and Nielsen, H. H., "Molecular Constants of Nitrous Oxide from Measurements of ν_2 at 17μ," *J. Chem. Phys.,* 24, 811. *50–9876.*

535. Lide, D. R., and Mann, D. E., "Infrared Spectrum and Structure of Perchloryl Fluoride," *J. Chem. Phys.,* 25, 1128. *51–5554.*

The infrared study has been carried out for the region 232–3333 cm^{-1}.

536. Lindeman, L. P., and Wilson, M. K., "Vibration Spectra of Some Mixed Halides of Boron," *J. Chem. Phys.,* 24, 242. *50–7592.*

Spectra were obtained for binary mixtures of BF_3, BCl_3, and BBr_3. Fundamental frequencies of BF_2Cl, $BFCl_2$, BF_2Br, $BFBr_2$, BCl_2Br, and $BClBr_2$ for molecules containing B^{10} and B^{11} were assigned.

537. Lindeman, L. P., and Wilson, M. K., "Vibrational Spectra of Some Deuterated Germanes," Z. *physik. Chem. (Frankfurt) (N.F.),* 9, 29. *51–2396.*

Spectra are obtained for GeD_4, GeD_3H, GeD_2H_2, and $GeDH_3$.

538. Lord, R. C., Robinson, D. W., and Schumb, W. C., "Vibrational Spectra and Structure of Disiloxane and Disiloxane-d_6," *J. Am. Chem. Soc.*, **78**, 1327. *50–9877.*

Spectra of gaseous and liquid samples have been obtained down to 250 cm^{-1}. The fundamentals were located for both the infrared and Raman spectra.

539. Lucchesi, P. J., and Glasson, W. A., "Infrared Investigation of Bound Water in Hydrates," *J. Am. Chem. Soc.*, **78**, 1347. *50–9878.*

The KBr-pellet technique was used to investigate the infrared absorption of H_2O bound in the following hydrates: $LiI\cdot 3H_2O$, $SrCl_2\cdot 6H_2O$, $SrBr_2\cdot 6H_2O$, $Na_3PO_4\cdot 12H_2O$, $AlCl_3\cdot 6H_2O$, $Al(NO_3)_3\cdot 9H_2O$, $SnCl_2\cdot 2H_2O$, and $SnCl_4\cdot 5H_2O$. The region 4000–800 cm^{-1} was studied.

540. Madden, R. P., and Benedict, W. S., "Structure of Perchlorylfluoride from High Resolution Infrared Spectra," *J. Chem. Phys.*, **25**, 594. *51–82.*

The infrared spectrum of ClO_3F was examined between 525 and 625 cm^{-1}.

541. Mashkevich, V. S., and Tolpygo, K. B., "Interaction of Vibrations of Nonpolar Crystals with Electric Fields," *Soviet Phys. "Doklady,"* **1**, 690. English Translation. *51–12581.*

Mathematical treatment of the absorption of infrared light by diamond, Si, and Ge crystals.

542. "Materials of the IXth All-Union Conference on Spectroscopy," *Izvest. Akad. Nauk S.S.S.R., Ser. Fiz.*, **18**, 627 ff (1954). *50–7584.*

543. Mathieu, J. P., Poulet, H., and Machiroux, R., "Vibration Spectra of the Fluorinated Salts of Zinc Hydrates," *J. phys. radium*, **17**, 122. *50–9154.*

The fluorinated salts of zinc hydrates of the form $MF_6Zn(OH_2)_6$, where M represents Si, Sn, Ti, or Zr were studied via infrared and Raman spectroscopy.

544. McKean, D. C., and Schatz, P. N., "Absolute Infrared Intensities of Vibration Bands in Ammonia and Phosphine," *J. Chem. Phys.*, **24**, 316. *50–7593.*

545. McKean, D. C., "Infrared Absorption Intensities and Bond Moments in Boron Trifluoride and Related Molecules," *J. Chem. Phys.*, **24**, 1002. *50–11112.*

546. Meal, J. H., and Wilson, M. K., "Infrared Spectra of Some Deuterated Silanes," *J. Chem. Phys.*, **24**, 385. *50–8327.*

Spectra of SiD_4, $SiHD_3$, and SiH_2D_2 were examined in the infrared region, 625–5000 cm^{-1}.

547. Meinnel, J., Eveno, M., and Trigolet, F., "The Effect of the Physical State and of Infrared Irradiation on the Absorption Properties of Very Pure Hexagonal Selenium Samples," *Compt. rend.*, **243**, 1761. *51–5553.*

548. Milligan, D. A., Brown, H. W., and Pimentel, G. C., "Infrared Absorption by the N_3 Radical," *J. Chem. Phys.*, **25**, 1080. *51–3290.*

549. Monfils, A., "Study of the Structure of Monochlorosilane from High-Dispersion Infrared Spectroscopy," *Acad. roy. Belg., Classe sci. Mém.*, **29**, No. 5, 52 pp. *51–4141*.

550. Morcillo, J., and Herranz, J., "Intensities of the Fundamental Vibration-Rotation Bands of Sulfur Dioxide. I. Experimental Determination," *Publs. inst. quim. fis. "Antonio de Gregorio Rocasolano,"* **10**, 162. *51–16098*.

551. Morcillo, J., and Herranz, J., "Intensities of the Fundamental Vibration-Rotation Bands of Sulfur Dioxide. II. Discussion of Results," *Publs. inst. quim. fis. "Antonio de Gregorio Rocasolano,"* **10**, 172. *51–16098*.

552. Morino, Y., "Infrared Spectra of Gaseous Hexachlorodisilane," *J. Chem. Phys.*, **24**, 164. *50–3897*.

553. Newman, C., O'Loane, J. K., Polo, S. R., and Wilson, M. K., "Infrared Spectra and Molecular Structures of SiH_3F, SiH_3Cl, and SiH_3Br," *J. Chem. Phys.*, **25**, 855. *51–4141*.

554. Nexsen, W. E., "Measurement and Analysis of the Rotational Fine Structure of the ν_2 Fundamental of Ozone," *Dissertation Abstr.*, **16**, 771. *50–10533*.

555. Nixon, E. R., "The Infrared Spectrum of Biphosphine," *J. Phys. Chem.*, **60**, 1054. *51–83*.

The spectra of gaseous biphosphine at 28° and of crystalline solid biphosphine at −180° were obtained in the infrared region. Results are also reported for deuterated biphosphine.

556. Otero, C., and Matutano, J. R. B., "An Infrared Spectroscopic Study of Sulfur Dichloride," *Anales real. soc. españ. fís. y quím. (Madrid)*, **52B**, 291. *50–12653*.

The spectra of gaseous and liquid SCl_2 and of its solution in CCl_4 were measured from 400–2000 cm^{-1}.

557. Paetzold, H. K., "The Infrared Absorption of Ozone," *Z. Naturforsch.*, 11a, 128. *51–4820*.

558. Palik, E. D., and Rao, K. N.,"Pure Rotational Spectra of Carbon Monoxide, Nitric Oxide, and Nitrous Oxide Between 100 and 600 Microns," *J. Chem. Phys.*, **25**, 1174. *51–5553*.

559. Pant, D. D., and Khandelwal, D. P., "Absorption Spectrum of Uranyl Nitrate in Aqueous Solutions," *Current Sci. (India)*, **25**, 255. *51–2391*.

560. Pemsler, J. P., and Planet, W. G., "Infrared Spectrum of PF_5," *J. Chem. Phys.*, **24**, 920. *50–9877*.

561. Penland, R. B., Lane, T. J., and Quagliano, J. V., "Infrared Absorption Spectra of Inorganic Coordination Complexes. VII. Structural Isomerism of Nitro- and Nitrito Pentammine-Cobalt (III) Chlorides," *J. Am. Chem. Soc.*, **78**, 887. *50–6919*.

562. Petch, H. E., Sheppard, N., and Megaw, H. D., "The Infrared Spectrum of Afwillite, $Ca_3 (SiO_3OH)_2 \cdot 2H_2O$, in Relation to the Proposed Hydrogen Positions," *Acta Cryst.*, **9**, 29. *50–5404*.

The region 2000–3500 cm^{-1} has been examined and the results discussed. Confirmation that both long and short hydrogen bonds are present in the afwillite structure is made on basis of the results.

563. Plyler, E. K., Tidwell, E. D., and Allen, H. C., "Near Infrared Spectrum of Nitrous Oxide," *J. Chem. Phys.*, **24**, 95. *50–4640.*

564. Pondy, P. R., and Beachell, H. C., "Near Infrared Spectra of Diborane, Pentaborane, and Decaborane," *J. Chem. Phys.*, **25**, 238. *50–15236.*

565. Potts, W. J., and Wright, N., "Quantitative Infrared Absorption Spectroscopy in Water Solution," *Anal. Chem.*, **28**, 1255. *50–14364.*

Water is found to be a satisfactory solvent for the 1000–1538 cm^{-1} region using a barium fluoride cell.

566. Powell, D. B., "Infrared Spectra and the Trans-Effect in Palladium and Platinum Complexes," *Chemistry and Industry*, 314. *50–11820.*

567. Powell, D. B., and Sheppard, N., "Infrared Spectra of Some Metal Ammines and Deuteroammines," *J. Chem. Soc.*, 3108. *51–856.*

568. Powell, D. B., "Infrared Spectra of Metal Ammines and Related Compounds. II. The Trans-Effect in Platinous Complexes," *J. Chem. Soc.*, 4495. *51–3290.*

569. Ramsay, D. A., "Absorption Spectra of Free PH$_2$ and PD$_2$ Radicals," *Nature*, **178**, 374. *51–850.*

570. "Review of Fundamental Developments in Analysis," *Anal. Chem.*, **28** (4).

571. Rocchicciaoli, C., "Determination of the Structure of Metallic Chlorates by Infrared Absorption Spectrography," *Compt. rend.*, **242**, 2922. *50–15236.*

Spectra covering the range 270–1900 cm^{-1} have been obtained for the chlorates of Na, K, Mg, Ca, Sr, Ba, Cr, Nd, Co, Ni, Cu, Ag, Zn, Cd, and Pb.

572. Rossman, K., France, W. L., Rao, K. N., and Nielsen, H. H., "Infrared Spectrum and Molecular Constants of Carbon Dioxide. II. Levels 10°0 and 02°0, 10°1 and 02°1 Coupled by Fermi Resonance," *J. Chem. Phys.*, **24**, 1007. *50–1112.*

573. Rossmann, K., Rao, K. N., and Nielson, H. H., "Infrared Spectrum and Molecular Constants of Carbon Dioxide. I. ν_2 of C^{12}O$_2$^{16} at 15μ," *J. Chem. Phys.*, **24**, 103. *50–4640.*

574. Rossmann, K., and Straley, J. W., "Fundamental Absorption Bands of Hydrogen Telluride," *J. Chem. Phys.*, **24**, 1276. *50–12651.*

575. Sevchenko, N. A., and Florinskaya, V. A., "Reflection and Transmittance Spectra of the Different Modifications of Silica in the Wave Length Range of 7 to 24μ," *Doklady Akad. Nauk S.S.S.R.*, **109**, 1115. *51–6338.*

576. Shaw, J. H., "Nitric Oxide Fundamental," *J. Chem. Phys.*, **24**, 399. *50–8326.*

A re-examination of the 5.3μ NO fundamental was made using a high resolution spectrometer. Constants calculated were in agreement with existing data.

577. Shcherba, C. D., and Yakovleva, T. V., "Preparation of Silver Chloride Windows for Cells," *Pribory i Tekh. Eksperimenta,* No. 3, 101. *52–6934.*

578. Shufler, S. L., Sternberg, H. W., and Friedel, R. A., "Infrared Spectrum and Structure of Chromium Hexacarbonyl, $Cr(CO)_6$," *J. Am. Chem. Soc.,* **78,** 2687. *50–14365.*

579. Sidorov, T. A., and Sobolev, N. N., "The Isotopic Shift in the Infrared Spectrum of Boric Acid and Its Structure," *Optika i Spektroskopiya,* **1,** 393. *51–4820.*

The region 450–4000 cm^{-1} was examined for spectral shifts in $B(OH)_3$ frequencies using the isotope B^{10}.

580. Simon, A., Waldmann, K., and Steger, E., "Constitution of Acid Sulfites. V. Structure of the Pyrosulfite Ion and the Reaction Mechanism of the Formation of Pyrosulfite on Partially Neutralizing Sulfurous Acid," *Z. anorg. u. allgem. Chem.,* **288,** 131. *51–7859.*

581. Skjöldelrand, R., "An Infrared Spectrometer and Its Use for the Isotopic Analysis of Heavy Water," *Appl. Sci. Res. B,* **5** (5), 401. *50–11062.*

582. Smith, R. A., Jones, F. E., and Chasmar, R. P., "The Detection and Measurement of Infrared Radiation," Amsterdam: Swets and Zeitlinger. *51–7161.*

583. Staats, P. A., Morgan, H. W., and Goldstein, J. H., "Infrared Spectrum of TCN," *J. Chem. Phys.,* **25,** 582. *51–78.*

584. Staats, P. A., Morgan, H. W., and Goldstein, J. H., "Infrared Spectra of T_2O, THO, and TDO," *J. Chem. Phys.,* **24,** 916. *50–9876.*

Spectra have been obtained for the vapor phase of T_2O, THO, and TDO from 700–7000 cm^{-1}.

585. Steele, W. C., "Infrared Absorption of Lanthanum, Scandium, and Indium Borate and the Force Constants of Borate Ion," *J. Chem. Phys.,* **25,** 1184. *51–5554.*

Spectra were observed and analyzed for the region 500–1429 cm^{-1}.

586. Sternglanz, H., "Use of Water as an Infrared Solvent," *Appl. Spectroscopy,* **10,** No. 2, 77. *50–12652.*

587. Sweeney, D. M., Nakagawa, I., Mizushima, S., and Quagliano, J. V., "Infrared Absorption Spectra of Inorganic Coordination Complexes. VIII. Normal Vibrations of Tetracyanoplatinate (II) Ion," *J. Am. Chem. Soc.,* **78,** 889. *50–6920.*

The spectrum of $K_2Pt(CN)_4 \cdot 3H_2O$ was determined and discussed for the region 250–5000 cm^{-1}.

588. Szepesy, G. L., Császár, J., and Lehotai, L., "Studies on the Light Absorption of H_2O–Ethanol Solutions in the Near Infrared Spectrum Range," *Acta Univ. Szegediensis, Acta Phys. et Chim.* (N.S.), **2,** 149. *51–15272.*

An explanation of the absorption spectra is given for the 833 cm^{-1} region.

589. Tagirov, R. B., "The Existence of the HO$_2$ Radical," *Zhur. Fiz. Khim.*, **30**, 949. *50–16387*.

The infrared spectrum of a hydrogen flame has been measured from 667–4000 cm^{-1} giving peaks which occur around 1305 cm^{-1}. The peaks cannot be ascribed to O$_3$, H$_2$O, H$_2$O$_2$ or OH$^-$.

590. Tarte, P., "Vibrational Spectrum and Force Constants of Solid Sodium Nitrite," *Ann. soc. sci. Bruxelles Ser. I.*, **70**, 244. *51–7860*.

Assignments are made for the fundamental frequencies of the NO$_2^-$ ion based on infrared and Raman spectra.

591. Thompson, H. W., and Green, B. A., "Fundamental Vibration Band of Nitric Oxide," *Spectrochim. Acta*, **8**, 129. *51–78*.

The rotational structure of the fundamental band of NO was measured from 1804.74–1971.21 cm^{-1} under high resolution.

592. Tinkham, M., "Energy-gap Interpretation of Experiments on Infrared Transmission Through Superconducting Films," *Phys. Rev.*, **104**, 845.

593. Van Horne, B. H., and Hause, C. D., "Near Infrared Spectrum of DCl," *J. Chem. Phys.*, **25**, 56. *50–14363*.

The first and second overtones of DCl have been obtained in the 4167 cm^{-1} and 6250 cm^{-1} regions.

594. Wiener, R. N., "Infrared Spectra of Molecular Crystals—Dinitrogen Tetroxide and Sulphur Dioxide," *Dissertation Abstr.*, **16**, 865. *50–11820*.

595. Wiener, R. N., and Nixon, E. R., "Infrared Spectrum of Solid Sulfur Dioxide," *J. Chem. Phys.*, **25**, 175. *50–13609*.

596. Woodward, L. A., and Roberts, H. L., "Raman and Infrared Absorption Spectra of Osmium Tetroxide. Relation to the Structure of the Perrhenate and Tungstate Ions in Aqueous Solution," *Trans. Faraday Soc.*, **52**, 615. *51–83*.

597. Yoshinago, H., and Oetjen, R. A., "Optical Properties of Indium Antimonide in the Region 20 to 200μ," *Phys. Rev.*, **101**, 526. *50–6907*.

598. Zaĭtsev, G. A., and Neporent, B. S., "Anisotropy of the Absorption of Gypsum Crystals in the Infrared," *Soviet Phys., JETP*, **2**, 733. *50–15233*.

1957

599. Allen, H. C., Plyler, E. K., and Blaine, C. R., "Infrared Spectrum of Carbonyl Sulfide," *J. Chem. Phys.*, **26**, 400. *51–7860*.

600. Allen, H. C., Plyler, E. K., and Blaine, C. R., "Some Infrared Bands of Deuterium Sulfide," *J. Research Nat'l. Bur. Standards*, **59**, 211. *52–2538*.

The regions 2000 cm^{-1} and 2778 cm^{-1} have been observed and analyzed for D$_2$S.

601. Asano, S., and Tomishima, Y., "Rotational Lattice Vibration in Complex Crystals. III. Vibrational Frequencies in $NaClO_4$ Crystals," *J. Phys. Soc. Japan*, **12**, 900. *52–888.*

602. Austin, I. G., and Sheard, A., "Optical Properties of Bi_2Te_3–Bi_2Se_3 Alloys," *J. Electronics and Control*, **3**, 236. *52–17415.*

603. Babushkin, A. A., "Use of Infrared Spectroscopy in the Study of Adsorption and Catalysis Phenomena," *Porerkhnost. Khim. Soedinen. i Rol v Yavleniyakh Adsorbtsii, Sbornik Trudov Konferents. Adsorbtsii*, 246. *51–17454.*

604. Baker, A. W., "Solid State Anomalies in Infrared Spectroscopy," *J. Phys. Chem.*, **61**, 450. *51–11069.*

605. Bakerman, S., "Molecular Spectroscopy: Infrared Band Shapes and Vibrational Parameters in NF_3," *Dissertation Abstr.*, **17**, 1906. *52–878.*

606. Bass, A. M., and Broida, H. P., "Sharp Line Absorption in Silica Near 3400 cm^{-1}," *J. Opt. Soc. Amer.*, **47** (2), 163.

607. Benedict, W. S., and Plyler, E. K., "Vibration-Rotation Bands of Ammonia. II. The Molecular Dimensions and Harmonic Frequencies of Ammonia and Deuterated Ammonia," *Can. J. Phys.*, **35**, 1235. *52–878.*

608. Bersuker, I. B., "Infrared Spectrum of Symmetric Molecules and Crystals," *Optika i Spektroskopiya*, **2**, 671. *51–16076.*
   Mathematical.

609. Bethke, G. W., and Wilson, M. K., "Comments on the Vibrational Spectrum of Borine Carbonyl," *J. Chem. Phys.*, **27**, 978. *51–13572.*

610. Bicelli, L. P., "Infrared Absorption Spectra of Sulfamic Acid and Some Sulfamates. III. Potassium Bromide Region," *Ann. chim. (Rome)*, **47**, 1380. *52–6932.*

611. Bonino, G. B., and Fabbri, G., "The Infrared Absorption Spectrum of Potassium Cuprocyanide in Aqueous Solution and in the Crystalline State," *Atti accad. nazl. Lincei. Rend., Classe sci. fiz., mat. e nat.*, **22**, 402. *52–5126.*

612. Brame, E. G., Jr., Cohen, S., Margrave, J. L., and Meloche, V. W., "Infrared Spectra of Inorganic Solids," *J. Inorg. and Nuclear Chem.*, **4**, 90. *51–9318.*

   The infrared spectra of Li_2O_2, $Li_2O_2 \cdot 8H_2O$, Na_2O_2, $Na_2O_2 \cdot 8H_2O$, $Na_2O_2 \cdot 8D_2O$, NaO_2, KO_2, CaO_2, $CaO_2 \cdot 8H_2O$, SrO_2, and BaO_2 are given using a modified KBr disc technique in the range 667–5000 cm^{-1}. The spectra show no characteristic sharp bands for peroxide and superoxide.

613. Brame, Jr., E. G., Margrave, J. L., and Meloche, V. W., "Infrared Spectra of Inorganic Solids. II. Oxides, Nitrides, Carbides, and Borides," *J. Inorg. and Nuclear Chem.*, **5**, 48. *51–17447.*

   The region 667–5000 cm^{-1} was used to determine spectral behavior of Li_3N, Cu_3N, BN, AlN, Mg_3N_2, Zn_3N_2, B_2O_3, Cr_2O_3, Ga_2O_3, Al_2O_3, B_4C, SiC, Mo_2B, CrN, ZrB_2 and TiB_2.

614. Brügel, W., "Einführung in die Ultrarotspektroskopie," 2nd ed. Darmstadt: D. Steinkopff. *52–5989.*

615. Bulanin, M. O., "Structure of Absorption Bands of Liquid H_2O, D_2O, and HDO Determined by the Structure of Their Molecules," *Optika i Spektroskopiya*, **2**, 557. *51–16097.*

616. Cabannes-Ott, C., "Structure of Some Natural Hydroxides of the Type XO·OH: Diaspore, Manganite, Goethite, Lepidocrocite," *Compt. rend.*, **244**, 2491. *51–14420.*

617. Caglioti, V., Sartori, G., and Scrocco, M., "Infrared Spectrophotometric Study of Cyanocomplexes of Iron (II and III), Chromium (III), and Manganese (l, II, and III)," *Atti accad. nazl. Lincei, Rend., Classe sci. fiz., mat. e nat.*, **22**, 266. *52–879.*

618. Ceccaldi, M., Thro, C., and Roth, E., "Influence of Dissolved Salts on the Infrared Absorption Spectra of Isotopic Varieties of Water in the Liquid State," *Cahiers phys.*, No. 73, 37 (1956); *Comm. énergie atomique (France)*, Rappt. No. **649**, 42. *52–3515.*

    An investigation was made of the effects of NaF, NaCl, KCl, and $CaCl_2$ on the infrared absorption bands of H_2O, HDO, and D_2O.

619. Clark, S. P., "Absorption Spectra of Some Silicates in the Visible and Near Infrared," *Am. Mineralogist*, **42**, 732. *52–2530.*

620. Costa, G., Pauluzzi, E., and Puxeddu, A., "Infrared Spectra of Chromous and Cupric Acetates," *Gazz. chim. ital.*, **87**, 885. *52–1763.*

621. Cotton, F. A., and Wilkinson, G., "Infrared Spectrum of Iron Dodecacarbonyl," *J. Am. Chem. Soc.*, **79**, 752. *51–7147.*

622. Coulon, R., and Hai, V., "Infrared Spectra of Mixtures of Hydrobromic Acid and Various Compressed Gases: Perturbation of Hydrobromic Acid Bands and Frequency of Combination Between Hydrobromic Acid and Hydrogen," *Compt. rend.*, **245**, 2247. *52–6929.*

623. Dahl, L. F., and Rundle, R. E., "Polynuclear Metal Carbonyls. III. Infrared Analysis of Iron Tetracarbonyl," *J. Chem. Phys.*, **27**, 323. *51–17450.*

624. Dasgupta, S., and Sinha, A. P. B., "Infrared Absorption by Copper and Nickel Manganites," *Trans. Faraday Soc.*, **53**, 909. *52–6932.*

    The spectra were obtained for the region 5800–350 cm^{-1}. The compressibility and the Debye temperature for these substances were calculated from the force constants used.

625. Durie, R. A., and Ramsay, D. A., "Absorption Spectra of the Halogen Monoxides," *Can. J. Phys.*, **36**, 35. *52–4315.*

    The absorption spectra of ClO, BrO, and IO were observed during photolysis of Cl_2—O_2, Br_2—O_2, and I_2—O_2 mixtures.

626. Edgell, W. F., and Moynihan, R. E., "Infrared Band Contours. I. Spherical Top Molecules," *J. Chem. Phys.*, **27**, 155. *51–17450.*

627. Elliot, J. P., Judd, B. R., and Runciman, W. A., "Energy Levels in Rare-Earth Ions," *Proc. Roy. Soc. (London)*, **A240**, 509. *51–15247.*

The tensor-operator and group-theoretical methods are used to determine the various contributions to the Hamiltonian of a rare-earth ion. The Coulomb interaction between ions, the spin-orbit coupling of the electrons, and the term arising from the influence of an external electrostatic field occurring when the rare-earth ion is present in a crystal lattice are considered.

628. Erley, D. S., "2,2-Dimethoxypropane as a Drying Agent for Preparation of Infrared Samples," *Anal. Chem.*, **29** (10), 1564.

629. Fabbri, G., "Infrared Spectrum of Crystalline Potassium Cyanocobaltate (III) at Liquid Nitrogen Temperatures," *Atti accad. nazl. Lincei. Rend., Classe sci. fiz., mat. e nat.*, **22**, 488. *51–17448.*

630. Fateley, W. G., and Lippincott, E. R., "Normal Coordinate Analysis of the Vibrational Spectrum of Iron Pentacarbonyl," *Spectrochim. Acta,* **10**, 8. *52–9763.*

631. Fletcher, W. H., and Begun, G. M., "Fundamental of $N^{15}O$," *J. Chem. Phys.*, **27**, 579. *52–878.*

632. Gatehouse, B. M., Livingstone, S. E., and Nyholm, R. S., "Infrared Spectra of Nitrato-Coordination Complexes," *J. Chem. Soc.*, 4222. *52–879.*

   The spectra of nitratocomplexes of metals were investigated between 4000 and 700 cm^{-1}. Characteristic bands of the coordinated nitrato groups were assigned.

633. Gaunt, J., and Ainscough, J. B., "The Molecular Structure of Niobium Pentachloride," *Spectrochim. Acta,* **10**, 52. *52–9763.*

634. Gaunt, J., and Ainscough, J. B., "The Molecular Structure of Antimony-pentafluoride," *Spectrochim. Acta,* **10**, 57. *52–9763.*

635. Giguère, P. A., and Harvey, K. B., "Infrared Absorption Spectrum of Nitrous Oxide in the Solid State," *Spectrochim. Acta,* **9**, 204. *51–14419.*

   The infrared spectrum of solid N_2O at $-175°$ was measured in the 400–5000 cm^{-1} region.

636. Gorman, M., "Evidence from Infrared Spectroscopy for Hydrogen Bonding," *J. Chem. Educ.*, **34**, 304. *51–11855.*

637. Gray, P., and Waddington, T. C., "Fundamental Vibration Frequencies and Force Constants in the Azide Ion," *Trans. Faraday Soc.*, **53**, 901. *52–6930.*

638. Gush, H. P., Hare, W. F. J., Allin, E. J., and Welsh, H. L., "Double Transitions in the Infrared Spectrum of Solid Hydrogen," *Phys. Rev.*, **106**, 1101. *52–82.*

639. Hadley, G. F., "Theoretical Study of the Hyperfine Structure in Inversion Spectra of the Deutero-ammonias," *J. Chem. Phys.*, **26**, 1482. *51–16098.*

640. Hall, G. R., Herniman, P. D., and Walter, A. J., "Spectro-photometric Studies of Plutonium in Nitric Acid Solution. I," *Atomic Energy Research Estab.*, C/R–712, 22 pp. *52–873.*

Spectra are given for Pu in tri-, quadri-, and sexivalent form in the range 400–1000 mμ.

641. Harbeke, G., and Lautz, G., "Infrared Measurements of Trivalent Metallic Tellurides to Determine the Relationship of Temperature to Electron Activation Energy," *Optik*, **14**, 547.   *52–8745.*

The transmission of crystals of Ga_2Te_3 and In_2Te_3 in the infrared was measured from 20°–650°K.

642. Higgins, H. G., "Use of Potassium Chloride Disks in the Infrared Examination of Fibrous Cellulose and Other Solid Materials," *Australian J. Chem.*, **10**, 496.   *52–3517.*

643. Hobbs, W. E., "Infrared Spectrum of Chromyl Fluoride," *U. S. Atomic Energy Comm.*, **K–1325**, 32 pp.   *51–15274.*

Spectra of CrO_2F_2 in the 277–5000 cm^{-1} region and of CrO_2Cl_2 in the 400–5000 cm^{-1} region are given.

644. Hrostowski, H. J., and Kaiser, R. H., "Infrared Absorption of Oxygen in Silicon," *Phys. Rev.*, **107**, 966.   *52–2538.*

645. Jones, L. H., "Vibrational Spectrum and Structure of Metal-Cyanide Complexes in the Solid State.   I. $KAg(CN)_2$," *J. Chem. Phys.*, **26**, 1578.   *51–17448.*

646. Jones, L. H., "Vibrational Spectrum and Structure of Metal-Cyanide Complexes in the Solid State.   II. $KAu(CN)_2$," *J. Chem. Phys.*, **27**, 468.   *52–879.*

647. Jones, L. H., "Vibrational Spectrum and Structure of Metal-Cyanide Complexes in the Solid State.   III. $Hg(CN)_2$," *J. Chem. Phys.*, **27**, 665.   *52–879.*

648. Kalbus, G. E., "Infrared Examination of Inorganic Materials," *Dissertation Abstr.*, **17**, 2413.   *52–3515.*

649. Kern, E., "Determination of the Optical Constants of Neodymium in the Visible and in the Near Infrared," *Z. Physik*, **148**, 38.   *52–2532.*

650. Kessler, R., and Riccius, D., "Absorption of Germanium in the Short-Wave Infrared," *Z. Naturforsch*, **12a**, 443.   *51–16081.*

651. Kislovskiĭ, L. D., "Representation of Optical Characteristics of Absorbing Media in Infrared Region by Means of a Resonator Model with Viscous Friction.   II.   Alkali-Halide Crystals," *Optika i Spectroskopiya*, **2**, 186.   *51–16074.*

652. Last, J. T., "Infrared Absorption Studies on $BaTiO_3$ and Related Materials," *Phys. Rev.*, **105**, 1740.   *51–13572.*

653. LeFèvre, R. J. W., Oh, W. T., Reece, I. H., and Werner, R. L., "Infrared Absorption Spectra of Metal Hyponitrites," *Australian J. Chem.*, **10**, 361.   *51–16098.*

Spectra are reported for Pb, Ba, Co, and Mg-hyponitrites from 4000–400 cm^{-1}.   No appreciable absorption occurs beyond 1160 cm^{-1}. Nujol and hexachlorobutadiene mulls were used.

654. Lovell, R. J., "Intensities, Bond Moments, Molecular Structure and Spectra for $COCl_2$ and $CSCl_2$," *Dissertation Abstr.*, **17**, 2649.

655. Maarsen, J. W., and Nobel, P. C., "Vibrational Spectrum and Force Constants of P_4S_3," *Rec. trav. chim.*, **76**, 757.

656. Macfarlane, G. G., McLean, T. P., Quarrington, J. E., and Roberts, V., "Fine Structure in the Absorption-Edge Spectrum of Germanium," *Phys. Rev.*, **108**, 1377.

657. Mann, D. E., and Fano, L., "Vibrational Spectrum and Force Constants of Diboron Tetrachloride," *J. Chem. Phys.*, **26**, 1665. *51–17451*.

658. Marcus, R. A., and Fresco, J. M., "Infrared Absorption Spectra of Nitric Acid and Its Solutions," *J. Chem. Phys.*, **27**, 564. *52–879*.

659. Martinez, J. V., and Wagner, E. L., "Vibrational Spectra and Structure of Phosphonium and Deuterophosphonium Iodides," *J. Chem. Phys.*, **27**, 1110. *52–4320*.

   The spectra of films of PH_4I and PD_4I were obtained at $-78°$ and $190°$ in the range 4000–400 cm^{-1}. Powder and Nujol spectra were obtained at room temperature.

660. Mathieu, J. P., and Poulet, H., "Vibrational Spectrum of Carborundum," *Compt. rend.*, **244**, 2794. *51–14419*.

661. Mayhood, J. E., "Infrared Intensities and Bond Moments in Sulfur Dioxide," *Can. J. Phys.*, **35**, 954. *51–15274*.

662. Miller, F. A., and Cousins, L. R., "Infrared and Raman Spectra of Vanadium Oxytrichloride," *J. Chem. Phys.*, **26**, 329. *51–7860*.

663. Miloslavskii, V. K., "Optical Properties of Thin Layers of Cadmium Oxide in the Infrared Region of the Spectrum," *Optika i Spektroskopiya*, **3**, 251. *52–2549*.

   The spectra of thin layers of CdO were obtained in the infrared from 625–10,000 cm^{-1}. The complex structure of the bands is discussed.

664. Morgan, H. W., Staats, P. A., and Goldstein, J. H., "Infrared Spectrum of NT_4Cl," *J. Chem. Phys.*, **27**, 1212. *52–4319*.

665. Morgan, H. W., Staats, P. A., and Goldstein, J. H., "Infrared Spectra of $N^{15}H_3$ and $N^{15}H_4{}^+$," *J. Chem. Phys.*, **27**, 1212. *52–4319*.

666. Motulevich, G. P., and Shubin, A. A., "Determination of Optical Constants of Metals in the Infrared Region," *Optika i Spektroskopiya*, **2**, 633. *51–16081*.

667. Murata, H., and Kawai, K., "Normal Frequencies of Octahedral $M(XY)_6$ Molecules," *J. Chem. Phys.*, **27**, 605. *52–877*.

   Calculated and observed values for the fundamental frequencies for $Cr(CO)_6$ and $Mo(CO)_6$ are compared.

668. Murata, H., and Kawai, K., "Normal Frequencies of Tetrahedral $M(XY)_4$ Molecules," *J. Chem. Phys.*, **26**, 1355. *51–14420*.

669. Mutschin, A., and Maenuchen, K., "Infrared Absorption Spectra of Different Phosphorus Compounds. I. Alkali Orthophosphates," *Z. anal. Chem.*, **156**, 241. *51–16098*.

Spectra in the 400–5000 cm^{-1} range are given for H_3PO_4, $NaH_2PO_4 \cdot 2H_2O$, $Na_2HPO_4 \cdot 12H_2O$, $Na_3PO_4 \cdot 12H_2O$ and $(NH_4)_2HPO_4$.

670. Nakagawa, I., Penland, R. B., Mizushima, S., Lane, P. J., and Quagliano, J. V., "Infrared Absorption Spectra of Inorganic Coordination Complexes. XI. Infrared Studies of Mercuric Amido-Bromide, $Hg(NH_2)Br$," *Spectrochim. Acta*, **9**, 199–203. *51–14419*.

Spectra for cubic and rhombic forms of $Hg(NH_2)Br$ were measured in the 286–5000 cm^{-1} region.

671. Nakamoto, K., Fujita, J., Tanaka, S., and Kobayashi, M., "Infrared Spectra of Metallic Complexes. IV. Comparison of the Infrared Spectra of Unidentate and Bidentate Complexes," *J. Am. Chem. Soc.*, **79**, 4904. *52–3516*.

The spectra of selected sulfato, carbonato, oxalato, and acetato metallic complexes were measured in the 5000–400 cm^{-1} region.

672. Palmer, C. H., "Long-Path Water-Vapor Spectra with Pressure Broadening. I. 20μ to 31.7μ. II. 29μ to 40μ," *J. Opt. Soc. Am.*, **47**, 1024. *52–877*.

673. Perry, J. A., and Bain, G. H., "General Procedures for Setting Up for Infrared Differential Analysis of Multicomponent Mixtures," *Anal. Chem.*, **29** (8), 1123. *51–16192*.

674. Person, W. B., Erickson, R. E., and Buckles, R. E., "Infrared Spectrum of Bromine in Benzene," *J. Chem. Phys.*, **27**, 1211. *52–4320*.

675. Pistorius, C. W. F. T., "Evaluation of Force Constants of Tetrahedral Hydrides from Raman and Infrared Data," *J. Chem. Phys.*, **27**, 965. *52–2539*.

Force constants were calculated for the following: CH_4, CD_4, SiH_4, GeH_4, NH_4^+, ND_4^+, PH_4^+, and AlH_4^-.

676. Pullin, A. D. E., "Infrared and Raman Spectroscopy," *Ann. Repts. Progr. Chem. (Chem. Soc. London)*, **53**, 7. *51–15245*.

A review.

677. Reding, F. P., and Hornig, D. F., "Vibrational Spectra of Molecules and Complex Ions in Crystals," *J. Chem. Phys.*, **27**, 1024. *52–4319*.

678. Rice, S. A., and Klemperer, W., "Spectra of the Alkali Halides. II. Infrared Spectra of the Sodium and Potassium Halides, Rubidium Chloride, and Cesium Chloride," *J. Chem. Phys.*, **27**, 573. *52–878*.

Spectra were observed for NaCl, NaBr, NaI, KCl, KBr, RbCl, CsCl in the region of the fundamental vibration frequency.

679. Roy, D. M., and Roy, R., "Hydrogen-deuterium Exchange in Clays and Problems in the Assignment of Infrared Frequencies in the Hydroxyl Region," *Geochim. et Cosmochim. Acta*, **11**, 72. *51–7858*.

680. Savage, C. M., and Edwards, T. H., "Infrared Spectrum of Hydrogen Sulfide in the 2.6 Micron Region," *J. Chem. Phys.*, **27**, 179. *51–17448*.

681. Sharpless, N. E., and Munday, J. S., "Infrared Spectra of Heteropoly Acid Salts," *Anal. Chem.*, **29**, 1619. *52–5125*.

The spectra of ammonium 12-tungstophosphate, ammonium 12 molybdophosphate, ammonium 12-tungstoarsenate, ammonium 12-molybdoarsenate, ammonium 12-tungstosilicate, ammonium 12-molybdosilicate, ammonium 12-tungstoborate, ammonium 12-molybdomanganate, and ammonium 12-molybdotitanate were obtained in the region 1200–625 cm^{-1}.

682. Sidorov, T. A., and Sobolev, N. N., "Infrared Spectrum and Molecular Structure of Phosphorus Anhydride," *Optika i Spektroskopiya,* **2,** 710, 717. *51–17450.*

683. Sidorov, T. A., and Sobolev, N. N., "Infrared and Raman Spectra of Boron Oxide. II. The Infrared Spectrum and Structure of Boron Oxide Molecule," *Optika i Spektroskopiya,* **3,** 560. *52–7854.*

The region 416–4000 cm^{-1} was investigated. The formula, B_4O_6, was obtained from the spectral data.

684. Smith, R. A., Jones, F. E., and Chasmar, R. P., "The Detection and Measurement of Infrared Radiation," Amsterdam: Swets and Zeitlinger.

685. Snyder, R. G., and Hisatsune, I. C., "Infrared Spectrum of Dinitrogen Tetroxide," *J. Mol. Spectroscopy,* **1,** 139. *51–17449.*

The spectrum of N_2O was measured between 5500 and 320 cm^{-1} for the gas at 23°C, the pure liquid at 10°, the liquid in CS_2 solution at 23°, and for the solid at −180°.

686. Spitzer, W. G., and Fan, H. Y., "Determination of Optical Constants and Carrier Effective Mass of Semiconductors," *Phys. Rev.,* **106,** 882. *52–92.*

Absorption studies in the range 287–2000 cm^{-1} have been made on n- and p-type Ge, Si, and InSb and on n-type InAs.

687. Spitzer, W. G., and Fan, H. Y., "Infrared Absorption in n-type Silicon," *Phys. Rev.,* **108,** 268. *52–4330.*

Absorption from 222–10,000 cm^{-1} was studied for As, Sb, P, and As-Sn impurities of various concentrations in n-type silicon.

688. Steiger, E., "Spectroscopic Investigation of the State of Bonding in Phosphoric Acid Derivatives," *Z. Elektrochem.,* **61,** 1004. *52–4319.*

The infrared spectra are reported for: $(NH_2)_3PO$, $(NH_2)_3PS$, $(NH_2)_2POOH$, $NaPO_3NH_3$, $Na_2PO_3NH_2$, $Ba(PO_3NH_3)_2$, $Ba(PO)_3NH_2 \cdot H_2O$, $Mg(PO_3NH_3)_2$, $MgPO_3NH_2 \cdot 7H_2O$, $(PhO)_2PO$ in NH_3, $PhO(NH_2)_2PO$, and $Na_6N(PO_3)_3$.

689. Stern, F., and Talley, R. M., "Optical Absorption in p-Type Indium Arsenide," *Phys. Rev.,* **108,** 158. *52–3527.*

690. Svatos, G. F., Sweeny, D. M., Mizushima, S., Curran, C., and Quagliano, J. V., "Infrared Absorption Spectra of Inorganic Coordination Complexes. XII. The Characteristic NH_3 Deformation Vibrations of Solid Inorganic Complexes," *J. Am. Chem. Soc.,* **79,** 3313. *51–16099.*

Infrared spectra of solid metal ammine complexes were studied. An explanation is proposed for the deformation frequencies determined.

691. Tai, H., and Underwood, A. C., "Infrared Spectrophotometry of Sulfate Ion. Combining Freeze-Drying with KBr Disc Technique," *Anal. Chem.*, **29** (10), 1430. *52–1857.*
The spectra of sulfates of Cd, Zn, Li, K, Na, Al, and Mg are given in the region 1000–1250 cm^{-1}.

692. Terenin, A. N., "Infrared Spectra of Surface Compounds on Silicate Adsorbents," *Poverkhnost. Khim. Soedinen. i Rol v Yavleniyakh Adsorbtsii, Sbornik Trudov Konferents. Adsorbtsii*, 206. *51–17393.*
A review.

693. Thiel, M. V., Becker, E. D., and Pimentel, G. C., "Infrared Studies of Hydrogen Bonding of Water by the Matrix Isolation Technique," *J. Chem. Phys.*, **27**, 486. *52–881.*

694. Tramer, A., and Wierzchowski, K. L., "Vibration Spectrum and Structure of Carbonylcyanide," *Bull. acad. polon. sci., Classe III*, **5**, 411, 417. *52–878.*
The infrared spectra from 714–4000 cm^{-1} and Raman spectra of $CO(CN)_2$ have been used to furnish data for calculation of force constants and absorption coefficients.

695. Treiber, E., Gierer, J., Rehnstrom, J., and Almin, K. E., "Ultraviolet and Infrared Absorption of Carbon Diselenide," *Acta Chem. Scand.*, **11**, 752. *52–6924.*

696. Vuagnat, A. M., and Wagner, E. L., "Vibrational Spectra and Structure of Solid Sulfamic Acid and the Sulfamate Ion," *J. Chem. Phys.*, **26**, 77. *51–6339.*
The KBr disk technique was used for obtaining spectra of sulfamic acid, sodium and potassium sulfamates, and the corresponding deuteriorated compound from 500–4000 cm^{-1} at different temperatures.

697. Wedepohl, P. T., "Electrical and Optical Properties of Type IIb Diamonds," *Proc. Phys. Soc. (London)*, **70B**, 177. *51–17415.*

698. Weston, R. E., and Brodasky, T. F., "Infrared Spectrum and Force Constants of the Nitrite Ion," *J. Chem. Phys.*, **27**, 683. *52–1762.*
Infrared spectra were observed for microcrystalline $NaNO_2$, KNO_2, and $AgNO_2$ and for aqueous solutions of $NaNO_2$ and KNO_2.

699. Wilmshurst, J. K., and Bernstein, H. J., "Infrared and Raman Spectra of Phosphorus Pentachloride," *J. Chem. Phys.*, **27**, 661. *52–878.*

700. Wood, D. L., "Infrared Absorption Bands in α-Quartz," *J. Chem. Phys.*, **27**, 1438. *52–5973.*

701. Yang, A. C., and Garland, C. W., "Infrared Studies of Carbon Monoxide Chemisorbed on Rhodium," *J. Phys., Chem.*, **61**, 1504. *52–3515.*
The spectrum from 1700–4000 cm^{-1} was studied as a function of coverage for CO on rhodium surfaces supported on a high area, nonporous alumina (Al on C).

1958

702. Addison, C. C., and Gatehouse, B. M., "The Infrared Spectra of Anhydrous Transition Metal Nitrates," *Chem. and Ind. (London)*, 464. *52–19450.*

703. Aliev, M. I., and Khalilor, A. K., "Effect of Iodine on the Optical Properties of Selenium," *Doklady Akad. Nauk Azerbaïdzhan. S.S.R.*, 14, No. 1, 9. *52–9777.*

Absorption, transmission, and reflection spectra of thin films of Se containing different concentrations of iodine (0.0–1.38%) were obtained in the visible and infrared regions.

704. Amr El Sayed, M. F., and Sheline, R. K., "Infrared Spectrum and Structure of the $Ni(CN)_4^{-4}$ Ion," *J. Am. Chem. Soc.*, 80, 2047. *52–14327.*

705. Anti Kainen, P. J., "Infrared Absorption Spectra of Inorganic Compounds in Aqueous Solution. I. Some Oxyanions of Sulfur," *Suomen Kemistilehti*, 31B, 223. *52–17958.*

Characteristic bands between 947 and 1,290 cm^{-1} were observed for SO_4^{-2}, SO_3^{-2}, $S_2O_3^{-2}$, $S_4O_6^{-2}$ in aqueous solution.

706. Arneth, R., "Absorption of Zinc Oxide Crystals in the Infrared Spectrum," *Naturwiss.*, 45, 282. *52–19450.*

707. Babushkin, A., Kovalev, I. F., and Emel' yanova, V. M., "Vibrational Spectra of Molecular Compounds of Boron Trifluoride with Nitrogen- and Oxygen-containing Substances. I. $BF_3 \cdot NH_3$ and $BF_3 \cdot ND_3$," *Optika i Spektroskopiya*, 4, 468. *52–12556.*

708. Balakov, V. V., and Suetin, V. F., "Optical Transmission of Monocrystalline Germanium," *Optika i Spektroskopiya*, 4, 415. *52–16888.*

Transmission of samples of germanium was observed in the region 714–5000 cm^{-1}.

709. Bass, A. M., and Broida, H. P., "Absorption Spectra of Solids Condensed at Low Temperatures from Electric Discharges," *J. Mol. Spectroscopy*, 2, 42. *52–10717.*

Products of electrical discharge in N,H,O, H_2O, and NH_3 (including free radicals such as H, NH, OH, and CN) were condensed on silica plates cooled to 4.2°K and the absorption spectra measured from 0.22 to 3.5μ.

710. Begun, G. M., and Fletcher, W. H., "Infrared Spectra of the Isotopic Nitrous Oxides," *J. Chem. Phys.*, 28, 414. *52–9758.*

The spectra of $N^{14}N^{15}O^{16}$, $N^{15}N^{14}O^{16}$ and $N^{15}N^{15}O^{16}$ were observed from 500–4000 cm^{-1}. Comparison was made with spectra of $N^{14}N^{14}O^{16}$.

711. Bellamy, L. J., "The Infrared Spectra of Complex Molecules," 2nd Ed. London: Methuen and Co.

712. Bertin, E. P., Nakagawa, I., Mizushima, S. I., Lane, T. J., and Quagliano, J. V., "Infrared Absorption Spectra of Inorganic Coordination Com-

plexes. XIII. Hexamminecobalt (II) Halides and Diammine Mercury (II) Halides," *J. Am. Chem. Soc.*, **80**, 525. *52–6931*.

The three characteristic deformation bands of Co(II) ammine halides were observed at approx. 1600, 1170, and 630 cm^{-1}.

713. Bigorgne, M., "Vibrational Spectrum of Nickel Carbonyl. Energy of the Ni—C Bond," *Compt. rend.*, **246**, 1685. *52–12555*.

Force constants and thermodynamic quantities are calculated.

714. Bonino, G. B., and Fabbri, G., "Infrared Absorption Spectra of Potassium Ruthenicyanide in the Crystalline State and in Aqueous Solution," *Atti accad. naz. Lincei Rend. Classe sci. fix. mat. e nat.*, **23**, 191. *52–12557*.

Data are available for the anhydrous and trihydrated molecule to 25μ.

715. Brame, E. G., Jr., Johnson, F. A., Larsen, E. M., and Meloche, V. W., "Infrared Spectra of Inorganic Solids. III. Octacyano Complexes of Tungsten (IV), (−V) and Molybdenum (IV), (−V) dihydrate and anhydrous," *J. Inorg. and Nuclear Chem.*, **6**, 99. *52–11568*.

Using the KBr-disk technique, 8 octacyano complexes were examined in the region 2–23μ.

716. Brown, T. L., "Infrared Intensities and Molecular Structure," *Chem. Rev.*, **58**, 581.

717. Buchler, A., and Klemperer, W., "Infrared Spectra of the Alkaline-Earth Halides. I. Beryllium Fluoride, Beryllium Chloride, and Magnesium Chloride," *J. Chem. Phys.*, **29**, 121. *52–17957*.

718. Bulanin, M. O., and Orlova, N. D., "Investigation of Modifications in Vibration-rotational Spectra of Some Simple Molecules in the Process of Dissolution," *Optika i Spektroskopiya*, **4**, 569. *52–15239*.

The degree of interaction between solutes (HCl, DCl, HBr, DBr, HF, H_2O, and D_2O) and various solvents has been investigated via infrared spectroscopy.

719. Busing, W. R., and Morgan, H. W., "Infrared Spectrum of Calcium Hydroxide," *J. Chem. Phys.*, **28**, 998.

A single crystal of $Ca(OH)_2$ was studied at room temperature and at −196°C.

720. Caldwell, R. S., "Optical Properties of Tellurium and Selenium," *Dissertation Abstr.*, **18**, 2173. *52–16888*.

721. Claasen, H. H., Weinstock, B., and Malm, J. G., "Vibrational Spectra and Thermodynamic Properties of ClF_3 and BrF_3," *J. Chem. Phys.*, **28**, 285. *52–8731*.

722. Crook, A., and Taylor, P. J., "Simple Mulling Technique for the Preparation of Samples for Infrared Spectroscopy," *Chem. and Ind. (London)*, 95. *52–5977*.

723. Davis, P. W., and Oetjen, R. A., "Far Infrared Spectra of Several Pyramidal Trihalides," *J. Mol. Spectroscopy*, **2**, 253. *52–15241*.

Spectra of PCl_3, PBr_3, $SbCl_3$, $SbBr_3$, and $AsCl_3$ have been recorded in the region 85–550 cm^{-1}.

724. Giguère, P. A., and Zengin, N., Infrared Spectra of Hydrogen Fluoride in the Crystalline State," *Can. J. Chem.*, **36**, 1013. *52–16033*.

Spectral data are obtained for HF at $-180°$ covering the region 300–5000 cm^{-1}.

725. Goubeau, J., and Mitschelen, H., "Vibrational Spectrum of $BF_3 \cdot NH_3$," *Z. Physik. Chem. (Frankfurt)*, **14**, 61. *52–5977*.

The spectrum of solid $BF_3 \cdot NH_3$ was reported for the 4000–300 cm^{-1} region.

726. Goubeau, J., and Reyhing, J., "Vibration Spectra and Structure of Some Thiocyanates of Silicon," *Z. anorg. u. allgem. Chem.*, **294**, 96. *52–12556*.

Infrared spectrum in the region 280–3000 cm^{-1} was obtained for $Si(NCS)_4$. Raman spectra were reported for other thiocyanates of Si.

727. Gray, P., and Waddington, T. C., "Fundamental Vibration Frequencies and Force Constants in the Azide Ion," *Trans. Faraday Soc.*, **53**, 901. *52–6930*.

The absorption spectra are given for the azides of NH_4^+, Li, Na, K, Rb, Cs, Ca, Sr, and Ba. The solids were prepared and tested as mulls using Nujol or hexachloro-butadiene. The NaCl and KCl regions were explained.

728. Haeusler, C., and Barchewitz, P., "Measurement of the Vibrational-rotational Band of HCl^{35} and HCl^{37} at 1.76μ," *Compt. rend.*, **246**, 3040. *52–17958*.

729. Hansler, R. L., "Recent Studies (on HCl, H_2S, NH_3, and DCl) in the Spectral Region from 40 to 140 Microns," *Dissertation Abstr.*, **18**, 620. *52–6929*.

730. Harvey, K. B., and Bass, A. M., "Infrared Absorption of Oxygen Discharge Products and Ozone at 4°K," *J. Mol. Spectroscopy*, **2**, 405. *52–19503*.

731. Hexter, R. M., "High-Resolution, Temperature-Dependent Spectra of Calcite," *Spectrochim. Acta*, **10**, 28.

732. Hexter, R. M., "Infrared Spectroscopic Investigation of Anion Rotational Disorder in Sodium Nitrate," *Spectrochim. Acta*, **10**, 291. *52–9762*.

The region 5000–3000 cm^{-1} was studied for $NaNO_3$ at temperatures of 20°, 270°, and 302°, and of molten $NaNO_3$.

733. Hieber, W., and Jahn, A., "Infrared Spectra of Various Types of Inorganic Nitric Oxide Compounds," *Z. Naturforsch*, **13b**, 195. *52–17957*.

734. Hiebert, G. L., and Hornig, D. F., "Infrared Spectra of HCl–HBr Mixed Crystals," *J. Chem. Phys.*, **28**, 316. *52–8730*.

735. Hirota, E., "Rotational Structure of the Infrared Absorption Spectrum of Hydrogen Peroxide Vapor," *J. Chem. Phys.*, **28**, 839. *52–15240*.

736. Hobbs, W. E., "Infrared Absorption Spectra of Chromyl Fluoride and Chromyl Chloride," *J. Chem. Phys.*, **28**, 1220. *52–16869*.

737. Hrostowski, H. J., and Fuller, C. S., "Extension of Infrared Spectra of III–V Compounds by Lithium Diffusion," *Phys. and Chem. Solids*, **4**, 155.

738. Hrostowski, H. J., and Kaiser, R. H., "Absorption Spectrum of Bismuth-doped Silicon," *Phys. and Chem. Solids*, **4**, 315.   *52–16041*.

739. Hrostowski, H. J., and Kaiser, R. H., "Infrared Spectra of Group III Acceptors in Silicon," *Phys. and Chem. Solids*, **4**, 148.   *52–16041*.

The spectra of B-, Al-, Ga-, and In-doped Si were investigated at 4.2°K.

740. Hrostowski, H. J., and Kaiser, R. H., "Infrared Spectra of Heat-treatment Centers in Silicon," *Phys. Rev. Letters*, **1**, 199.   *52–19487*.

741. Jones, L. H., "Systematics in the Vibrational Spectra of Uranyl Complexes," *Spectrochim. Acta*, **10**, 395.   *52–9759*.

742. Jones, L. H., "Polarized Infrared Spectrum of Potassium Thiocyanate," *J. Chem. Phys.*, **28**, 1234.   *52–16870*.

743. Jones, L. H., "Vibrational Spectrum of Nickel Carbonyl," *J. Chem. Phys.*, **28**, 1215.   *52–16871*.

744. Jones, L. H., and McLaren, E., "Infrared Absorption Spectra of Sulfur Dioxide and Carbon Dioxide in Aqueous Solution," *J. Chem. Phys.*, **28**, 995.   *52–15240*.

745. Kessler, F. R., and Schnell, J., "Infrared Spectrum and Carrier Mobility in the Self-conductance Region of Silica," *Z. Naturforsch*, **13a**, 458.   *52–19516*.

746. Kotov, Y. I., Tyulin, V. I., and Taterskii, V. M., "Spectrum of the Combination Scattering of Gaseous Carbon Dioxide,"*Optika i Spektroskopiya*, **4**, 271.   *52–15241*.

CO_2, at 1.5–2 atm., was studied in the infrared region.   Analysis of the data gives a rotational const. of 0.3895 ± 0.0004 cm^{-1} and symmetrical mode frequencies of 1285.7 and 1388.2 cm^{-1}.

747. Kranendonk, J. van, "Induced Infrared Absorption in Gases—Calculation of the Binary Absorption Coefficients of Symmetrical Diatomic Molecules," *Physica*, **24**, 347.   *52–17955*.

748. Kuipers, G. A., "The Spectrum of Monomeric Hydrogen Fluoride: Line Shapes, Intensities and Breadths," *J. Mol. Spectroscopy*, **2**, 75.

The 2.5μ fundamental of HF was measured at 117° and at pressures varying from 200–3860 mm. Hg with a high resolution grating spectrometer.

749. Lewis, J., and Wilkinson, G., "Infrared Spectra of Osmium-Nitrogen Compounds," *J. Inorg. and Nuclear Chem.*, **6**, 12.   *52–8730*.

Spectra were observed for potassium osmate and nitrilopentachloroosmate.

750. Linton, H. R., and Nixon, E. R., "Infrared Spectra of Silyl and Silyl-d$_3$ Cyanides," *Spectrochim. Acta*, **10**, 299.   *52–9762*.

Gaseous state spectra of silyl and silyl-d_3 cyanides were examined over the 300–3500 cm^{-1} region.

751. Linz, Jr., A., and Herrington, K., "Electrical and Optical Properties of Synthetic Calcium Titanate Crystal," *J. Chem. Phys.*, **28**, 824.

The region 0.3–7 μ was investigated using a 1.9 mm crystal of CaTiO$_3$.

752. Lothian, G. F., "Absorption Spectrophotometry," The Macmillan Company, New York.

A book which contains sections on infrared spectroscopy.

753. Maki, A., and Decius, J. C., "Infrared Spectrum of Cyanate Ion as a Solid Solution in a Potassium Iodide Lattice," *J. Chem. Phys.*, **28**, 1003.

754. Meloche, V. W., and Kalbus, G. E., "Anomalies in the Infrared Spectra of Inorganic Compounds Prepared by the Potassium Bromide Pellet Technique," *J. Inorg. and Nuclear Chem.*, **6**, 104. *52–11569.*

Factors responsible for apparent exchange between inorganic compounds and the matrix are enumerated and discussed.

755. Miyazawa, T., "Infrared Absorption of Cyanogen in the Cesium Iodide Region and CN Bond Moment," *J. Chem. Phys.*, **29**, 421. *52–19454.*

756. Mutschin, A., and Maennchen, K., "Infrared Absorption Spectra of Different Phosphorus Compounds II. Alkali Pyrophosphates," *Z. Anal. Chem.*, **160**, 81. *52–13422.*

Spectral data obtained in the region 1–40 μ are reported for H$_4$P$_2$O$_7$, NaH$_3$P$_2$O$_7$, Na$_2$H$_2$P$_2$O$_7$, Na$_3$HP$_2$O$_7$·H$_2$O, Na$_3$HP$_2$O$_7$·9H$_2$O, Na$_4$P$_2$O$_7$·10H$_2$O, Na$_4$P$_2$O$_7$, and K$_4$P$_2$O$_7$.

757. Narayanan, P. S., and Lakshmanan, B. R., "Infrared and Raman Spectra of Witherite (BaCO$_3$) and Strontianite (SrCO$_3$)," *J. Indian Inst. Sci.*, **40A**, 1. *52–19450.*

758. Noto, T., Sawada, H., Sato, Y., Kotera, K., Goto, H., Fukuba, N., and Takahashi, T., "Infrared Absorption Spectra of Heavy Water Hydrates," *Tanabe Seiyaku Kenkyu Nempô*, **3**, 48. *52–17956.*

The rock salt region was studied. The spectra of anhydrous and heavy water$_{60}$ hydrated barium chloride were compared.

759. Ockman, N., Infrared and Raman Spectra of Single Crystals of Ordinary Ice," *Dissertation Abstr.*, **18**, 1466. *52–13420.*

760. O'Dwyer, M. F., "Infrared Spectra and Normal Coordinate Analysis of Ironpentacarbonyl," *J. Mol. Spectroscopy*, **2**, 144–51. *52–11568.*

Vapor and liquid phase at 25° were investigated between 400 and 4000 cm^{-1}. Analysis suggests a tetragonal pyramidal model.

761. Olsen, A. L., "High-temperature Cell for Infrared Spectroscopy," *Anal. Chem.*, **30**, 158. *52–5977.*

A cell is described for heating KBr disks as high as 300°.

762. Penneman, R. A., and Jones, L. H., "Infrared Absorption of Gold Monocyanide," *J. Chem. Phys.*, **28**, 169. *52–7854.*

A strong absorption band is observed for AuCN at 2239 cm^{-1}.

763. Piper, W. W., Marple, D. T. F., and Johnson, P. D., "Optical Properties of Hexagonal Zinc Sulfide Single Crystals," *Phys. Rev.*, **110**, 323.

764. Pistorius, C. W. F. T., "Force Constants of Tetrahedral Molecules," *J. Chem. Phys.*, **28**, 514.   *52–9763.*

765. Pullin, A. D. E., and Pollock, J. McC., "Spectra of Solutions of Silver and Lithium Perchlorates in Acetone," *Trans. Faraday Soc.*, **54**, 11. *52–15243.*

766. Rosenstock, H. B., "Infrared Absorption by Sodium Chloride-Type Lattices," *Phys. and Chem. Solids*, **4**, 201.   *52–16038.*

767. Schultz, J. W., and Eggers, D. F., "Bond Moments and Bond Moment Derivatives of $C_2{}^{12}N_2{}^{14}$ and $C^{12}C^{13}N_2{}^{14}$ from Infrared Intensities," *J. Mol. Spectroscopy*, **2**, 113.   *52–11568.*

768. Serratosa, J. M., and Bradley, W. F., "Infrared Absorption of OH Bonds in Micas," *Nature*, **181**, 111.   *52–10719.*

769. Sevchenko, N. A., and Florinskaya, V. A., "Infrared Transmission Spectra of Porous and Quartzoid Glasses," *Optika i Spektroskopiya*, **4**, 189. *52–13421.*

770. Sidorov, T. A., "Infrared Spectra at Low Temperatures and the Structure of Quartz and Cristobalite," *Optika i Spektroskopiya*, **4**, 800. *52–16885.*

   Spectra of powdered glass taken in the region $2.5–24\mu$ at room temperature and at liquid–N_2 temperature were compared with those of quartz and cristobalite taken under similar conditions.

771. Sidorov, T. A., and Sobolev, N. N., "Infrared and Combination Spectra of Boron Oxide. III. Interpretation of the Vibrational Spectrum of Boron Oxide and Calculation of the Isotope Effect," *Optika i Spektroskopiya*, **4**, 9.   *52–15240.*

772. Silin, V. P., "Optical Properties of Metals in the Infrared Region," *Zhur. Eksptl. i Teoret. Fiz.*, **34**, 707.   *52–9773.*

773. Spitzer, and Fan, H. Y., "Effect of Neutron Irradiation on Infrared Absorption in Silicon," *Phys. Rev.*, **109**, 1011.   *52–11580.*

774. Stepanov, B. I., and Prima, A. M., "Vibrational Spectra of Silicates. I. Calculation of Frequencies and Intensities of Spectral Lines of Silicates," *Optika i Spektroskopiya*, **4**, 734.   *52–16870.*

775. Steger, E., "Spectroscopic Investigations of Condensed Phosphates and Phosphoric Acids. IV. The Infrared Spectra of Some Tetrametaphosphates," *Z. anorg. u. allgem. Chem.*, **294**, 1.   *52–12557.*

   Assignments are made for frequencies observed in the rock salt region for $Al_4(P_4O_{12})_3$, $Cu_2P_4O_{12}$, $Mg_2P_4O_{12}$, $(NH_4)_4P_4O_{12}$, $Na_4P_4O_{12}\cdot4H_2O$, and $Na_4P_4O_{12}$.

776. Szymanowski, W., Wiśniewski, B., Golebiowski, B., and Olszewska, L., "Application of Pressed-powder Methods to Investigations of Infrared Absorption Spectra of Solids," *Bull. acad. polon. sci., Ser. sci., math., astron. et phys.*, **6**, 223.   *52–13421.*

Absorption curves are given for $BaTiO_3$, polystyrene, coal, and inositol in KBr disc.

777. Tanner, K. N., and King, R. L., "Infrared Spectra of Free Radicals," *Nature*, **181**, 963. *52–14327.*

Photolysis of hydrazine was studied using a CaF_2 prism instrument.

778. Terenin, A. N., Filimonov, V., and Bystror, D., "Infrared Spectra of Addition Compounds of Metal Halides," *Z. Elektrochem.*, **62**, 180. *52–10721.*

Spectra of NO, MeCN, C_5H_5N, cyclohexene, Et_2O, Me_2CO, and MeOH with $AlCl_3$, $AlBr_3$, and $SnCl_4$ were obtained from 8000–700 cm^{-1}.

779. Waggener, W. C., "Measurement of the Absorption Spectra of Neptunium Ions in Heavy Water Solution from 0.35 to 1.85μ," *J. Phys. Chem.*, **62**, 382.

780. Ward, W. M., "Infrared Spectrum of Deuterophosphine," *Dissertation Abstr.*, **18**, 1823. *52–14327.*

781. Wardzyński, W., "Infrared Absorption in Alkali Halide Crystals with Anionic Impurities," *Acta Phys. Polon*, **17**, 29. *52–19477.*

Impurities, on the order of 10^{-2} mole percent, were introduced into the lattices of KCl, KBr, and KI. The effects of temperature and ultraviolet radiation on the induced infrared absorptions at 7 and 8μ were noted.

782. Wentink, Jr., T., "Triatomic Linear Molecules Containing Carbon and Oxygen, Sulfur, Selenium, or Tellurium. I. Vibrational Spectra of CS_2, CSe_2, SCSe, and SCTe," *J. Chem. Phys.*, **29**, 188. *52–17957.*

783. Wentink, Jr., T., and Tiensuu, V. H., "Vibrational Spectra of BBr_3 and BI_3," *J. Chem. Phys.*, **28**, 826. *52–15240.*

Gas, liquid and CS_2-solution phases of BBr_3 and gas, solid, and sol'n phases of BI_3 were observed in the infrared at room temperature.

784. Willis, J. B., "Vibrational Spectroscopy and Its Application in Structural Inorganic Chemistry," *Revs. Pure Appl. Chem.*, **8**, 101. *52–16858.*

METAL-ORGANIC COMPLEXES

785. Lecomte, J., "Infrared Absorption Spectra of Metallic Acetylacetonates," *Discussions Faraday Soc.*, No. 9, 125 (1950). *46–3408.*

Spectra from 525 to 1750 cm^{-1} are given for the acetylacetone chelates of Be,Cr,Fe^{+3},Cu,Zn,Th, and U. The spectra indicate that the compounds are enolic and probably have cyclic structure. The principal metal-sensitive region lies between 600 and 700 cm^{-1}. The bonding of the metal to the ligand is not completely understood.

786. Dorough, G. D., Miller, J. R., and Huennekens, F. M., "Spectra of the Metallo Derivatives of α, β, γ, δ–Tetraphenylporphine," *J. Am. Chem. Soc.*, **73**, 4315 (1951). *46–5968.*

787. Falk, J. E., and Willis, J. B., "Infrared Spectra of Porphyrins and Their Iron Complexes," *Australian J. Sci. Research*, **A4**, 579 (1951).

The spectra of certain porphyrins, hemes and related compounds were recorded from 670–4000 cm^{-1} using Nujol mulls and chloroform solutions.

788. Cooke, I., Herschmann, C., and Susz, B. P., "Infrared Spectra of Complexes of Benzophenone, Acetophenone, and Benzoyl Chloride with Aluminum Chloride and Bromide," *Arch. sci. (Geneva)*, **5**, 262 (1952). *49–5968.*

789. Cooke, I., and Susz, B., "Infrared Spectra of the Complex of Benzophenone and Aluminum Chloride," *Arch. sci.*, **5**, 105 (1952).

About 15 bands, ranging from 1657–672 cm^{-1}, were observed for the $C_6H_5COC_6H_5 \cdot AlCl_3$ complex.

790. Duval, Cl., Freymann, R., and Lecomte, J., "An Attempt at Interpretation of the Infrared Spectra of Metal Acetylacetonates," *Bull. soc. chim. France*, 106 (1952). *47–43.*

Infrared spectra of acetylacetonates of Be^{+2}, Mg^{+2}, Al^{+3}, Sc^{+3}, Cr^{+3}, Fe^{+3}, CO^{+2}, CO^{+3}, Cu^{+2}, Zn^{+2}, and Sm^{+3} are obtained for the region 526–1786 cm^{-1}. Conclusions are given based on correlations of the spectra with those of acetone and acetylacetone.

791. Lippincott, E. R., Mercier, P., and Tobin, M. C., "The Vibrational Spectra of Some Tin and Germanium Halogen Metalorganic Compounds," *J. Phys. Chem.*, **57**, 939 (1953). *48–2477.*

The infrared spectra of $SnMe_3I$ and $SnMe_2I_2$ from 667–3333 cm^{-1} are given along with Raman spectra of $SnMe_3I$, $SnMe_2I_2$, $GeEtCl_3$, and $GeEt_2Cl_2$.

792. Lippincott, E. R., and Nelson, R. D., "The Vibrational Spectra and Structure of Ferrocene and Ruthenocene," *J. Chem. Phys.*, **21**, 1307 (1953). *47–11002.*

793. Mizushima, S., and Quagliano, J. V., "Structure of Ligands in Inorganic Coordination Compounds by Infrared Spectra," *J. Am. Chem. Soc.*, **75**, 4870 (1953).

The forbidden frequency of the nitrate ion in $[Cu\langle SC(NHCH_2)_2\rangle_4]NO_3$ and that of the sulfate ion in $[Cu(NH_3)_4]SO_4 \cdot H_2O$ were observed as weak infrared absorptions.

794. Bellamy, L. J., and Branch, R. F., "The Infrared Spectra of Chelate Compounds. II. Metal Chelate Compounds of β-Diketones and of Salicylaldehyde," *J. Chem. Soc.*, 4491 (1954). *49–3663.*

Two peaks (1550–1600 and 1280–1390 cm^{-1}) were observed for metal chelate compounds of β-diketones. A single peak (1585–1681 cm^{-1}) was observed for different bivalent metal complexes of salicylaldehyde. The CO frequencies for acetylacetonates do not vary appreciably with change in metal.

795. Bryant, B. E., Pariaud, J. C., and Fernelius, W. C., "Infrared Spectra of Chelate Compounds. I. A Study of the Carbonyl Frequencies of the Hydrogen and Metal Chelates of the Substituted Cycloheptatrienones," *J. Org. Chem.,* **19**, 1889 (1954). *49–12131.*

The infrared studies were made of tropolone and various derivates of of it in an effort to study the effect of varying Y, X, and Z.

796. Claassen, H. H., and Zielen, A. J., "Structure of the Perrhenate Ion," *J. Chem. Phys.,* **22**, 707 (1954).

Absorption spectra of aqueous solutions of perrhenic acid and $NaReO_4$ were obtained in the infrared region. The spectra suggest a probable tetrahedral structure for the perrhenate ion.

797. Cooke, I., Susz, B. P., and Herschmann, C., "The Infrared Spectrum of Complexes Formed by Aluminum Halides. II. Complexes of Benzoylchloride and Bromide and of Maleic and Phthalic Anhydrides; Variation of the Spectrum in the Course of the Friedel-Crafts Ketone Synthesis," *Helv. Chim. Acta,* **37**, 1280 (1954). *48–12555.*

798. Susz, B. P., and Cooke, I., "The Infrared Spectrum of Complexes Formed by Aluminum Halides. I. Complexes of Acetophenone and Benzophenone; Comparison with the Spectra of Various Organic Compounds Presenting the Aluminum-Oxygen Bond," *Helv. Chim. Acta,* **37**, 1273 (1954). *48–12555.*

799. Faust, J. P., and Quagliano, J. V., "The Trans Effect in Inorganic Coordination Compounds. I. Ultraviolet and Infrared Studies of Cis- and Trans-Dinitrotetrammine-Cobalt (III) Chloride," *J. Am. Chem. Soc.,* **76**, 5346 (1954). *49–2188.*

The strong absorption bands at 1333 cm^{-1} and 833.3 cm^{-1} are discussed. The spectral data support N–metal bonding in complexes of this type.

800. Lane, T. J., Sen, D. N., and Quagliano, J. V., "Potassium Bromide Disk Method for the Infrared Studies of Coordination Compounds," *J. Chem. Phys.,* **22**, 1855 (1954). *49–2191.*

Absorption studies in the infrared region were made of tetrakis(ethylenethiocarbamide)Cu(I) nitrate, ethylenethiocarbamide, and KNO_3.

801. Stone, K. G., "Infrared Spectra of Magnesium and Bismuth 8-Quinolinolates," *J. Am. Chem. Soc.,* **76**, 4997. (1954). *49–2871.*

802. Jones, L. H., "Infrared Spectra and Structure of the Crystalline Sodium Acetate Complexes of U(VI), Np(VI), Pu(VI), and Am(VI). Compari-

son of Metal-oxygen Bond Distance and Bond Force Constant in This Series," *J. Chem. Phys.*, **23**, 2105 (1955). *50–3083.*

803. Merritt, P. E., and Wiberley, S. E., "Infrared Absorption Spectra of Cis-trans Isomers of Coordination Compounds of Cobalt (III)," *J. Phys. Chem.*, **59**, 55 (1955). *49–3661.*

804. Mizushima, S., Ichishima, I., Nakagawa, I., and Quagliano, J. V., "Infrared Studies of Inorganic Coordination Compounds. II. Infrared and Raman Spectra of 1,2 dithiocyanatoethane in Relation to a New Type of Optical Isomerism of Coordination Compounds," *J. Phys., Chem.*, **59**, 293 (1955). *49–11419.*

805. Nakahara, A., "Dimethylglyoximato-cobalt (III) Complexes. III. Direct Evidence for the Planar Coordination of Two Dimethylglyoximate Ions in Bis(dimethylglyoximato)cobalt (III) Complexes," *Bull. Chem. Soc. Japan*, **28**, 473 (1955).

806. Orgel, L. E., "Spectra of Transition-Metal Complexes," *J. Chem. Phys.*, **23**, 1004 (1955).

807. Sen, D. N., Mizushima, S., Curran, C., and Quagliano, J. V., "Infrared Absorption Spectra of Inorganic Coordination Complexes. I. The Nature of Chelation Bonding in Bis(glycino)copper(II) monohydrate and Bis(glycino)nickel(II)dihydrate," *J. Am. Chem. Soc.*, **77**, 211 (1955). *50–6919.*

808. Sidorov, A. N., and Terenin, A. N., "Infrared Spectra of Phthalocyanines and the Action of Gaseous Compounds on Them," *Doklady Akad. Nauk S.S.S.R.*, **104**, 575 (1955).

The effect of various metals (Co, Fe, Cu, Mg, and Zn) on the infrared spectra of phthalocyanine is observed and discussed.

809. Svatos, G. F., Curran, C., and Quagliano, J. V., "Infrared Absorption Spectra of Inorganic Coordination Complexes. V. The N—H Stretching Vibration in Coordination Compounds," *J. Am. Chem. Soc.*, **77**, 6159 (1955). *50–3086.*

810. Sweeny, D. M., Curran, C., and Quagliano, J. V., "Infrared Absorption Spectra of Inorganic Coordination Complexes. IV. Infrared Spectrum of Bis(glycino)zinc Monohydrate," *J. Am. Chem. Soc.*, **77**, 5508 (1955). *50–1467.*

811. Sweeny, D. M., Mizushima, S., and Quagliano, J. V., "Infrared Absorption Spectra of Inorganic Coordination Complexes. VI. Molecular Structure of 1,2-Dimethylmercaptoethane and Its Metal Chelate Compounds," *J. Am. Chem. Soc.*, **77**, 6521 (1955). *50–4641.*

The infrared spectra of 1,2 dimethylmercaptoethane and its Pt, Pd, Cu, Hg, Cd, and Ni chelate derivatives were observed in the rock salt region.

812. Ueno, K., and Martell, A. E., "Infrared Study of Metal Chelates of Bisacetylacetone ethylenediimine and Related Compounds," *J. Phys. Chem.*, **59**, 998 (1955). *50–678.*

Frequency assignments were made from observed infrared spectra of bisacetylacetone ethylenediimine, related compounds, and the corresponding Cu, Ni, Co, Pd divalent chelate derivatives. Three bands (580–430 cm⁻¹) corresponding to vibrations of the covalent metal-ligand bonds were tentatively assigned.

813. Chalandon, P., and Susz, B. P., "Preparation and Infrared Spectra of Complexes Formed by Boron Trifluoride with Dipropyl Ketone, Acetophenone, and Benzophenone," *Arch. sci. (Geneva)*, **9**, 461 (1956).

814. Charles, R. G., *et al.*, "Infrared Absorption Spectra of Metal Chelates Derived from 8-hydroxyquinoline, 8-hydroxy-2-methylquinoline, and 8-hydroxy-4-methylquinoline," *Spectrochim. Acta*, **8** (1), 1 (1956). *50–13611.*

815. Filimonov, V. N., and Terenin, A. N., "Infrared Absorption Spectra of Some Organic Complexes with Aluminum Bromide and Tin Tetrachloride," *Doklady Akad. Nauk S.S.S.R.*, **109**, 799 (1956). *51–9320.*

816. Fujita, J., Nakamoto, K., and Kobayashi, M., "Infrared Spectra of Metallic Complexes. I. The Effect of Coordination on the Infrared Spectra of Ammine, Rhodanato, and Azido Complexes," *J. Am. Chem. Soc.*, **78**, 3295 (1956).

817. Graddon, D. P., "The Absorption Spectra of Complex Oxalates," *J. Inorg. Nuclear Chem.*, **3**, 308 (1956). *51–4139.*

818. Harkins, T. R., Walter, J. L., Harris, O. E., and Freiser, H., "An Infrared Study of the Metal Chelates of Some Imidazole Derivatives," *J. Am. Chem. Soc.*, **78**, 260 (1956). *50–7595.*

819. Mecke, R., and Funck, E., "Tautomerism and the Infrared Absorption Spectrum of Acetylacetone," *Z. Elektrochem.*, **60**, 1124 (1956). *51–6340.*

Acetylacetonates of Li, Na, K, Tl(I), and Ag were studied in the infrared region.

820. Morris, M. L., and Busch, D. H., "Properties and Infrared Absorption Spectra of Complexes of Cobalt (III) with Pentadentate Ethylenediaminetetracetic Acid and Hydroxyethylethylene-diaminetriacetic Acid," *J. Am. Chem., Soc.*, **78**, 5178 (1956). *51–856.*

821. Nakahara, A., Fujita, J., and Tsuchida, R., "Dimethylglyoximato cobalt (III) Complexes. IV. Intramolecular O—H—O Hydrogen Bonds in Bis(dimethylglyoximato) cobalt (III) Complexes," *Bull. Chem. Soc. Japan*, **29**, 296 (1956).

822. Rosenberg, A., "Infrared Absorption Spectra of Amino-acid-metal Chelates at Liquid-air Temperatures," *Acta Chem. Scand.*, **10**, 840 (1956). *52–17961.*

823. Vuagnat, A. M., and Susz, B. P., "Infrared Spectrum of the Complex of Acetophenone and Mercuric Chloride," *Arch. sci. (Geneva)*, **9**, 325 (1956). *51–5556.*

824. Zeil, W., Dautel, R., and Honsberg, W., "The Infrared Spectra of Coordination Compounds of Aluminum Hydride with Trimethylamine and Tetrahydrofuran," *Z. Elektrochem.*, **60**, 1131 (1956). *51–6340.*

825. Filimonov, V. N., Bystrov, D. S., and Terenin, A. N., "Infrared Spectra of Molecular Compounds with Metal Halides," *Optika i Spektroskopiya*, **3**, 480 (1957). *52–4321.*

The infrared absorption spectra of $AlBr_3$, $AlCl_3$, and $SnCl_4$ complexes of NO, acetonitrile, pyridine, cyclohexene, acetone, and MeOH were observed in the 8000–700 cm^{-1} region.

826. Fujita, J., Nakamoto, and Kobayashi, M., "Infrared Spectra of Metallic Complexes. III. The Infrared Spectra of Metallic Oxalates," *J. Phys. Chem.*, **61**, 1014 (1957). *52–82.*

The spectra of oxalates of Al, Co, Cr, Fe, Cu, and Ni were studied. A discussion of the effect of the metal ion on frequency shifts is given.

827. Gagnaux, P., Janjic, D., and Susz, B. P., "Preparation and Infrared Spectra of Complexes of Aluminum Bromide and Aromatic Nitro Derivatives," *Arch. sci. (Geneva)*, **10**, 257 (1957). *52–3516.*

Techniques for investigating complexes of $AlBr_3$ with $PhNO_2$, $p\text{-}MeC_6H_4NO_2$, $p\text{-}ClC_6H_4NO_2$, $p\text{-}NO_2C_6H_4NO_2$, and $p\text{-}Me_3CC_6H_4NO_2$ are presented.

828. Hoffmann, E. G., and Schomburg, G., "Infrared Absorption and Association in Dialkylaluminum Hydrides," *Z. Elektrochem.*, **61**, 1101 (1957).

829. Holtzclaw, Jr., H., Collman, J. P., "Infrared Absorption of Metal Chelate Compounds of 1,3 Diketones," *J. Am. Chem. Soc.*, **79**, 3318 (1957). *51–16099.*

The spectra are described for the copper chelates of 1,3 diketones and the acetylacetone chelates of 4 different metals.

830. Kiss, A. I., and Csaszar, J., "Light Absorption of Chelate Complexes. II. Mechanism of Light Absorption of Acetylacetonate Complexes," *Acta Chim. Acad. Sci. Hung.*, **13**, 49 (1957). *52–9760.*

Spectra of the acetylacetonates were obtained between 5000 and 50,000 cm^{-1}. Complexes for the following ions were studied: Be(II), Mg(II), Zn(II), Cd(II), Al(III), Th(IV), Cr(III), Mn(III), Fe(III), Co(II and III), Ni(II), Pd(II), and Cu(II).

831. Kriegsmann, H., "Spectroscopic Investigations of Silicon Compounds. II. Spectroscopic Investigation of the Si—X—Si Bridge Bonds in Hexamethyldisiloxane and Its NH, CH_2, and S Analogs," *Z. Elektrochem.*, **61**, 1088 (1957).

832. Lakshmanan, B. R., "Infrared Absorption Spectra of Copper Potassium Oxalate, Copper Sodium Oxalate, and Copper Ammonium Oxalate," *J. Indian Inst. Sci.*, **39A**, 30 (1957). *51–10237.*

833. Nakamoto, K., Fujita, J., Tanaka, S., and Kobayashi, M., "Infrared Spectra of Metallic Complexes. IV. Comparison of the Infrared Spectra of

Unidentate and Bidentate Complexes," *J. Am. Chem. Soc.*, **79**, 4904 (1957). *52–3516.*

The spectra of selected sulfato, carbonato, oxalato, and acetato metallic complexes were measured in the 5000–400 cm^{-1} region.

834. Penland, R. B., Mizushima, S., Curran, C., and Quagliano, J. V., "Infrared Absorption Spectra of Inorganic Coordination Complexes. X. Studies of Some Metal-urea Complexes," *J. Am. Chem. Soc.*, **79**, 1575 (1957). *51–9318.*

Spectra were obtained for the following complexes in the 2–35μ region: $Pd(NH_2CONH_2)_2Cl_2$, $Pt(NH_2CONH_2)_2Cl_2$, $[Cr(OC(NH_2)_2)_6]Cl_3$, $[Fe(OC(NH_2)_2)_6]Cl_3$, $Zn (OC(NH_2)_2)_2Cl_2$, and $Cu(OC(NH_2)_2)_2Cl_2$.

835. Phillips, J. P., and Deye, J. F., "Infrared Spectra of Oxine Chelates," *Anal. Chim. Acta*, **17**, 231 (1957). *52–6932.*

The infrared spectra from 667–5000 cm^{-1} of 33 derivatives of 8-quinolinol (oxine) in KBr disks were obtained.

836. Polstyanko, L. L., Kazitsyna, L. A., and Terentev, A. P., "Study of the Structure of Chelates by Their Infrared and Ultraviolet Spectra," *Khim. Nauka i Prom.*, **2**, 797 (1957).

The chelates studied were prepared from Schiff bases and salts of Cu, Ni, Pd, Be, Zn, and Cd or from a metal salicylaldehyde and the corresponding ammine.

837. Rosenberg, A., "The Infrared Absorption Spectra of Some Amide and Dipeptide Metal Chelates," *Acta Chem. Scand.*, **11**, 1390 (1957). *52–10714.*

Amide and dipeptide chelates of Cu, Ni, and Zn were prepared and studied. A shift in the resonance equilibrium of the peptide group was revealed from a study of the spectra.

838. Schmelz, M. J., Miyazawa, T., Mizushima, S., Lane, T. J., and Quagliano, J. V., "Infrared Absorption Spectra of Inorganic Coordination Complexes. IX. Infrared Spectra of Oxalato Complexes," *Spectrochim. Acta*, **9**, 51 (1957). *51–11068.*

839. Schomburg, G., and Hoffmann, E. G., "Infrared Spectroscopic Investigation of Aluminum Hydride Derivatives," *Z. Elektrochem.*, **61**, 1110 (1957).

Spectra are reported for: $AlH_3 \cdot NMe_3$, $AlH_3 \cdot 2NMe_3$, $AlH_3 \cdot NEt_3$, H_2AlNEt_2, Et_2AlNEt_2, $Et_2AlH \cdot NEt_2$, $(Et_2N)_2AlH$, $EtOAlHEt$, $AlH_2Br \cdot NEt_3$, $AlHBr_2 \cdot Et_2O$, $AlHl_2 \cdot Et_2O$, $HAlCl_2 \cdot NEt_3$, and $HAlBr_3 \cdot NEt_2$.

840. Stewart, J. E., "Infrared Absorption Spectra of Urea, Thiourea, and Some Thiourea-Alkali Halide Complexes," *J. Chem. Phys.*, **26**, 248 (1957). *51–7864.*

841. Tarte, P., and Laurent, P. A., "Comparative Study of the Vibrational Spectra of 1,4 Dioxane, Mercuric Chloride, and the Dioxane-Mercuric Chloride Complex," *Bull. soc. chim. France*, 403 (1957). *51–9317.*

842. Ueno, K., "Infrared Absorption Spectra of o-Hydroxyazobenzene and Its Metal Chelate Compounds," *J. Am. Chem. Soc.*, **79**, 3066 (1957). *51–12661.*

843. Zeitler, V. A., and Brown, C. A., "The Infrared Spectra of Some Ti–O–Si, Ti–O–Ti, and Si–O–Si Compounds," *J. Phys. Chem.*, **61**, 1174 (1957). *52–883.*

Infrared spectra are given for tetrakis(triphenylsiloxy)titanium, tetrakis(trimethylsiloxy)titanium, tetraxis(triphenyl-siloxy)silane, tetrabutoxy and tetraiso propoxytitanium, a condensed butoxytitanium ester, and $Ti[O_5Si_4(C_6H_5)_8]_2$.

844. Barceló, J. R., "The Infrared Spectrum of Some Metallic Chelate Compounds. I. Rubeanates," *Spectrochim. Acta,* **10**, 245 (1958). *52–9765.*

The Cu, Ni, Co, Ag, and Hg derivatives of rubeanic acid (the diamine of thioxalic acid) have been examined in the infrared region.

845. Brown, D. A., "Use of 4p Orbitals in Metal Aromatic Complexes," *J. Chem. Phys.*, **29**, 1086 (1958). (European Research Associates, s.a., 95 rue Gatti de Gamond, Brussels, Belgium.)

846. Cotton, F. A., and Reynolds, L. T., "The Structure and Bonding of Cyclopentadienylthallium and Bis(cyclopentadienyl)magnesium," *J. Am. Chem. Soc.*, **80**, 269 (1958). *52–9765.*

847. Daasch, L. W., "Infrared Spectrum of Antimony Trichloride-benzene Complex," *J. Chem. Phys.*, **28**, 1005 (1958).

848. Dryden, R. P., and Winston, A., "Infrared Spectra of Some Metal Chelates of β-diketones," *J. Phys. Chem.*, **62**, 635 (1958). *52–13422.*

Solutions of various chelates of β-diketones with Al, Cu, Zr, or Ti were studied in the 1650–1500 cm^{-1} region.

849. Sawyer, D. T., and Paulsen, P. J., "Properties and Infrared Spectra of Ethylenediaminetetraacetic Acid Complexes. I. Alkaline Earth Chelates," *J. Am. Chem. Soc.*, **80**, 1597 (1958). *52–12557.*

850. Stromatt, R. W., "Infrared Study of Zirconium Tetramandelate, and Stabilities of Metal Chelates of Some α-amino Acids and Mandelic Acid," *Dissertation Abstr.*, **18**, 1609 (1958). *52–14330.*

851. West, R., and Riley, R., "Infrared Spectra of Metal Acetylacetonates in the Sodium Chloride Region," *J. Inorg. and Nuclear Chem.*, **5**, 295 (1958). *52–8732.*

Spectra are presented for the acetylacetonates of Cs, K, Na, Li, Tl, Ag, Ca, Mg, Be, Co^{II}, Cu, Zn, Pd, La, Al, Fe, Cr, and Co^{III}.

852. Yamaguchi, A., Penland, R. B., Mizushima, S., Lane, J. T., Curran, C., and Quagliano, J. V., "Infrared Absorption Spectra of Inorganic Coordination Compounds. XIV. Infrared Studies of Some Metal Thiourea Complexes," *J. Am. Chem. Soc.*, **80**, 527 (1958). *51–6923.*

SUPPLEMENTARY LIST OF REFERENCES

1954

S-1. Amat, G., "Vibration-Rotation Spectrum of Nitrous Oxide," *J. phys. radium,* **15**, 636. *52–17957.*

S-2. Coulon, R., Galatry, L., Oksengorn, B., Robin, S., and Vodar, "Perturbation of Some Infrared Absorption Frequencies by Gases Compressed to the Order of 1000 Atmospheres," *J. phys. radium,* **15**, 641. *52–17956.*

Spectra of H_2, N_2, and CO_2 under high pressure, and the spectrum of HCl pressurized with N_2 and A are reported.

S-3. Ellis, J. W., and Vanderberg, R. M., "The Near Infrared Absorption and the Dispersion of Ice and Other Crystals," *J. phys. radium,* **15**, 612. *52–17956.*

S-4. Fahrenfort, J., deKluiver, H., and Babeliowsky, T. P. J. H., "Infrared Absorption Induced in Carbon Dioxide Under Pressure," *J. phys. radium,* **15**, 617. *52–17956.*

Carbon dioxide, 1–125 atmospheres and at temperatures up to 135°C, was investigated in the spectral region 700–7300 cm^{-1}.

S-5. Langseth, A., "Infrared and Raman Spectra of Simple Linear Molecules," *J. phys. radium,* **15**, 614. *52–17956.*

The spectra of CO_2, COS, and CS_2 were observed between 3 and 25μ.

S-6. Nielson, A. H., Shelton, R. D., and Fletcher, W. H., "The Infrared Spectrum and the Molecular Constants of Sulfurous Anhydride," *J. phys. radium,* **15**, 604. *52–17957.*

1955

S-7. Sheppard, N., "Study of Molecular Structure by Infrared and Raman Spectroscopy," *Glasnik Khem. Drushtra, Beograd,* **20**, 221. *52–15225.*

A lecture.

1956

S-8. Bonino, G. B., and Fabbri, G., "Infrared Absorption of Potassium Cobalticyanide in the Crystalline State and in Solution," *Atti accad. nazl. Lincei, Rend., Classe Sci. fis., mat. e nat.,* **21**, 246.

S-9. Brazdzhyunas, P. P., and Vishchakas, Yu. K., "Optical Properties of Polycrystalline Layers of Cadmium Selenide," *Lietuvos. T. S. R. Mokslu Akad. Darbai Ser. B.,* No. 4, 21. *53–10989.*

Reflectivity and light absorption of thin films of CdSe are reported for the visible and near-infrared regions.

S-10. Busch, E., and Winkler, U., "Determination of the Characteristic Values of Semiconductors by Means of Electrical, Optical, and Magnetic Measurements," *Ergeb. exakt. Naturw.*, **29**, 145. *53–873*.

A review.

S-11. Fan, H. Y., "Infrared Absorption in Semiconductors," *Repts. Progr. Phys.*, **19**, 107. *54–1085*.

1957

S-12. Bicelli, L. P., "Infrared Absorption Spectra of Some Salts of the Sulfamic Acid. II. Zinc, Copper, Cobalt, and Nickel Salts," *Rend. ist. lombardo sci.*, Pt. I, **91**, 76. *52–10719*.

The region $2–15\mu$ was studied. Only in the $8–9\mu$ region did sizable differences occur.

S-13. Cagliotti, V., Sartori, G., and Scrocco, M., "Infrared Spectrum and Internal Force-Constants of the Complex Ion $Cr(CN)_6^{-3}$," *Atti accad. nazl. Lincei, Rend., Classe sci. fis., mat. e nat.*, **23**, 355. *52–10715*.

S-14. Dodd, R. E., Woodward, L. A., and Roberts, H. L., "Molecular Vibrations of Group VI Decafluorides. I. Infrared and Raman Spectra of Disulfur Decafluoride and Ditellurium Decafluoride," *Trans. Faraday Soc.*, **53**, 1545. *53–14687*.

S-15. Donovan, B., and March, N. H., "The Absorption by Free Carriers in Semiconductors," *Proc. Phys. Soc. (London)*, **70B**, 883.

Examination of infrared absorption in n-type Ge to test the theory.

S-16. Dupuis, T., "Infrared Absorption Spectra of Sulfuric Acid and Its Salts," *Congr. groupe. avance. methodes anal. spectrog. prod. met.*, **10e**, 109. *53–21160*.

Na, K, NH_4, Ag, Tl, Ba, Ca, and Sr derivatives of sulfate, thiosulfate, amine sulfonate, and selenosulfate ion were studied.

S-17. Duval, C., and Wadier, C., "Thermogravimetric and Infrared Spectrographic Study of Chromite Minerals," *Congr. groupe. avance. methodes anal. spectrog. prod. met. 10e Paris*, 101. *54–1069*.

Chromites of Ba, Ag, Zn, Cd, and Co were examined in the NaCl and CsBr regions. A discussion of the principal bands is given.

S-18. Falk, M., and Giguère, P. A., "Infrared Spectrum of the H_3O^+ Ion in Aqueous Solutions," *Can. J. Chem.*, **35**, 1195. *52–13421*.

Solutions of mineral acids in water at 25° were examined in the region 400–5000 cm^{-1}.

S-19. Fontana, P., and Fabbri, G., "Investigation in the Infrared Spectrum of Copper Basic Chlorides and Their Anticryptogamic Use," *Boll. sci. fac. chim. ind. Bologna*, **15**, 109. *52–19513*.

S-20. Gross, E. F., and Shulton, A. A., "Interaction of Molecular and Lattice Vibrations in Crystals and the Infrared Spectrum," *Doklady Akad. Nauk S.S.S.R.*, **115**, 689. [*Soviet Phys.* "*Doklady*," **2**, 371 (1957).] 52–15257.

The theory of the interaction is confirmed by spectral data obtained for $Ba(NO_3)_2$ and $Pb(NO_3)_2$.

S-21. Häfele, H. G., "Analysis of Infrared Absorption Spectra of Various Nitrate Crystals Within the Framework of the Individual Cell Model," *Z. Physik*, **148**, 262. 54–7339.

Spectral data are reported for the following nitrates: $NaNO_3$, $ZnSO_4 \cdot 7H_2O$, $Ce(NO_3)_3 \cdot 6H_2O$, $Mg(NO_3)_2 \cdot 6H_2O$, and $Pr_2Zn_3(NO_3)_{12} \cdot 24H_2O$.

S-22. Mitchell, E. W. J., and Rigden, J. D., "The Effects of Radiation on the Near Infrared Absorption Spectrum of α-quartz," *Phil. Mag.* (8), **2**, 941. 52–13420.

S-23. Moss, T. S., Smith, S. D., and Hawkins, T. D. F., "Absorption and Dispersion of Indium Antimonide," *Proc. Phys. Soc. (London)*, **70B**, 776.

The range covered for absorption coefficient determinations was 1.5–7.5μ.

S-24. Setkina, O. N., and Gopshteïn, N. M., "Infrared Absorption Spectra of Clay Minerals," *Trudy Leningrad. Tekhnol. Inst. im. Lensoveta*, **37**, 79. 53–2800.

S-25. Sosnowski, L., "Optical Transmissions in Semiconductors," *Postępy Fiz.*, **8**, 131. 54–2954.

Review.

S-26. Wilmshurst, J. K., and Bernstein, H. J., "The Infrared and Raman Spectra of Disulfur Decafluoride," *Can. J. Chem.*, **35**, 191. 53–12831.

The spectrum of the vapor from 2000–290 cm^{-1} and that of the solid (liquid N_2 temperature) from 1000–400 cm^{-1} were reported. Using also the Raman data for the liquid, assignments were made assuming D_{4d} or D_{4h} symmetry.

S-27. Woodward, L. A., and Roberts, H. L., "Molecular Vibrations of Group VI Decafluorides. II. Force Field Calculations for Sulfur Decafluoride," *Trans. Faraday Soc.*, **53**, 1557. 53–14687.

S-28. Yakovleva, T. V., "Spectroscopic Study of Solutions of HNO_3–N_2O_4–H_2O," *Zhur. Neorg. Khim.*, **2**, 2782. 52–15242.

A study of the mechanism for the decomposition of nitric acid was undertaken using infrared spectroscopy to obtain the necessary data.

S-29. Yatsenko, A. F., "Optical Transmission Spectrum of Barium Titanate," *Soviet Phys.-Tech. Phys.*, **2**, 2257. 52–17958.

The spectra of $BaTiO_3$, single crystal and powdered, were obtained in the region 0.4–23μ.

1958

S-30. Babushkin, A. A., "Spectroscopic Investigation of the Structure of Some Complex Compounds," *Izvest. Akad. Nauk S.S.S.R., Ser. Fiz.*, **22**, 1131.   *53–861.*

The compounds investigated were $BF_3 \cdot NH_3$, $BF_3 \cdot ND_3$, $BF_3 \cdot NH_2D$, and $BF_3 \cdot NHD_2$.   Other studies involved various coordination compounds of water and sodium para- or meta-tungstate.

S-31. Babushkin, A. A., Gribov, L. A., and Gel'man, A. D., "The Nature of the Bond Between the Central Atom and Some Unsaturated Molecules in Complex Compounds of Platinum," *Doklady Akad. Nauk S.S.S.R.*, **123**, 461.   *53–3880.*

S-32. Babushkin, A. A., Gribov, L. A., Guseva, N. G., and Emel'yanova, V. M., "Vibrational Spectra of Boron Trifluoride Molecular Compounds with Nitrogen- and Oxygen-Containing Substances.   II.   Structure of Molecular Compounds of Boron Trifluoride with Methanol, Ethanol, and Water," *Optika i Spektroskopiya*, **5**, 256.   *53–1919.*

S-33. Benedict, W. S., Plyler, E. K., and Tidwell, E. D., "Vibration-Rotation Bands of Ammonia.   III.   The Region 3.2–4.3 Microns," *J. Chem. Phys.*, **29**, 829.   *53–3879.*

S-34. Berkowitz, J., "Molecular Structure and Vibrational Spectra of Alkali Halide Dimers," *J. Chem. Phys.*, **29**, 1386.   *53–6758.*

S-35. Bigorgne, M., "Vibration Spectrum of Nickel Carbonyl.   Strength and Nature of the Bonds," *J. Inorg. and Nuclear Chem.*, **8**, 113.   *53–5868.*

S-36. Bird, G. R., Dauti, A., and Lord, R. C., "Pure Rotational Absorption of NO_2 in the 50–200μ Region," *Spectrochim. Acta*, **12**, 247.   *53–4901.*

S-37. Blinc, R., and Hadži, D., "Infrared Spectra of Some Ferroelectric Compounds With Short Hydrogen Bonds," *Mol. Phys.*, **1**, 391.   *53–19569.*

Data are reported for KH_2PO_4, $NH_4H_2PO_4$, NaH_2PO_4, KH_2AsO_4, $NH_4H_2AsO_4$, $Ag_2H_3IO_6$, $(NH_4)_2H_3IO_6$ and the corresponding deuterated compounds.   A quantum-mechanical interpretation of the findings is offered.

S-38. Bokiĭ, G. B., and Plyusnina, I. I., "Infrared Absorption Spectra of Cyclic Silicates in the 7–21μ Wave-Length Range.   (Determination of the Structure of Silicates from Their Infrared Spectra)," *Nauch. Doklady Vyssheĭ Shkoly, Geol.-Geograf. Nauki*, No. 3, 116.   *53–16698.*

Monocrystalline samples of bentonite, catapleiite, eudyalite, elpidite, cordierite, vorobyevite, beryl, aquamarine, and tourmaline were studied.

S-39. Borchert, R., and Jubitz, W., "Infrarottechnik," Berlin: Verlag Technik.   *53–14719.*

S-40. Boyle, W. S., and Noziéres, P., "Band Structure and Infrared Absorption of Graphite," *Phys. Rev.*, **111**, 782.   *53–58.*

S-41. Brown, D. A., "Vibration Frequencies of Some Tetrahedral Hydride Ions," *J. Chem. Phys.*, **29**, 451. *53–48*.

S-42. Brückner, R., and Scholze, H., "Infrared Bands of Freshly Prepared and Weathered B_2O_3 Glass," *Glastechn. Ber.*, **31**, 417. *53–3890*.

S-43. Bush, G., and Vinkrep, U., "Determination of the Basic Characteristics of Semiconductors by Electrical, Optical, and Magnetic Methods," *Poluprovod. v Nauke i Tekh., Akad. Nauk S.S.S.R. Inst. Poluprovod.*, 2 (A. F. Ioffe, editor, Moscow: Izdatel. Akad. Nauk S.S.S.R.) 7. *54–61*. Review.

S-44. Cagliotti, V., Sartori, G., and Furlani, C., "Analysis of the Vibrational Spectrum of the Complex Ion $Cr(CN)_6^{-3}$," *Atti accad. nazl. Lincei, Rend., Classe sci., fix., mat. e nat.*, **25**, 260. *53–17668*.

S-45. Cagliotti, V., Sartori, G., and Scrocco, M., "Infrared Spectra of Hexacoordinated Cyanide Complexes," *J. Inorg. and Nuclear Chem.*, **8**, 87. *53–7762*.

S-46. Califano, S., "Force Constants for the Hexafluorides XF_6," *Atti accad. nazl. Lincei, Rend., Classe sci. fis., mat. e nat.*, **25**, 284. *53–19557*. Calculations from spectroscopic data.

S-47. Califano, S., and Czerny, M., "Absorption of Sodium Chloride and Potassium Bromide in the Shortwave Infrared," *Z. Physik*, **150**, 1. *53–16691*.

S-48. Ceccaldi, M., Goldman, M., and Roth, E., "Absorption Spectra Between 0.8 and 30μ of Mixtures of H_2O—D_2O in the Liquid State," *Comm. energie at. (France), Rappt.* No. 818, 623. *53–12825*.

S-49. Chatt, J., Duncanson, L. A., and Shaw, B. L., "Influence of Ligands on the Platinum-Hydrogen Stretching Frequency in a Series of Complex Hydrides of Platinum (II). A Complex Hydride of Platinum," *Chem. and Ind. (London)*, 859. *53–859*.

Compounds of the type Y_2PtHX, where X is a halogen, nitrate, nitrite, cyanide, or SCN group and Y is an alkyl phosphide or arsenide group, (R_3M), were studied.

S-50. Chatt, J., Duncanson, L. A., and Venanzi, L. M., "Infrared Spectroscopic Evidence of an Interaction Between the NH Bonds of Coordinated Amines and the Non-Bonding d-Electrons of Metal Atoms," *J. Inorg. and Nuclear Chem.*, **8**, 67. *53–5867*.

S-51. Colpa, J. P., and Ketelaar, J. A. A., "Absorption Intensity of Simultaneous Vibrational Transitions in Gas Mixtures," *Physica*, **24**, 1035. *53–10958*.

S-52. Colpa-Boonstra, J. P., and Ketelaar, J. A. A., "II. Pressure-Induced Rotational Absorption of Hydrogen," *Mol. Phys.*, **1**, 343. *53–19561*.

S-53. Colpa-Boonstra, J. P., and Ketelaar, J. A. A., "The Pressure-Induced Rotation Absorption Spectrum of Hydrogen," *Mol. Phys.*, **1**, 14. *53–856*.

Absorption data of hydrogen and hydrogen-foreign gas mixtures, pressures ranging from 20–150 atmospheres, are reported for various temperatures. Absorption of hydrogen increases with foreign gas addition and intensities are proportional to gas densities.

S-54. Cotten, F. A., Danti, A., Waugh, J. S., and Fessenden, R. W., "Carbon-13 Nuclear Resonance Spectrum and Low-Frequency Infrared Spectrum of Iron Pentacarbonyl," *J. Chem. Phys.*, 29, 1427. *53–7766.*

Bands observed at 93 and 72 cm^{-1} are consistent with a D_{3h} model.

S-55. Coulon, R., "Experimental Study of the Infrared Absorption Spectra of Several Compressed Gases and Mixtures of Gases," *J. recherches centre natl. recherche sci., Labs. Bellevue (Paris)*, No. 45, 305. *53–15762.*

Mixtures of N_2 and O_2, pure H_2, H_2 and HCl, H_2 and N_2O, CO and N_2, HBr and N_2, HBr and A, HBr and H_2, HF and N_2, HCl and A, HCl and O_2, and HCl and He were studied. Thorough experimental details and mathematical interpretation of results are given.

S-56. Crow, T. T., and Lagemann, R. T., "Infrared Spectrum of Sulfuryl Bromofluoride," *Spectrochim. Acta*, 12, 143. *53–4904.*

S-57. Curl, Jr., R. F., and Pitzer, K. S., "The Spectrum and Structure of Disiloxane," *J. Am. Chem. Soc.*, 80, 2371. *53–49.*

Spectra of disiloxane were obtained from 700–2400 cm^{-1} using the matrix isolation technique. Si—O—Si bond angle was calculated.

S-58. Demidenkova, I. V., and Shcherba, L. D., "Changes in the Infrared Spectrum of Ammonia During Transition from the Gaseous to the Liquid State," *Izvest. Akad. Nauk S.S.S.R., Ser. Fiz.*, 22, 1122. *53–857.*

S-59. Deubner, A., Schreiber, G., and Schubert, R., "Investigation in the Near Infrared of Absorption by Artificially Prepared Lithium Fluoride Crystals," *Optik*, 15, 734. *53–12835.*

S-60. Dupuis, T., "Infrared Absorption Spectra of the Metallic Chromates and Alkaline Halochromates," *Compt. rend.*, 246, 3332. *53–858.*

S-61. Ebsworth, E. A. V., Hall, J. R., MacKillop, M. J., McKean, D. C., Sheppard, N., and Woodward, L. A., "Vibrational Spectra and Structure of Trisilylamine and Trisilylamine-d$_9$," *Spectrochim. Acta*, 13, 202. *53–6759.*

Gaseous $N(SiH_3)_3$ and $N(SiD_3)_3$ were studied from 4000–400 cm^{-1}. The data suggest a planar structure for NSi_3.

S-62. Fabbri, G., and Cappellina, F., "Infrared Spectrum of Potassium Octacyanotungstate in the Crystalline State and in Aqueous Solution," *Atti accad. nazl. Lincei, Rend., Classe sci. fis., mat. e nat.*, 25, 299. *53–17668.*

S-63. Falk, M., and Giguére, P. A., "Infrared Spectra and Structure of Selenious Acid," *Can. J. Chem.*, 36, 1680. *53–6757.*

Methanolic solutions of H_2SeO_3 and D_2SeO_3 and films of H_2SeO_3 on AgCl plates were examined from 3000–400 cm^{-1}. The data are consistent with the structure $(HO)_2SeO$.

S-64. Farmer, V. C., "The Infrared Spectra of Talc, Saponite, and Hectorite," *Mineral. Mag.*, **31**, 829. *53–1918.*

The spectra of these minerals in the region 400–4000 cm^{-1} are similar.

S-65. Filimonov, V. N., "Electronic Absorption Bands of ZnO and TiO_2 in the Infrared Region of the Spectrum," *Optika i Spektroskopiya*, **5**, 709. *53–9818.*

S-66. Frasco, D. L., "Interpretation of the Vibrational Spectra of Solid Hydroxyl-Ammonium Salts," *Dissertation Abstr.*, **19**, 1219.

S-67. Gailar, N. M., "ν_2 Band of HDO and the Design and Construction of an Infrared Spectrometer," *Dissertation Abstr.*, **19**, 839.

S-68. Garing, J. S., "High-Resolution Study of the 6-, 10-, and 16-μ Vibration-Rotation Bands of Ammonia," *Dissertation Abstr.*, **19**, 839.

S-69. Gatehouse, B. M., "Survey of the Infrared Spectra of NO_2 in Metal Complexes," *J. Inorg. and Nuclear Chem.*, **8**, 79. *53–5868.*

S-70. Gatehouse, B. M., and Comyns, A. E., "Infrared Spectra of Uranyl Nitrate Hydrates and Rubidium Uranyl Nitrate," *J. Chem. Soc.*, 3965. *53–1918.*

Spectra of hydrated uranyl nitrate and hydrated rubidium uranyl nitrate were obtained from 700–3700 cm^{-1}.

S-71. Gatehouse, B. M., Livingstone, S. E., and Nyholm, R. S., "Infrared Spectra of Some Nitrato and Other Oxyanion Coordination Complexes," *J. Inorg. and Nuclear Chem.*, **8**, 75. *53–5868.*

S-72. Gilfert, J. C., and Williams, D., "Pressure Modulation of Infrared Absorption. I. Entire Vibration-Rotation Bands," *J. Opt. Soc. Am.*, **48**, 765.

Pressure-modulation absorption bands of CO, N_2O, methane, and propane are discussed.

S-73. Gillis, R. G., "The Intensity of Infrared Absorption Bands—A Bibliography," *Australian, Commonwealth, Dept. Supply Defence Standards Labs. Tech. Memo*, **2**, 48 pp. *53–14673.*

S-74. Griffith, W. P., Lewis, J., and Wilkinson, G., "Infrared Spectra of Transition Metal-Nitric Oxide Complexes. II. Complexes Involving NO^- Ion," *J. Inorg. and Nuclear Chem.*, **7**, 38. *53–50.*

S-75. Groskaufmanis, A., Shakalina, A., and Liepina, L., "Vibrational Spectrum of the O—H Group, and Bound Water in the Molecule," *Latvijas Valsts Univ. Kim. Fak. Zinātniskie Raksti*, **22**, No. 6, 107. *53–12831.*

Spectra between 1.25 and 1.65μ indicate that O—H exists in aqueous solutions of many aluminum salts. Salts investigated were $Al(OH)_2Cl$, $Al(OH)Cl_2$, $AlCl_3$ and other neutral aluminum salts.

S-76. Harbeke, G., and Lautz, G., "The Infrared Absorption of Gallium Telluride and Indium Telluride," Z. *Naturforsch.*, 13A, 775. *53–5878*.

Absorption spectra were obtained at temperatures from 20°–650°K.

S-77. Harihan, T. A., "The Force Constants of Some Polyatomic Molecules and Ions," *J. Indian Inst. Sci.*, 40, 89. *53–18627*.

Calculations are made for $OPBr_3$, $SPBr_3$, $GaBr_4^{-2}$, $InBr_4^{-2}$, $TlBr_4^{-2}$, $TlBr_4^{-2}$, and $CdBr_4^{-2}$.

S-78. Heilmann, G., "Optical Constants n and k of Lithium Fluoride in the Region of the Infrared Reststrahlen Band," Z. *Naturforsch.*, 13a, 238. *53–2785*.

S-79. Hexter, R. M., "Infrared Absorption Spectra of Crystalline Brucite [$Mg(OH)_2$] and Portlandite [$Ca(OH)_2$]," *J. Opt. Soc. Am.*, 48, 770. *53–4902*.

S-80. Hooge, R. N., and Ketelaar, J. A. A., "Assignment of the Vibrational Frequencies of S_2X_2 Molecules," *Rec. trav. chim.*, 77, 902. *53–3881*.

Molecules of the S_2X_2 type where X is H, methyl, or halogen were studied. A band at ca. 250 cm^{-1} was assigned to the SS stretching mode.

S-81. Horák, M., "Technique of Measurement of Infrared Spectra of Solids," *Chemi (Prague)*, 10, 710. *53–21125*.

Review.

S-82. Hornig, D. F., White, H. F., and Reding, F. P., "The Infrared Spectra of Crystalline H_2O, D_2O, and HDO," *Spectrochim. Acta*, 12, 338. *53–4901*.

Samples prepared by freezing the liquid or condensing the vapor were studied at temperatures to $-190°$C in the region 3700–200 cm^{-1}.

S-83. Huldt, L., and Staflin, T., "Infrared Absorption of Photogenerated Free Carriers into Germanium," *Phys. Rev. Letters*, 1, 236. *53–59*.

S-84. Huldt, L., and Staflin, T., "Valence Band Structure of Silicon," *Phys. Rev. Letters*, 1, 313. *53–874*.

S-85. Jones, L. H., "Vibrational Spectrum and Structure of Metal-Cyanide Complexes in the Solid State. IV. $K_3Cu(CN)_4$," *J. Chem. Phys.*, 29, 463. *53–1920*.

S-86. Jones, W. D., "Vibrational Relaxation Time Studies on Carbon Monoxide, by the Infrared Spectrophone Method," *Dissertation Abstr.*, 19, 456.

S-87. Josien, M. L., Grange, P., and Lascombe, J., "Study of Hydrofluoric Acid Dissolved in Carbon Tetrachloride and Some Aromatic Solvents by Infrared Spectroscopy," *Compt. rend.*, 246, 3339. *53–2785*.

Bands corresponding to polymerized $(HF)_n$ molecules were located at 3550 and 3300 cm^{-1}.

S-88. Kirillov, E. A., Nesterovskaya, E. A., and Gol'denberg, A. B., "The Infrared Region of the Absorption Spectrum of Interior Centers in

Fine-Grained Silver Bromide and Silver Chloride Emulsions," *Pratsi Odes'k. Derzhav. Univ. im. I. I. Mechnikova, Ser. Fiz.,* **148**, No. 6, 15. *53–21186.*

S-89. Klier, M., "Temperature Dependence of the Optical Constants of Lithium and Sodium Fluorides in the Infrared," *Z. Physik,* **150**, 49. *53–21204.*

S-90. Kostyshin, M. T., "Optical Constants of Germanium in the Region 2–25 Microns," *Optika i Spektroskopiya,* **5**, 312. *53–1927.*

S-91. Kriegsmann, H., and Forster, W., "Spectroscopic Investigations of Silicon Compounds. V. The Vibration Spectrum of Trisilylamine," *Z. anorg. u. allgem. Chem.,* **298**, 212. *53–7762.*

S-92. Krogh-Moe, J., "The Infrared Spectra of Some Vitreous and Crystalline Borates," *Arkiv Kemi,* **12**, 475. *53–2785.*

Alkali halide disks containing crystalline and vitreous samples of alkali borates were examined between 5000 and 667 cm^{-1}.

S-93. Lafon, J., "Raman and Infrared Spectra of the Double Quanidine-Aluminum Sulfate," *Compt. rend.,* **247**, 2120. *53–21160.*

S-94. Lazarev, A. N., "Absorption Spectrum of KH_2PO_4 in the Region of Hydroxyl Valence Vibration," *Zhur. Tekh. Fiz.,* **27**, 426. *53–4902.*

Absorption data for the region 4000–1818 cm^{-1} is reported.

S-95. Lehmann, W. J., Ditter, J. F., and Shapiro, I., "Infrared Spectra of Partially Deuterated Diboranes," *J. Chem. Phys.,* **29**, 1248. *53–6758.*

S-96. Lely, J. A., and Kröger, F. A., "Optical Properties of Pure and Doped Silicon Carbide," *Semiconductors and Phosphors, Proc. Intern. Colloq., Garmisch-Partenkirchen,* 514. *53–16709.*

S-97. Lewis, J., Irving, R. J., and Wilkinson, G., "Infrared Spectra of Transition Metal-Nitric Oxide Complexes. I. Complexes Involving Donation From the NO^+ Ion," *J. Inorg. and Nuclear Chem.,* **7**, 32. *53–50.*

S-98. Linton, H. R., and Nixon, E. R., "Vibrational Spectrum of Disilyl Sulfide," *J. Chem. Phys.,* **29**, 921. *53–3880.*

A value of 100 degrees has been estimated for the Si–S–Si angle on basis of infrared and Raman spectral data obtained for SiH_3SSiH_3 and its deuterated analog.

S-99. Linton, H. R., and Nixon, E. R., "Infrared Spectrum and Force Constants of Silyl-d_3-Iodide," *Spectrochim. Acta,* **12**, 41. *53–4903.*

Gaseous SiD_3I was studied from 4000–300 cm^{-1}.

S-100. Lippincott, E. R., Valkenburg, A. V., Weir, C. E., and Bunting, E. N., "Infrared Studies on Polymorphs of Silica and Germania," *J. Research Natl. Bur. Standards,* **61**, No. 1, 61 (Research Paper 2885). *53–5876.*

The region 4000–300 cm^{-1} was investigated for coesite, cristobalite, quartz, vitreous silica, hexagonal and tetragonal GeO_2 and vitreous germania.

S-101. Lygin, V. I., "Variation of the Infrared Absorption Spectra of the Hydroxyl Groups of Porous Glass and Silica Gel During Thermal Dehydration," *Vestnik Moskov. Univ., Ser. Mat., Mekh., Astron., Fiz., Khim.*, **13**, No. 1, 223.   53–2799.

S-102. Majumdar, A. K., Duval, C., and Lecomte, J., "A New Case of Isomerism Revealed by Infrared Spectrometry," *Compt. rend.*, **247**, 302. 53–3879.

Two isomeric forms of $Co(NH_3)_3(NO_2)_3$ were revealed by means of infrared spectrometry.

S-103. Mathieu, J. P., "Vibration Spectra and Structure of Coordination Complexes," *J. Inorg. and Nuclear Chem.*, **8**, 33.   53–5864.

A review.

S-104. Matossi, F., "Infrared Absorption of n-Conducting Indium Arsenide," *Z. Naturforsch.*, **13a**, 767.

S-105. McDonald, R. S., "Surface Functionality of Amorphous Silica by Infrared Spectroscopy," *J. Phys. Chem.*, **62**, 1168.   53–2804.

S-106. McKean, D. C., "Force Constants, Interbond Angle, and Solid State Spectrum of Disiloxane," *Spectrochim. Acta*, **13**, 38.   53–6762.

S-107. Meyer, H. J. G., "Infrared Absorption by Conduction Electrons in Germanium," *Phys. Rev.*, **112**, 298.   53–3895.

S-108. Miloslavskiĭ, V. K., and Kovalenko, N. A., "Absorption of Zinc Oxide in the Infrared Region of the Spectrum," *Optika i Spektroskopiya*, **5**, 614.   53–10958.

A maximum at 1818 cm^{-1} is observed in samples of ZnO when absorption is measured from $10,000$–625 cm^{-1}.

S-109. Mitra, S. S., "Infrared and Raman Spectra of Brucite, $Mg(OH)_2$," *Dissertation Abstr.*, **19**, 841.   53–2784.

S-110. Mitsuishi, A., Yoshinaga, H., and Fujita, S., "Far-Infrared Absorption of Sulfides, Selenides, and Tellurides of Zinc and Cadmium," *J. Phys. Soc. Japan*, **13**, 1235.   53–2785.

S-111. Mitsuishi, A., Yoshinaga, H., and Fujita, S., "Far-Infrared Absorption of Ferrites," *J. Phys. Soc. Japan*, **13**, 1236.   53–2785.

The region 500–10 cm^{-1} was investigated for $ZnFe_2O_4$, $NiFe_2O_4$, $CoFe_2O_4$, and $MgFe_2O_4$.

S-112. Mizushima, S., Nakagawa, I., Schmelz, M. J., Curran, C., and Quagliano, J. V., "Infrared Absorption Spectra of Inorganic Coordination Complexes. XVII.   Infrared Spectra of Platinum (II) and Palladium (II) Ammine Complexes," *Spectrochim. Acta*, **13**, 31.   53–6757.

The assignment of bands in the 5000–667 cm^{-1} region for 9 inorganic complexes is reported.

S-113. Nakagawa, I., Mizushima, S., Saraceno, A. J., Lane, T. J., and Quagliano, J. V., "Infrared Absorption Spectra of Inorganic Coordination Complexes. XV.   Normal Vibrations of Sulfamic Acid, H_3N^+ $-SO_3^-$," *Spectrochim. Acta*, **12**, 239.   53–4902.

S-114. Nakamoto, K., Fujita, J., and Murata, H., "Infrared Spectra of Metallic

Complexes. V. Nitro and Nitrito Complexes," *J. Am. Chem. Soc.*, **80**, 4817. *53–12832.*

S-115. Narasimhan, P. T., "Infrared Intensities and the Nature of the Chemical Bond. I. Variation of Hybridization With Bond Length in SO_2, NH_3, and PH_3," *Proc. Natl. Instl. Sci. India, Pt. A*, **24**, 55. *53–857.*

S-116. Newman, R., "Optical Properties of n-Type Indium Phosphide," *Phys. Rev.*, **111**, 1518. *53–2811.*

S-117. Ockman, N., "The Infrared and Raman Spectra of Ice," *Advance in Phys.*, **7**, 199. *53–8793.*
Review.

S-118. Orssmann, K., "High-Resolution Study of Some Vibration-Rotation Bands of $C^{12}O_2^{16}$ and H_2Te," *Dissertation Abstr.*, **19**, 341.

S-119. Pistorius, C. W. F. T., "Potential Field and Force Constants of Octahedral Molecules," *J. Chem. Phys.*, **29**, 1328. *53–7762.*
Calculations are made for SF_6, SeF_6, TeF_6, ReF_6, IrF_6, UF_6, NpF_6, PuF_6, $TiCl_6^{-2}$, $SeCl_6^{-2}$, $SnCl_6^{-2}$, $SbCl_6^{-2}$, $SnBr_6^{-2}$, MoF_6 and WF_6.

S-120. Pitaevskiĭ, L. P., "Anomalous Skin Effect in the Infrared Region," *Zhur. Ekspt. i Teoret. Fiz.*, **34**, 942. *53–1912.*

S-121. Plyler, E. K., and Acquista, N., "Transmission and Reflectance of Cesium Iodide in the Far-Infrared Region," *J. Opt. Soc. Am.*, **48**, 668. *53–3878.*

S-122. Powell, J. M., and Kurnick, S. W., "Indium Antimonide Infrared Filter," *J. Appl. Phys.*, **29**, 1129. *53–874.*
Transmission data for InSb (n-type) with 10^{17} donors/c.c. are reported at 0° and 25°.

S-123. Prigent, J., "Infrared Absorption Spectra of Anhydrous Uranyl Halides," *Compt. rend.*, **247**, 1737. *53–10961.*

S-124. Pryce, M. H. L., and Runciman, W. A., "The Absorption Spectrum of Vanadium Corundum," *Discussions Faraday Soc.*, No. **26**, 34. *53–15765.*

S-125. Sartori, G., Furlani, C., and Damiani, A., "Vibrational Frequencies of Water in Complexes," *J. Inorg. and Nuclear Chem.*, **8**, 119. *53–5868.*

S-126. Saum, G. A., "Fundamental Optical Absorption in the II A—VI B Compounds," *Dissertation Abstr.*, **19**, 342.

S-127. Saumagne, P., and Josien, M. L., "Valence Vibrations of H_2O, D_2O, and HDO Molecules in Organic Solvents," *Bull. soc. chim. France*, 813. *53–18626.*

S-128. Schatz, P. N., "Potential Function of NF_3," *J. Chem. Phys.*, **29**, 481. *53–858.*

S-129. Schatz, P. N., and Levin, I. W., "Absolute Infrared Intensities of the Fundamental Vibrations of NF_3," *J. Chem. Phys.*, **29**, 475. *53–858.*

S-130. Serratosa, J. M., and Bradley, W. F., "Determination of the Orientation of OH Bond Axes in Layer Silicates by Infrared Absorption," *J. Phys. Chem.*, **62**, 1164. *53–2804.*

S-131. Sheldon, J. C., and Tyree, S. Y., "Addition Compounds of Metal Halides with POX$_3$ Compounds," *J. Am. Chem. Soc.*, 80, 4775. *53–3880*.

S-132. Siebert, H., "Infrared Spectra of Cobalt (III) Complexes With Ammonia and Anions of Oxyacids as Ligands," *Z. anorg. u. allgem. Chem.*, 298, 51. *53–7762*.

Co(III) complexes of NH$_3$ and anions of oxyacids (CO$_3^{-2}$, HCO$_2^-$, C$_2$O$_4^{-2}$, NO$_2^-$, NO$_3^-$, SO$_4^{-2}$, ONO$^-$, SO$_3^{-2}$) were studied in the region 4000–600 cm^{-1}.

S-133. Smith, D. F., "Molecular Properties of Hydrogen Fluoride," *Proc. U. N. Intern. Conf. Peaceful Uses At. Energy, 2nd, Geneva*, 28, 130. *54–68*.

Pressure-broadening of HF lines by other gases is described. Absorption shifts related to complexes and polymer structures are discussed.

S-134. Spinar, L. H., and Margrave, J. L., "Absorption Spectra of Gaseous Alkali Metal Hydroxides at High Temperatures," *Spectrochim. Acta*, 12, 244. *53–4902*.

Temperatures up to 1000° have been employed in the absorption studies of LiOH, NaOH, KOH, and RbOH.

S-135. Stammreich, H., Bassi, D., Sala, O., and Siebert, H., "The Vibrational Spectrum of the Dichromate Ion," *Spectrochim. Acta*, 13, 192. *53–6757*.

S-136. Steger, E., "Spectroscopic Investigation of Condensed Phosphates and Phosphoric Acids. V. Structural Differences of the Trimetaphosphate Ion in Crystal and in Solution," *Z. anorg. u. allgem. Chem.*, 29, 305. *53–1918*.

S-137. Stekhanov, A. I., "Structure of the OH Vibration Band in Crystal Spectra Containing a Hydrogen Bond," *Izvest. Akad. Nauk S.S.S.R., Ser. Fiz.*, 22, 1109. *53–869*.

Infrared and Raman spectra reveal a large, complex-structured band for crystals containing the OH group. At low temperature the band was found to consist of narrow bands and sharp lines. Among the 20 crystals studied were gypsum, Seignette salt, and NaH$_2$PO$_4$.

S-138. Štokr, J., and Schneider, B., "Vibrational Spectra of Some Halogenated Silanes. II. Vibrational Spectra of Trichlorohalogen Silanes," *Chem. listy*, 52, 985. *53–49*.

Raman and infrared data are reported for the region 450–2000 cm^{-1}.

S-139. Tarte, P., "Researches on the Deformation Frequencies of OH. I. Infrared Spectra of Basic Copper Salts," *Spectrochim. Acta*, 13, 107. *53–6757*.

S-140. Vincent-Geisse, J., Queyrel, M., and Lecomte, J., "Infrared Optical Constant Determination of Very Absorbing Solids," *Compt. rend.*, 247, 1330. *53–21190*.

Results are reported for quartz and calcite.

S-141. Waddington, T. C., "Infrared Spectra, Structure, and Hydrogen Bonding in Ammonium Salts," *J. Chem. Soc.*, 4340. *53–3880.*

Spectra-structure correlations are made for the following ammonium salts: NH_4N_3, NH_4HF_2, NH_4NCO, NH_4NCS, NH_4NO_3, NH_4ClO_4, NH_4BF_4, NH_4BPh_4, NH_4PF_6, NH_4SO_3F, and $NH_4SO_3CH_3$.

S-142. Wickersheim, K. A., "Preparation of Thin Crystalline Samples of the Alkali Hydroxides for Infrared Absorption Studies," *J. Chem. Phys.*, **29**, 1197. *53–5867.*

S-143. Yamamoto, G., and Sasamori, T., "Calculation of the Absorption of the 15μ Carbon Dioxide Band," *Sci. Repts. Tohoku Univ. Fifth Ser.*, **10**, 37. *53–13776.*

S-144. Yaroslavskiĭ, N. G., and Stanevich, A. E., "Rotational Spectrum of Water in the Long-Wave Infrared Region $50–1500\mu$ ($200–7$ cm^{-1})," *Optika i Spektroskopiya*, **5**, 384. *53–10958.*

S-145. Yatsenko, A. F., "Infrared Absorption Spectra of Perovskite-Type Ferroelectric Crystals," *Izvest. Akad. Nauk S.S.S.R., Ser. Fiz.*, **22**, 1456. *53–5878.*

Absorption data and force constants are reported for $PbTiO_3$, $BaTiO_3$, $CaTiO_3$, $SrTiO_3$, $PbZrO_3$, $BaZrO_3$, $SrZrO_3$, $BaSnO_3$, $SrSnO_3$, and WO_3.

1959

S-146. Adams, R. V., and Douglas, R. W., "Infrared Studies on Various Samples of Fused Silica With Special Reference to the Bands Due to Water," *J. Soc. Glass Technol.*, **43**, 1471. *53–15766.*

S-147. Akhmanova, M. V., "Infrared Absorption Spectra of Minerals," *Uspekhi Khim.*, **28**, 312. *53–11979.*

Review.

S-148. Allpress, J. G., and Hambly, A. N., "Infrared Spectra of Uranyl Compounds. I. Uranyl Nitrates," *Australian J. Chem.*, **12**, 569. *54–5245.*

Anhydrous and hydrated uranyl nitrates were studied between 3800 and 700 cm^{-1}.

S-149. Arneth, R., "Absorption of ZnO Single Crystals in the Infrared," *Z. Physik*, **155**, 595. *53–18635.*

Pure and doped ZnO crystals were studied between 10,000 and 700 cm^{-1}.

S-150. Bán, M. I., "Vibrational Symmetries of Tetracyanonickelate (II) Ion," *Acta Chim. Acad. Sci. Hung.*, **19**, 35. *53–19557.*

S-151. Barraclough, C. G., Lewis, J., and Nyholm, R. S., "Stretching Frequencies of Metal-O Double Bonds," *J. Chem. Soc.*, 3552. *54–6306.*

The region 900–1100 cm^{-1} has been associated with a stretching frequency of the metal-oxygen bond. Compounds studied contained Cr—O, Mn—O, V—O, Re—O, Mo—O, or Ti—O bonds.

S-152. Benesi, H. A., "Infrared Spectrum of Magnesium Hydroxide," *J. Chem. Phys.*, **30**, 852. *53–13776.*

S-153. Benesi, H. A., and Jones, A. C., "An Infrared Study of the Water-Silica Gel System," *J. Phys. Chem.*, **63**, 179. *53–10958.*

Infrared spectrum of physically adsorbed water is compared with that of "unbound" water.

S-154. Bernard, M. P., "Infrared Absorption Spectrum at Low Temperature of Crystalline D-Substituted Seignette Salt (7500–5300 cm⁻¹)," *Compt. rend.*, **248**, 1153. *53–15766.*

S-155. Bertin, E. P., Mizushima, S., Lane, T. J., and Quagliano, J. V., "Infrared Absorption Studies of Inorganic Coordination Complexes. XXI. Nitrosopentammine Cobalt Halides and Nitrate," *J. Am. Chem. Soc.*, **81**, 3821. *54–4149.*

S-156. Bertin, E. P., Penland, R. B., Mizushima, S., Curran, C., and Quagliano, J. V., "Infrared Absorption Studies of Inorganic Coordination Complexes. XX. Cobalt (III) Ammine Complexes Containing Some Coordinated Anions," *J. Am. Chem. Soc.*, **81**, 3818. *54–4149.*

S-157. Biermann, W. J., and Gilmour, J. B., "Hydronium Ion Absorption in the region 1.7μ," *Can. J. Chem.*, **37**, 1249. *54–69.*

S-158. Block, H. A., "Vibrational Study of the Hexammine-Cobalt (III) Ion," *Trans. Faraday Soc.*, **55**, 867. *54–6305.*

Potassium chloride pellets containing $Co(NH_3)_6Cl_3$ were examined from 5000–416 cm⁻¹.

S-159. Bor, G., and Markó, L., "Infrared Spectrum of Dicobalto Octacarbonyl," *Spectrochim. Acta*, 747. *54–4149.*

Principal absorption bands for $Co_2(CO)_8$ in the LiF region are reported.

S-160. Boyle, W. S., "Far Infrared Magnetooptic Effects from Impurities in Germanium," *Phys. and Chem. Solids*, **8**, 321. *53–12849.*

Magnetooptic effects were observed in Ge-doped with arsenic and phosphorus.

S-161. Braunholtz, J. T., Hall, G. E., Mann, F. G., and Sheppard, N., "Infrared Spectra and Hydrogen Bonding in Compounds Containing X(:O). OH Groups," *J. Chem. Soc.*, 868. *53–11994.*

Bands associated with OH vibrations are studied for compounds of the type X(:O). OH, where X is P, As, S, Se, and C.

S-162. Buchanan, R. A., "Near Infrared Spectra of Crystalline Alkali Hydroxides," *J. Chem. Phys.*, **31**, 870. *54–6304.*

S-163. Burnside, P. B., "Pure Rotational Absorption Spectrum of Deuterium Sulfide," *Dissertation Abstr.*, **19**, 3329. *53–18626.*

S-164. Caldwell, R. S., and Fan, H. Y., "Optical Properties of Tellurium and Selenium," *Phys. Rev.*, **114**, 664. *53–18638.*

Studies were made on Te and trigonal and amorphous Se to wavelengths of 152μ using polarized radiation.

S-165. Catalano, E., and Milligan, D. E., "Infrared Spectra of H_2O, D_2O, and HDO in Solid Argon, Krypton, and Xenon," *J. Chem. Phys.*, **30**, 45. *53–9812.*

S-166. Church, C. H., "High-Resolution Electric Field-Induced Infrared Absorption Spectra of H_2 and D_2," *Dissertation Abstr.*, **20**, 1398. *54–4147.*

S-167. Claassen, H. H., "Force Constants of Metal Hexafluorides," *J. Chem. Phys.*, **30**, 968. *53–17668.*

S-168. Cleek, G. W., and Scuderi, T. G., "Effect of Fluorides on Infrared Transmittance of Certain Silicate Glasses," *J. Am. Ceram. Soc.*, **42**, 599. *54–5245.*

S-169. Cleek, G. W., Villa, J. J., and Hahner, C. H., "Refractive Indexes And Transmittances of Several Optical Glasses in the Infrared," *J. Opt. Soc. Am.*, **49**, 1090. *54–1069.*

Transmission data for the 10,000–2000 cm^{-1} region of thirteen optical glasses, including eight flint glasses, are reported.

S-170. Colpa-Boonstra, J. P., "Rotational Spectra of Pure Molecular Hydrogen Induced by Pressure," *Colloq. intern. centre natl. recherche sci.* *(Paris)*, **No. 77.** *53–21155.*

S-171. Cotton, F. A., Down, J. L., and Wilkinson, G., "Infrared Spectra of Manganese Carbonyl Hydride and Deuteride," *J. Chem. Soc.*, 833. *53–10960.*

Spectra of $HMn(CO)_5$ and $DMn(CO)_5$ are analyzed for the 3000–400 cm^{-1} region.

S-172. Coulon, R., and Hai, V., "Some New Results on the Infrared Spectra of Mixtures of Compressed Gases," *Coll. internl. centre natl. recherche Sci. (Paris)*, **No. 77,** 99. *54–2937.*

S-173. Courtoy, C. P., "Infrared Spectra of Carbon Dioxide at High Dispersion and Constant Molecular Concentration," *Ann. soc. sci. Bruxelles*, *Ser. I*, **73**, 5. *53–15762.*

Observed spectra in the region 3440–8100 cm^{-1} for CO_2 enriched with 66% C^{13} are reported and discussed.

S-174. Cronemeyer, D. C., "Infrared Absorption of Reduced Rutile TiO_2 Single Crystals," *Phys. Rev.*, **113**, 1222. *53–16709.*

Plane parallel plates (resistivity, 0.01–3 ohm-m.) were studied. Maximum absorption occurs at ~ 0.75 ev for samples with resistivity > 0.04 ohm-m. normal to the c-axis, and at 1.18 ev. for samples with resistivity < 0.03 ohm-m.

S-175. Danti, A., and Lord, R. C., "Pure Rotational Absorption of Ozone and Sulfur Dioxide from 100 to 200 Microns," *J. Chem. Phys.*, **30**, 1310. *53–17667.*

S-176. Dows, D. A., "Torsional Vibrations in Carbon Dioxide and Nitrous Oxide Crystals," *Spectrochim. Acta*, **13**, 308.

Films of CO_2 & N_2O were observed from 778–574 cm^{-1}.

S-177. Drouard, E., "The Infrared Absorption Spectra of Single Crystals of Lithium Hydroxide Monohydrate," *Compt. rend.*, **249**, 665. *54–6303.*

S-178. Dunlap, J. L., "Infrared Intensities, Bond Moments, and Bond Moment Derivatives for PF_3 and POF_3," *Dissertation Abstr.*, **20**, 1398. *54–4147.*

S-179. Duval, C., and Lecomte, J., "Infrared Absorption Spectra of Mixed Crystals: $CuSO_4$ and $ZnSO_4$ and Their Interpretation," *Compt. rend.*, **248**, 1977. *53–14686.*

S-180. Duyckaerts, G., "The Infrared Analysis of Solid Substances," *Analyst*, **84**, 201. *53–16691.*

A review.

S-181. Ebsworth, E. A. V., Taylor, R., and Woodward, L. A., "Vibrational Spectra and Structures of Disilyl Sulfide, Disilyl Sulfide-d_6, Disilyl Selenide, and Disilyl Selenide-d_6," *Trans. Faraday Soc.*, **55**, 211. *54–69.*

Data, obtained from 4000–400 cm^{-1}, are consistent with a non-linear Si—X—Si structure.

S-182. Edgell, W. F., Asato, G., Wilson, W., and Angell, C., "Infrared Spectra of Metal Carbonyl Hydrides," *J. Am. Chem. Soc.*, **81**, 2022. *53–13777.*

In the region 5000–333 cm^{-1}, spectra of $DCo(CO)_4$, $H_2Fe(CO)_4$, $HDFe(CO)_4$, $HMn(CO)_5$, $DMn(CO)_5$ and similar compounds were determined and discussed.

S-183. Fan, H. Y., and Ramdas, A. K., "Infrared Absorption in Neutron-Irradiated Silicon," *Phys. and Chem. Solids*, **8**, 272. *53–12848.*

Studies of radiation (deuteron, neutron, electron) effects on n- and p-type silicon are reported.

S-184. Fan, H. Y., and Ramdas, A. K., "Infrared Absorption and Photoconductivity in Irradiated Silicon," *J. Appl. Phys.*, **30**, 1118. *54–1080.*

S-185. Fateley, W. G., Bent, H. A., and Crawford, Jr., B., "Infrared Spectra of the Frozen Oxides of Nitrogen," *J. Chem. Phys.*, **31**, 204. *54–1069.*

Matrix isolation technique was used to study structures of nitrogen oxides in the infrared region.

S-186. Fisher, P., and Fan, H. Y., "Optical and Magnetooptical Effects of Group III Impurities in Germanium," *Phys. Rev. Letters*, **2**, 456. *54–2955.*

S-187. Folman, M., and Yates, D. J. C., "Infrared Studies of Physically Adsorbed Polar Molecules and of the Surface of a Silica Adsorbent Containing Hydroxyl Groups," *J. Phys. Chem.*, **63**, 183. *53–10964.*

S-188. Frasco, D. L., and Wagner, E. L., "Interpretation of the Infrared Spectra of the Solid Hydroxylammonium Halides," *J. Chem. Phys.*, **30**, 1124. *53–16692.*

Films of hydroxyl ammonium halides and their deuterated analogs were examined at 25°, −78° and −180° from 400–4000 cm⁻¹.

S-189. Frevel, L. K., "Infrared Absorption Spectra of Dilute Solid Solutions at Low Temperature," *Spectrochim. Acta*, 557. *54–6305*.

S-190. Fujii, S., "Infrared Spectra of Coal," *Nenryô Kyôkaishi*, **38**, 442. *54–5233*.

A review.

S-191. Gaizauskas, V., and Welsh, H. L., "Infrared Absorption of CO_2 Gas Induced by Pressure," *Coll. intern. centre natl. recherche sci. (Paris)*, No. 77, 171. *54–2932*.

S-192. Gamo, I., "Calculation of the Fundamental Vibrations of CO_2 and CS_2," *J. phys. radium*, **20**, 839. *54–4148*.

S-193. Gandy, H. W., "Optical Transmission of Heat-Treated Strontium Titanate," *Phys. Rev.*, **113**, 795. *53–13789*.

S-194. Garland, C. W., "Effect of Poisoning on the Infrared Spectrum of Carbon Monoxide Adsorbed on Nickel," *J. Phys. Chem.*, **63**, 1423. *54–5249*.

S-195. Geick, R., "Measurements on Cerium Bromide in the Region of its Infrared Oscillation," *Z. Naturforsch.*, **14a**, 196. *53–10958*.

Transmission data are recorded for CsBr layers (0.19–2.5 microns thick) in the region 91–66 cm⁻¹.

S-196. Gilbert, J. C., and Williams, Dudley, "Pressure Modulation of Infrared Absorption, II, Individual Lines in Vibration-Rotation Bands," *J. Opt. Soc. Am.*, **49**, 212. *53–8806*.

Near-infrared spectra of CO, N_2O, CH_4, C_3H_8, under pressure changes have been reported.

S-197. Glemser, O., "Binding of Water in Ferric Hydrates," *Nature*, **183**, 1476. *54–5245*.

S-198. Goubeau, J., Heubach, E., Paulin, D., and Widmaier, I., "The Vibration Spectra of Some Silicon Cyanates," *Z. anorg. u. allgem. Chem.*, **300**, 194. *53–21155*.

S-199. Goubeau, J., and Hummel, D., "Vibrational Spectra of Various Boron-Oxygen Compounds," *Z. physik. Chem. (Frankfurt)*, **20**, 15. *54–1070*.

S-200. Greene, F. T., and Margrave, J. L., "Infrared and Visible Spectra of Gaseous B_2S_3 at High Temperatures," *J. Am. Chem. Soc.*, **81**, 5555. *54–6305*.

S-201. Griffith, W. P., Cotton, F. A., and Wolkinson, G., "Infrared Spectrum and Structure of $K_4[Ni(CN)_3CO]_2$," *J. Inorg. and Nuclear Chem.*, **10**, 23.

S-202. Griffith, W. P., Lewis, J., and Wilkinson, G., "Infrared Spectra of Transition Metal-Nitric Oxide Complexes. IV. Penta Cyanonitrosyl Complexes of Chromium and Molybdenum," *J. Chem. Soc.*, 872 (1959). *53–11994*.

Infrared data are consistent with the structure: $K_3[Cr^I(CN)_5NO]$. $H_2O,K_4[Mo^{II}(OH)_2(CN)_5(NO)]$, and $K_3[Mo^V(OH)_4(CN)_4]$. $2H_2O$: for the complexes studied.

S-203. Hadni, A., Taurel, L., Paillette, M., and Lankoande, "The Infrared Spectrum in the 3μ Region of Different Samples of Clear Quartz and Quartz Irradiated by Neutrons," *Compt. rend.*, **248**, 211. *53–12004.*

S-204. Harvey, K. B., and Brown, H. W., "Infrared Studies of Certain Solids Condensed from a Discharge in the Gaseous State," *J. chim. phys.*, **56**, 745. *54–6304.*

Absorption bands of HNO and DNO were observed.

S-205. Hasse, J., "The Influence of Lattice Perturbations on the Optical Properties of Metal Layers," *Z. Physik*, **157**, 166. *54–1077.*

Data are reported for films of bismuth, gallium, tin, and silver for the region 40,000–2500 cm^{-1}.

S-206. Hershenson, H. M., "Infrared Absorption Spectra. Index for 1945–1957," New York Academic Press.

S-207. Hidalgo, A., and Mathieu, J. P., "The Infrared Absorption Spectra of Crystalline Cyanide Complexes," *Compt. rend.*, **249**, 233. *53–21204.*

S-208. Hirshberg, J. F., "Infrared Lattice Absorption in Crystals of Diamond Structure," *Dissertation Abstr.*, **19**, 2630.

S-209. Jahn, A., "Inorganic Compounds of Nitric Oxide. X. The N—O Stretching Frequencies of Nitric Oxide Complexes of Iron Group Metals," *Z. anorg. u. allgem. Chem.*, **301**, 301. *54–4150.*

S-210. Jones, W. J., and Orville-Thomas, W. J., "Infrared Spectrum and Structure of Dicyandiamide," *Trans. Faraday Soc.*, **55**, 193. *54–70.*

Solid dicyandiamide and its deuterated analog were investigated in the 5000–450 cm^{-1} region.

S-211. Katorski, A. R., "Crystal Field Effect on Vibrational Bands of Tetrahedral Molecules: Silane ν_3 Band," *Dissertation Abstr.*, **19**, 3147.

S-212. Kaye, W., "High Resolution Infrared Ammonia Spectrum," *Anal. Chem.*, **31**, 1127.

S-213. Kessler, F. R., "Infrared Absorption of Free Carriers Produced in Semiconductors by the Photo Effect," *Phys. and Chem. Solids*, **8**, 275.

S-214. Ketelaar, J. A. A., "Infrared Spectra of Compressed Gases," *Spectrochim. Acta*, **14**, 237. *53–14673.*

A review.

S-215. Ketelaar, J. A. A., and van der Elsken, J., "Frequency Shifts in the Infrared Absorption Spectrum of Complex Ions in Solid Solution," *J. Chem. Phys.*, **30**, 336. *53–10959.*

Infrared absorption of NO_3^-, HF_2^-, BH_4^-, NH_4^+, BF_4^-, and NO_2^- in alkali halide solution is reported. The observed frequency shifts were related, perhaps in a complex fashion, to the lattice parameter of the matrix.

S-216. Kimel, S., Hirshfeld, M. A., and Jaffe, J. H., "Pressure Induced Shifts of HCl Absorption Lines in the Infrared," *J. Chem. Phys.*, 31, 81. *54–68*.

S-217. Kiss, Z. J., Gush, H. P., and Welsh, H. L., "The Pressure-Induced Rotational Absorption Spectrum of Hydrogen, I. The Absolute Intensities," *Can. J. Phys.*, 37, 362. *53–8806*.

Spectral data for H_2 and H_2 pressurized with N_2, He, Ne, A, Kr, and Xe to total gas pressures of 250 atmospheres were obtained from 300–1400 cm^{-1}.

S-218. Kiss, Z. J., and Welsh, H. L., "Pressure-Induced Infrared Absorption of Mixtures of Rare Gases," *Phys. Rev. Letters*, 2, 166. *53–8806*.

S-219. Kiss, Z. J., and Welsh, H. L., "The Pressure-Induced Rotational Absorption Spectrum of Hydrogen. II. Analysis of the Absorption Profile," *Can. J. Phys.*, 37, 1249. *54–2930*.

S-220. Kolesova, V. A., "Infrared Absorption Spectra of Aluminum-Containing Silicates and Some Crystalline Aluminates," *Optika i Spektroskopiya*, 6, 38.

A characteristic band ascribed to the Al—O vibration was observed in the 720–780 cm^{-1} region.

S-221. Kranendonk, J. van, "Induced Infrared Absorption in Gases. Calculation of the Ternary Absorption Coefficients of Symmetrical Diatomic Molecules," *Physica*, 25, 337. *54–68*.

S-222. Kranendonk, J. van, and Kiss, Z. J., "Theory of the Pressure-Induced Rotational Spectrum of Hydrogen," *Can. J. Phys.*, 37, 1187. *54–67*.

S-223. Lascombe, J., Huong, P. V., and Josien, M. L., "Vibration-Rotation Structure in the Spectra of Some Simple Molecules in Solution," *Bull. soc. chim. France*, 1175. *54–2937*.

A review.

S-224. Linton, H. R., and Nixon, E. R., "Infrared Spectra of Methyl and Silyl Phosphines," *Spectrochim. Acta*, 146. *53–13777*.

Gaseous methyl and silyl phosphines were studied in the region 300–4000 cm^{-1}.

S-225. Lorenzelli, V., and Möller, K. D., "Absorption Spectrum of Phosphorus Trichloride in the Far Infrared," *Compt. rend.*, 248, 1980. *53–14686*.

A pyramidal model is suggested for PCl_3 on basis of infrared data obtained on the vapor from 500–222 cm^{-1}.

S-226. Louisfert, J., "Methods of Measurement and Fundamental Frequencies of Internal Vibration and Harmonics for Calcite, Dolomite, and Magnesite," *Compt. rend.*, 248, 1497. *53–14686*.

S-227. Louisfert, J., "Fundamental Frequencies of External Vibrations of Calcite, Dolomite and Magnesite," *Compt. rend.*, 248, 1150. *53–14686*.

S-228. Maki, A., and Decius, J. C., "Vibrational Spectrum of Cyanate Ion in Various Alkali Halide Lattices," *J. Chem. Phys.*, 31, 772. *54–4150*.

Spectra of cyanate ion in KI, KBr, KCl, and NaCl single crystals were obtained and discussed for the 600–5000 cm^{-1} region at temperatures from 150–480°K.

S-229. Mashkevich, V. S., "Electrical, Optical and Elastic Properties of Diamond-Type Crystals. III. Dispersion and Absorption of Light," *Zhur. Eksptl. i Teoret. Fiz.*, 36, 108. *53–12842.*

S-230. Mathieu, J. P., and Poulet, H., "CN Vibration Frequency in Complex Cyanides," *Compt. rend.*, 248, 2315. *53–21160.*

S-231. Meyer, H. J. G., "Theory of Infrared Absorption by Conduction Electrons in Germanium," *Phys. and Chem. Solids*, 8, 264. *53–12848.*

S-232. Miller, F. A., Carlson, G. L., and White, W. B., "Infrared and Raman Spectra of Chromyl Chloride," *Spectrochim. Acta*, 709. *54–4149.*

Fundamental frequencies of CrO_2Cl are assigned assuming C_{2v} symmetry for the molecule.

S-233. Mitchell, E. W. J., "A Review of Recent Work on Diamond," *Phys. and Chem. Solids*, 8, 444. *53–12844.*

S-234. Mizushima, S., and Nakagawa, I., "Infrared Spectra and Normal Vibrations of Inorganic Coordination Compounds," *Nippon Kagaka Zasshi*, 80, 124. *53–6757.*

S-235. Mould, H. M., Price, U. C., and Wilkinson, G. R., "A High-Resolution Study and Analysis of the ν_2 Ammonia Vibration-Rotation Band," *Spectrochim. Acta*, 313. *53–19568.*

S-236. Mutter, R., Mecke, R., and Luttke, W., "A New Infrared Absorption Spectrum of Ice," *Z. physik. Chem. (Frankfurt)*, 19, 8. *54–1069.*

S-237. Namba, M., "Optical Properties of Silicon Carbide in the Infrared Region," *J. Phys. Soc. Japan*, 14, 228. *53–14606.*

Room temperature transmission data of SiC crystals are reported for the range 4000–666 cm^{-1}.

S-238. Neuringer, L. J., "Effect of Pressure on the Infrared Absorption of Semiconductors," *Phys. Rev.*, 113, 1495. *53–17680.*

S-239. Newman, C., Polo, S. R., and Wilson, M. K., "Infrared Spectra of SiF_3H, SiF_3D, SiD_3F, and SiD_3Cl," *Spectrochim. Acta*, 793. *54–5245.*

S-240. Orr, S. F. D., "Recent Advances in Infrared Transmission," *Spectrochim. Acta*, 14, 86.

A review.

S-241. Oswald, F., "Optical Investigations of the Semi-conducting Mixed Crystal Series In (As_yP_{1-y})," *Z. Naturforsch.*, 14a, 374. *52–21193.*

S-242. Oswald, F., "Accuracy in the Determination of Absorption Coefficients of Semi-conductors in the Infrared Region," *Optik*, 16, 527. *54–7349.*

S-243. Overend, J., Youngquist, M. J., Curtis, E. C., and Crawford, Jr., B., "Vibrational Intensities XI. Carbon Dioxide and the Wilson-Wells Method," *J. Chem. Phys.*, 30, 532. *53–11992.*

S-244. Pastrnyak, I., "Infrared Absorption Spectrum for Cuprous Oxide," *Optika i Spektroskopiya*, 6, 107. *53–12831.*

S-245. Patty, R. R., and Lagemann, R. T., "Infrared Spectrum and Molecular

Structure of Carbonyl-Bromofluoride," *Spectrochim. Acta*, 60. 53–13778.

S-246. Peacock, R. D., and Sharp, D. W. A., "Infrared Spectra of Alkali Salts of Complex Fluoroacids," *J. Chem. Soc.*, 2762. *54–2938.*

S-247. Pelah, I., Lefkowitz, I., Kley, W., and Tunkelo, E., "Observations of Hydrogen Vibration Frequencies in Phosphates by Means of Inelastic Scattering of Cold Neutrons," *Phys. Rev. Letters*, **2**, 94. *53–8807.*

Infrared absorption measurements were used to confirm hydrogen vibration frequencies observed by inelastic neutron scattering.

S-248. Person, W. B., Humphrey, R. E., and Popov, A. I., "Infrared Spectra of Charge-Transfer Complexes. II. Iodine Cyanide Complexes," *J. Am. Chem. Soc.*, **81**, 273. *53–10959.*

S-249. Pistorius, C. W. F. T., "Valence-Type Force Constants of Nickeltetra-carbonyl," *Spectrochim. Acta*, 717. *54–5235.*

S-250. Poulet, H., and Mathieu, J. P., "Vibrational Spectra of Piezoelectric Crystals. VII. Potassium Cuprocyanide," *Spectrochim. Acta*, 932. *54–7430.*

S-251. Poulet, H., and Mathieu, J. P., "Vibration Spectra and Structure of Simple and Complex Mercury Cyanides," *Compt. rend.*, **248**, 2079. *53–16693.*

Spectral data are reported for $Hg(CN)_2$, $K_2[Hg(CN)_4]$ and $K_2[Hg_2(CN)_6]$.

S-252. Prokopová, H., and Vasko, A., "The Transmissivity of Arsenic Glass in the 15μ to 25μ Range," *Czechoslov. J. Phys.*, **9**, 270. *53–21156.*

S-253. Puranik, P. G., and Rao, M. L. N., "Evaluation of Force Constants of Osmium Tetroxide," *Current Sci. (India)*, **28**, 59. *53–14687.*

S-254. Pustinger, J. V., Cave, W. T., and Nielsen, M. L., "Infrared Spectra of Inorganic Phosphorus Compounds," *Spectrochim. Acta*, 909. *54–7339.*

Mull spectra of 55 compounds were obtained between 5000 and 650 cm^{-1}.

S-255. Randall, S. P., Greene, F. T., and Margrave, J. L., "The Infrared Spectra of Gaseous Magnesium Chloride, Magnesium Bromide, and Nickel Chloride at Elevated Temperatures," *J. Phys. Chem.*, **63**, 758. *53–18626.*

S-256. Rao, C. N. R., Ramachandran, J., and Shankar, P. S., "Characteristic Infrared Frequencies of Inorganic Cyanides, Cyanates, and Thio-Cyanates," *J. Sci. Ind. Research (India)*, **18B**, 169. *53–19568.*

S-257. Rao, K. N., Ryan, C. R., and Nielsen, H. H., "Wavelength Calibrations in Infrared Spectra. I. Some Problems Concerning the Determination of Absolute Positions of Infrared Lines," *J. Opt. Soc. Am.*, **49**, 216. *53–8805.*

S-258. Rinehart, R. W., "Induced Infrared Absorption in Mixed Gases at High Pressure," *Dissertation Abstr.*, **20**, 1606. *54–4147.*

S-259. Roberts, S., "Optical Properties of Nickel and Tungsten and Their Interpretation According to Drude's Formula," *Phys. Rev.*, 114, 104. *53–18638*.

Data are reported and discussed for different temperatures over the near-infrared region.

S-260. Rocchiccioli, C., "A Study of Anhydrous and Hydrated Bromate by Infrared Absorption Spectroscopy," *Compt. rend.*, 249, 236. *54–68*.

Anhydrous and/or hydrated bromates of Na, K, Ag, Ba, Sr, Pb, Co, Ni, Mg, Zn, and Cu are classified into two groups on basis of spectral data obtained in the 4000–300 cm^{-1} region.

S-261. Ryskin, Ya. I., "Infrared Absorption Spectra of Nitrates in Nonaqueous Solutions," *Optika i Spektroskopiya*, 6, 113. *53–12831*.

Absorption spectra of nitrates, such as $Ce(NO_3)_3.6H_2O$, were determined in non-aqueous solutions. Solvents used were ketones, esters, or paraffin oil.

S-262. Ryskin, Ya. I., Zemlyanukhin, V. I., Solov'eva, A. A., and Derbeneva, N. A., "Infrared Spectroscopic Study of the State of Water in Non-aqueous Solutions of Uranyl Nitrate," *Zhur. Neorg. Khim.*, 4, 393. *53–15765*.

S-263. Saksena, G. D., "Coriolis Perturbation and Molecular Constants Derived from Some Infrared OCS Bands," *Dissertation Abstr.*, 20, 701. *53–21156*.

S-264. Saksena, G. D., Wiggins, T. A., and Rank, D. H., "Molecular Constants of Carbonyl Sulfide and a Coriolis Perturbation," *J. Chem. Phys.*, 31, 839. *54–4148*.

S-265. Salvetti, O., "Force Constants in the Octahedral Molecular Structures of the Complex Hexacyanides," *Ricerca sci.*, 29, 531. *53–19557*.

Calculations are made for the force constants of $Fe(CN)_6{}^{-4}$, $Ru(CN)_6{}^{-4}$, and $Os(CN)_6{}^{-4}$.

S-266. Setkina, O., "Infrared Spectra of Minerals and Their Practical Application," *Zapiski Vsesoyuz. Mineral. Obshchestva*, 88, 39. *53–15766*.

Extensive study of the Si—O—Si group vibrations in a number of minerals.

S-267. Sheppard, N., "Infrared Spectra of Adsorbed Molecules," *Spectrochim. Acta*, 14, 249. *53–14673*.

A review.

S-268. Shigorin, D. N., "Infrared Absorption Spectra Study of Hydrogen Bonding and of Metal-Element Bonding," *Spectrochim. Acta*, 14, 198. *53–17668*.

S-269. Shklyarevskiĭ, I. N., and Padalka, V. G., "Measurement of the Optical Constants of Copper, Gold, and Nickel in the Infrared Region of the Spectrum," *Optika i Spektroskopiya*, 6, 78. *53–12844*.

Absorption measurements were made in the region 10,000–825 cm^{-1}.

S-270. Shklyarevskiĭ, I. N., and Padalka, V. G., "The Anomalous Skin-Effect and the Optical Constants of Copper, Silver, Gold, and Nickel in the Infrared Spectra Region," *Optika i Spektroskopiya*, 6, 776. *53–18637*.

S-271. Siebert, H., "Infrared Spectra of Telluric Acids, Tellurates, and Antimonates," *Z. anorg. u. allgem. Chem.*, 301, 161. *54–2938*.

Spectral data for the region 4000–400 cm^{-1} are reported and discussed for H_6TeO_6, $(H_2TeO_4)_x$, $Na_2H_4TeO_6$, $K_2H_4TeO_6.3H_2O$, $Na[Sb(OH)_6]$, $KSbO_3.2H_2O$, $Na_2HSb_3O_9.4H_2O$, $K_2HSb_3O_9.5H_2O$, $NaSbO_3$ and $KSbO_3$.

S-272. Simon, A., and Richter, H., "Spectroscopic Investigations of Condensed Phosphates and Phosphoric Acids. VI. The Structure of the Pyrophosphate Ion in Solution," *Z. anorg. u. allgem. Chem.*, 301, 154. *54–2938*.

S-273. Snyder, R. G., and Decius, J. C., "The Infrared Spectra of $N_2H_6Cl_2$ and $N_2H_6F_2$," *Spectrochim. Acta*, 13, 280. *53–8806*.

S-274. Spitzer, W. G., Kleinman, D. A., and Frosch., C. J., "Infrared Properties of Cubic Silicon Carbide Films," *Phys. Rev.*, 113, 133. *53–10981*.

Measured transmission and reflection of infrared radiation by cubic SiC are reported and discussed for the region 10,000–667 cm^{-1}.

S-275. Spitzer, W. G., Kleinman, D., and Walsh, D., "Infrared Properties of Hexagonal Silicon Carbide," *Phys. Rev.*, 113, 127. *53–10980*.

Measured transmission and reflectivity of infrared radiation by SiC are reported and discussed for the region 10,000–400 cm^{-1}.

S-276. Spitzer, W. G., and Whelan, J. M., "Infrared Absorption and Electron Effective Mass in N-Type Gallium Arsenide," *Phys. Rev.*, 114, 59. *53–18642*.

Absorption-carrier concentration measurements were made for single crystal n-GaAs for the region 11,770–400 cm^{-1}.

S-277. Staats, P. A., and Morgan, H. W., "Infrared Spectra of Solid Ammonia," *J. Chem. Phys.*, 31, 553. *54–2937*.

Films of NH_3 and ND_3 were observed at different temperatures and conditions of deposition.

S-278. Tai, H., "Infrared Spectrophotometry of Inorganic Anions," *Dissertation Abstr.*, 19, 2734. *53–15747*.

S-279. Thomas, D. G., "Infrared Absorption in Zinc Oxide Crystals," *Phys. and Chem. Solids*, 10, 47. *54–75*.

Measurements were made on pure and doped single crystals of ZnO at 78 and 300°K in the region 10,000–800 cm^{-1}.

S-280. Titeica, R., and Palade, G., "Infrared Absorption Spectra of Some Micas," *Rev. phys., Acad. rép. populaire Roumaine*, 4, 93. *54–5258*.

Spectra of biotite, phlogopite, lepidolite, muscovite, and zinnwaldite were obtained in the infrared to 400 cm^{-1}.

S-281. Tramer, A., "Vibration Spectrum of Sodium Nitrite," *Compt. rend.*, 248, 3546. *53–19579*.

S-282. Tramer, A., and Mathieu, J. P., "Vibration Spectrum and Structure of Hydrated Ba(NO₂)₂," *Compt. rend.*, **249**, 392. *54–1070*.

Raman and infrared spectra in the region 3500–30 cm^{-1} suggest the formula $Ba(NO_2)_2.H_2O$.

S-283. Vanderryn, J., "Infrared Spectrum of BF₃," *J. Chem. Phys.*, **30**, 331. *53–10957*.

S-284. Vannerberg, N. G., "Infrared Spectra of Some Peroxide Hydrates and Peroxidates," *Arkiv Kemi*, **14**, 107. *54–7339*.

S-285. Venkateswarlu, K., Somasundaran, V., and Krishna, M. G. P., "Potential Constants of XY₄ and XY₃Z Types of Molecules and Radicals," *Z. physik. Chem. (Leipzig)*, **212**, 145. *54–4148*.

S-286. Venkateswarlu, K., and Thirugnanasambandam, P., "Force Constants of Some Systems of the Bent Symmetrical XY₂ Type," *Z. physik. Chem. (Leipzig)*, **212**, 138. *54–4147*.

Calculations are made for H_2Se, D_2Se, SCl_2, F_2O, ClO_2, Cl_2O, NO_2, NO_2^+, NO_2^-, UO_2^{++}, $=CF_2$, $=CCl_2$, $=CBr_2$, and $=CI_2$.

S-287. Verdier, P. H., and Wilson, Jr., E. B., "Force Constant Calculations in Linear Triatomic Molecules from Infrared and Microwave Data," *J. Chem. Phys.*, **30**, 1372. *53–17667*.

Calculations for OCS and N₂O are discussed.

S-288. Vratny, F., "Infrared Spectra of Metal Nitrates," *Applied Spectroscopy*, **13**, 59. *53–16692*.

Spectral data for 35 compounds are presented for the region 5000–667 cm^{-1}.

S-289. Vratny, F., "Stress Relaxation and Exchange in Pellets Used for the Infrared Technique," *J. Inorg. and Nuclear Chem.*, **10**, 328.

A logarithmic curve is followed for lead nitrate pellets when exchange with KCl, water adsorption, or stress relaxation is considered.

S-290. Vu, H., and Vodar, B., "Disturbance of the Fundamental Band of Vibration-Rotation of Hydrogen Chloride, in Mixtures with Neutral Gases under High Pressures. Effect of Temperature," *Compt. rend.*, **248**, 2082. *53–16691*.

S-291. Vu, H., and Vodar, B., "Shift of the Fundamental Infrared Band of Hydrogen Chloride Dissolved in Liquefied Gases and in Solidified Gases under Pressure," *Compt. rend.*, **248**, 2469.

S-292. Weinstock, B., and Claassen, H. H., "Jahn-Teller Effect in the Vibrational Spectra of Hexafluorides," *J. Chem. Phys.*, **31**, 262. *54–2003*.

S-293. Weir, C. E., Lippincott, E. R., Valkenburg, A. V., and Bunting, E. N., "Infrared Studies in the 1- to 15-Micron Region to 30,000 Atmospheres," *J. Research Natl. Bur. Standards*, **63A**, 55. *54–2953*.

Studies were made of calcite, aragonite and several carbonates having both structures.

S-294. Wentnik, T., and Bauer, S. H., "Triatomic Linear Molecules Containing Carbon and Oxygen, Sulfur, Selenium or Tellurium, III. Absolute

Intensity of the σ_3 Band of CSe_2," *J. Chem. Phys.*, **31**, 834. *54–4149.*

S-295. Wickersheim, K. A., "Infrared Absorption Spectrum of Lithium Hydroxide," *J. Chem. Phys.*, **31**, 863. *54–6303.*

The spectrum of crystalline lithium hydroxide measured from 2500–8000 cm^{-1} was explained using factor group selection rules.

S-296. Wickersheim, K. A., and Hanking, B., "Infrared Absorption in CaF_2," *Physica*, **25**, 569. *54–4164.*

S-297. Wilkinson, G. R., Price, W. C., and Bradbury, E. M., "Applications of Polarized Infrared Radiation," *Spectrochim. Acta*, **14**, 284. *53–14673.* A review.

S-298. Woolley, D. D., "Infrared Investigation of Vanadia-Silica Gel Catalysts," *Dissertation Abstr.*, **19**, 1916. *53–9813.*

S-299. Yamaguchi, A., Ichishima, I., Shimanouchi, T., and Mizushima, S., "Far Infrared Spectrum of Hydrazine," *J. Chem. Phys.*, **31**, 843. *54–4150.*

S-300. Zengin, N., and Giguere, P. A., "Infrared Spectrum of Crystalline Hydrogen Persulfide," *Can. J. Chem.*, **37**, 632. *53–14689.*

Crystalline H_2S_2 was examined in the region 500–3500 cm^{-1}.

1960

S-301. Francis, A. B., and Carlson, A. I., "Cadmium Sulfide Infrared Optical Material," *J. Opt. Soc. Am.*, **50**, 118. *54–7349.*

METAL-ORGANIC COMPLEXES

S-302. Blinc, R., and Hadzi, D., "Infrared Spectra and Hydrogen Bonding in Nickel Dimethylglyoxime and Related Complexes," *J. Chem. Soc.*, 4536 (1958). *53–5869.*

S-303. Favini, G., and Paglia, E., "Absorption Spectra of Some Cobalt (II) and Cobalt (III) Complexes of Bipyridine and Phenanthroline," *J. Inorg. and Nuclear Chem.*, **8**, 155 (1958). *53–5865.*

S-304. Lumme, P. O., "Infrared Absorption of Some Bivalent Metal Chelates of 2-Pyridine Carboxylic and 2- and 8-Quinoline Carboxylic Acids," *Suomen Kemistilehti*, **31B**, 294 (1958). *53–4903.*

S-305. Rosenblum, M., "Correlation of Infrared Spectra With the Structure of Substituted Ferrocenes," *Chem. and Ind. (London)*, 953 (1958). *53–49.*

S-306. Sacconi, L., Caroti, G., and Paoletti, P., "Investigations on the Co-ordinative Power of Uranyl. III. Infrared Spectra of Some Complexes With β-Diketones," *J. Chem. Soc.*, 4257 (1958). *53–4903.*

Acetylacetone, benzoylacetone, and dibenzoylmethane complexes of uranyl ion, both anhydrous and crystallized with water, ammonia, or pyridine were studied in the infrared region.

S-307. Saraceno, A. J., Nakagawa, I., Mizushima, S., Curran, C., and Quagliano, J. V., "Infrared Absorption Spectra of Inorganic Coordination Complexes. XVI. Infrared Studies of Glycino-Metal Complexes," *J. Am. Chem. Soc.*, **80**, 5018 (1958). *53–3879.*

S-308. Terenin, A. N., Filimonov, V. N., and Bystrov, D. S., "Infrared Absorption Spectra of Molecular Compounds with Metal Halogen Compounds," *Izvest. Akad. Nauk S.S.S.R., Ser. Fiz.*, **22**, 1100 (1958). *53–860.*

Frequency shifts are observed in the spectra of molecular compounds of NO, pyridine, ethyl ether, methanol, cyclohexene, acetone, acetonitrile, acetic acid, ethyl acetate, and chloracetyl with metal halides such as $AlCl_3$, $SnCl_4$, $TiCl_4$, etc.

S-309. Cotton, F. A., Stammreich, H., and Wilkinson, G., "Raman and Infrared Spectra and Structure of Di-(π-Cyclopentadienyl-Iron) Tetracarbonyl," *J. Inorg. and Nuclear Chem.*, **9**, 3 (1959). *53–7762.*

S-310. Fritz, H. P., "Aromatic Complexes of Metals. XXVI. Infrared Studies on Cyclopentadienyl-Metal Complexes," *Chem. Ber.*, **92**, 780 (1959). *53–11994.*

Discussion of the degree of aromaticity of the cyclopentadienyl radical is given based on infrared spectra. The complexes involved are those of Fe, Ru, Ni, Os, Co, Mn, Cr, V, Sn, Pb, Be, Mg, Hg, ReH, RhH, Bi, La, Tl, K.

S-311. Gaufrés, R., and Mathieu, J., "Structure of the Group C_2O_4 in Potassium Aluminum Trioxalate," *Compt. rend.*, **248**, 81 (1959). *53–1194.*

S-312. Lane, T. J., Yamaguchi, A., Quagliano, J. V., Ryan, J. A., and Mizushima, S., "Infrared Absorption Studies of Inorganic Coordinated Complexes. XXII. Infrared Studies of Methyl Thiourea and its Metal Complexes," *J. Am. Chem. Soc.*, **81**, 3824 (1959). *54–4149.*

S-313. Martinette, M., Mizushima, S., and Quagliano, J. V., "Infrared Absorption Spectra of Inorganic Coordination Complexes. XIX. N-Methyl-Acetamidecadmium (II) Chloride," *Spectrochim. Acta*, 77 (1959). *53–13777.*

S-314. Nakamoto, K., McCarthy, P. J., and Martell, A. E., "Metal-Oxygen Stretching Frequencies in the Metal Chelate Compounds of β-Diketones," *Nature*, **183**, 459 (1959). *53–14679.*

Bands observed between 420–480 cm^{-1} are ascribed to Me—O vibrational modes in chelates of Cu^{+2}, Ni^{+2}, Co^{+2}, Pd^{+2} with acetyl- and benzoylacetone.

S-315. Powell, D. B., and Sheppard, N., "Infrared Spectrum of a Platinous Complex Having a Bridging Ethylene Diamine Group with the Trans-Configuration: [Bisethylene Tetrachloro-μ-Ethylenediaminediplatinum (II)]," *J. Chem. Soc.*, 3089 (1959). *54–2938.*

S-316. Rao, G. S., "The Effect of Complex Formation on the Infrared Spectra of Titanium Tetrafluoride and Tetrachloride," *Z. Naturforsch.*, **14b**, 689 (1959). *54–6304.*

Complexes with the organic ligands, pyridine, acetonitrile, propionitrile, benzonitrile were examined from 400–800 cm^{-1}.

S-317. Rao, G. A., "Unsymmetrical Nature of the Pyridine Complexes of TiF$_4$ and TiI$_4$," *Naturwissenschaften*, **46**, 556 (1959). *54–5245.*

S-318. Sawyer, D. T., and Paulsen, P. J., "Properties and Infrared Spectra of Ethylene Diamine Tetraacetic Acid (EDTA) Complexes. II. Chelates of Bivalent Ions," *J. Am. Chem. Soc.*, **81**, 816 (1959). *53–10965.*

S-319. Schmelz, M. J., Nakagawa, I., Mizushima, S., and Quagliano, J. V., "Infrared Absorption Spectra of Inorganic Coordination Complexes. XVIII. Infrared Studies of Malonato Metal Complexes," *J. Am. Chem. Soc.*, **81**, 287 (1959). *53–8808.*

INDEX TO BIBLIOGRAPHY

All references cited in the bibliography, except those pertaining to metal-organic complexes, are indexed. The numbers refer to entries in the bibliography; the letter S preceding a number refers to entries which appear in the supplementary reference list. The major headings are those of the principal element involved. In some cases it was necessary to include as major headings specific compounds or types of compounds, e.g., acids, alloys, ammonium compounds, crystals, minerals, hydroxides, water, etc. Intermetallic compounds are indexed under the more positive element, while compounds between metals and non-metals or complex ions are indexed under both positive and negative parts of the molecule. For example, indium antimonide is indexed only under the major heading, Indium; while indium phosphate is indexed under both headings, Indium and Phosphorus (phosphates). Books, reviews, summaries, and general or miscellaneous articles which do not readily fall into a specific group appear under the heading, General. It is suggested that the reader make liberal use of the entries indexed under General in order to insure complete coverage of the literature cited.

Acids
  cyanuric and deuterocyanuric, 94
  hydrazoic and deuterohydrazoic,
    345, 346
  hydrocyanic, 3
  isocyanic, 2
  perchloric, 131
Alloys, 105, 109
Aluminum, 105
  aluminate glasses, 358, S-220
  aluminates, S-220
  antimonide, 207, 223, 295
  aqueous solutions of salts of, S-75
  bromide, 778
  chloride, 530, 778
  fluoride, 83
  guanidine sulfate, S-93
  hydroxide, 434
  nitride, 613
  oxide, 369, 499, 613
    hydrated, 238
  sulfate, 691
  tetrametaphosphate, 775
Ammonia, 89, 124, 154, 245, 272,
  337, 419, 493, 503, 544, 607, 665,
  729, S-33, S-58, S-68, S-115, S-212,
  S-235, S-277
  adsorbed on silica, 439
  ammonia —d, and —d_2 mixed crys-
    tals, 425
  ammonia—oxygen flame, 347
  boron trifluoride—ammonia, 707,
    725, S-30
  deuterated, 110, 418, 639
  hydrates, 196
  liquid, medium for absorption spec-
    troscopy, 79
Ammonium compounds
  ammonium ion, 665
  arsenates, 98

azide, 346, 348, 727
bifluoride, 528
ferroelectric compounds, S-37
fluoborate, 15
fluoferrates, 21
halides, 9
heteropoly acid salts, 681
hydrogen bonding in salts, S-141
hydroxyl salts, S-66, S-188
phosphates, 98
substituted, 429
sulfate, selenosulfate, thiosulfate,
    and amine sulfonate, S-16
tetrametaphosphate, 775
tritium—substituted ammonium
    chloride, 664
Antimony
antimonates, S-271
cesium photocathode, 132
oxide, 103, 460
pentafluoride, 634
stibine and deuterated stibine, 158
tribromide, 723
trichloride, 723
Arsenic, 367
arsenates, 98, S-37
arsine, 6
glass, S-252
molybdoarsenates, 681
trioxide, 460
trichloride, 723
trisulfide, 479
tungstoarsenates, 681

Barium
azide, 727
barite, 301
borates, meta- and ortho-, 62
bromate, S-260
carbonate, 340, 757
chlorate, 571
chloride, 758
chromite, S-17
fluoride, 80

hyponitrite, 653
nitrate, S-20
nitrite, S-282
oxide, 140
peroxide, 612
sulfate (thiosulfate, selenosulfate,
    and amine sulfonate), S-16
titanate, 281, 652, 776, S-29
Beryllium
chloride, 717
fluoride, 717
Bismuth, S-205
oxide, 103
selenide, 43, 602
sulfide, 43
telluride, 43, 602
Boranes, 285
decaborane, 564
diborane, 308, 322, 564, S-95
exchange of deuterium between,
    525
pentaborane, 7, 255, 285, 564
Boron, 287
borate ion, 354, 585
boric acid, 323, 579
borides, 613
borine carbonyl, 609
carbide, 613
diboron tetrachloride, 657
halides, 536
hydrides, 285
metal salts of meta- and orthobo-
    rate, 62, 228, S-92
nitride, 613
oxide, 613, 683, 771
oxide glass, S-42
oxygen compounds, S-199
tribromide, 783
tricyanide, 500
trifluoride, 545, S-283
    complexes, S-32
trifluoride—ammonia, 707, 725,
    S-30
triiodide, 783

Boron (*cont.*)
  trisulfide, S-200
  tungstoborates, 681
Bromine, 674
  bromates, S-260
  bromides, 9, 102, 112, 115, 141,
    154, 157, 268, 372, 376, 379,
    407, 416, 437, 521, 531, 536,
    539, 622, 723, 734, 783, S-47,
    S-88, S-195, S-255
  monoxide, 625
  pentafluoride, 10, 246
  trifluoride, 246, 721

Cadmium
  ammine complex, 468
  chlorate, 571
  chromite, S-17
  fluoride, 80
  oxide, 663
    hydrated, 466
  selenide, S-9, S-110
  sulfamate, 453
  sulfate, 691
  sulfide, 365, 366, S-110, S-301
  telluride, S-110
Calcium, 324
  aluminate glasses, 358
  azide, 727
  calcite, 186, 731, S-140
  carbonate, 87, 388
  chlorate, 571
  diphosphate, 392
  fluoride, 80, S-296
  hydroxide, 719, S-79
  orthoborate, 62
  peroxide, 612
  sulfate, 170, 362, 440, 508, 598,
    S-16, S-137
  thiosulfate, selenosulfate, and
    amine sulfonate, S-16
  titanate, 751
Carbon
  carbides, 184, 613, S-96, S-237,

    S-274, S-275
  carbonates, 23, 81, 87, 186, 283,
    731, 757, S-140, S-293
  carbonyl bromofluoride, S-245
  carbonyl chloride (phosgene and
    thiophosgene), 96, 654
  carbonyl cyanide, 694
    nickel complex, S-201
  carbonyl sulfide, 39, 214, 599,
    S-263, S-264
  coals and coal products, 136, 776,
    S-190
  cyanogen, 755, 767
  diamond, 189, 218, 697, S-233
  dioxide, 3, 77, 99, 111, 113, 116,
    159, 233, 290, 311, 356, 446,
    529, 572, 573, 744, 746, S-2,
    S-5, S-118, S-143, S-173, S-176,
    S-191, S-192, S-243
    isotope ratio, 168, 274
  diselenide, 695, 782, S-294
  disulfide, 39, 245, 382, 444, 782,
    S-5, S-192
  graphite, S-40
  graphitic oxide, 363, 364
  isotope ratio, C^{13}/C^{12}, 27, 274
  metal carbonyls, 306, 359, 374,
    398, 483, 578, 621, 623, 630,
    667, 713, 743, 760, S-35, S-54,
    S-159, S-249
    hydrides, S-171, S-182
  monoxide, 34, 35, 36, 37, 46, 104,
    114, 222, 230, 312, 313, 421,
    484, 558, 701, S-72, S-86, S-194,
    S-196
  suboxide, 279, 302, 314
  sulfur-selenide, 782
  sulfur-telluride, 782
  tetrafluoride, 119
Cerium
  nitrate, S-21, S-261
Cesium
  antimony photocathode, 132
  azide, 727

bromide, 102, S-195
carbonyl, 306
chloride, 678
cobalt chloride complex, 267
iodide, 122, S-121
Chlorine
  carbonyl, phosgene and fluorinated
    derivative, 96
  chlorates, metallic, 106, 107, 185,
    571
  chlorides, 9, 56, 64, 66, 89, 92, 108,
    141, 154, 156, 157, 178, 202,
    222, 258, 267, 282, 303, 321,
    334, 372, 379, 386, 387, 428,
    521, 530, 531, 536, 539, 556,
    593, 633, 657, 662, 664, 699,
    717, 723, 728, 729, 734, 758,
    S-19, S-47, S-88, S-225, S-232,
    S-255, S-273, S-290, S-291
  chlorites, 17
  dioxide, 97
  impurities in liquid, 299, 300
  isotope ratio in HCl gas, 235
  monofluoride, 30
  monoxide, 625
  perchlorate, 59, 601
  trifluoride, 721
Chromium
  acetates, 620
  chlorate, 571
  chromates, S-60
  chromites, S-17
  chromyl chloride, 736, S-232
  chromyl fluoride, 736
  complex salts, 385, 468, 617
  dichromates, S-135
  halides, 643
  halochromates, S-60
  hexacarbonyl, 578, 667
  hexacyanide ion, S-13, S-44
  nitride, 613
  oxide, 613
  pentacyanonitrosyl complex, S-202

Cobalt
  bromate, S-260
  carbonyl, 359, S-159
    hydride, 483, S-182
    hydro-, 398
    nitrosyl, 398
  chlorate, 571
  chromite, S-17
  complex salts, 121, 252, 385, 408,
    409, 449, 468, 513, 712, S-132,
    S-155, S-156, S-158
  coordination compounds, cis-trans
    isomers of, 408
  ferrite, 436, S-111
  hyponitrite, 653
  sulfamate, S-12
Copper, 105, 205, 305, 454, S-269,
  S-270
  ammine complexes, 468
  basic salts, S-19, S-139
  bromate, S-260
  chlorate, 571
  cupric derivatives
    acetates, 620
    chlorides, 428
    general, 384
  cuprous derivatives
    oxide, 71, 412, S-244
    fluoride, 41
    fluosilicate, 83
    hydrated oxide, 466
    hydroxide, 467
    manganite, 624
    nitride, 613
  cyanide complexes, S-85, S-250
  sulfamate, S-12
  sulfate, S-179
  sulfate and nitrate in ammonia, 79
  tetrametaphosphate, 775
Crystals, 501
  alkali halide with anionic impuri-
    ties, 781
  carbon dioxide and hydrogen cyan-
    ide, low temperature spectra, 3

Crystals (*cont.*)
  diamond-structured, S-208, S-229
  hydrogen chloride—hydrogen bromide, mixed, 734
  non-polar, interaction of vibrations with electric fields, 541
  piezoelectric, 402
  polymorphic forms, identification of, 167
Cyanates, 753, S-198, S-228, S-256
  isothio-, 395
  thio-, 519, 726, 742, S-256
Cyanides, 38, 78, 142, 318, 445, 457, 472, 500, 583, 750, S-248, S-250, S-251, S-256
  ferro- and ferri-, 232, 328, 329, 456, 459
  hexacoordinated complexes, S-45, S-207, S-230, S-265
Cyanogen, 755, 767
  halides, 487

Deuterium, S-166
  bromide, 268, 416
  chloride, 154, 593, 729
  cyanide, 38, 78, 142, 318, 445, 472
  exchange, 525, 679
  fluoride, 441
  iodide, 416
  oxide, 144, 171, 441, 450, 451, 492, 495, 581, 615, S-48, S-67, S-165
  oxide hydrates, 758
  sulfide, 600, S-163
Dicyandiamide, S-210

Fluorine
  fluoborates, 15
  fluoferrates, 21
  fluorides, 8, 9, 10, 11 13, 14, 18, 21, 29, 30, 41, 54, 55, 60, 65, 73, 84, 100, 118, 119, 147, 198, 202, 221, 242, 246, 249, 263, 284, 291, 296, 360, 399, 404,

405, 406, 413, 415, 441, 465, 475, 476, 528, 532, 533, 536, 545, 560, 605, 634, 643, 707, 717, 724, 725, S-14, S-26, S-27, S-30, S-32, S-46, S-56, S-59, S-78, S-87, S-89, S-128, S-129, S-133, S-167, S-273, S-283, S-296
    carbonyl, COF$_2$, 96
    perchloryl, 535, 540
  fluorinated salts of zinc hydrates, 543
  fluoroacids, salts of, S-246
  fluoroxymethforane, 82
  fluosilicates, 83

Gallium, S-205
  antimonide, 206, 223, 295, 427
  arsenide, 223, 295, S-276
  oxide, 613
  telluride, 641, S-76
General
  anomalous skin effect, S-120
  automatic recording, 271
  books, reviews, reports, 40, 90, 108, 134, 151, 153, 197, 209, 245, 250, 256, 275, 276, 277, 315, 316, 400, 401, 430, 438, 462, 502, 510, 542, 570, 582, 604, 614, 648, 676, 677, 684, 711, 716, 752, 784, S-39, S-73, S-81, S-103, S-180, S-206, S-214, S-223, S-233, S-240, S-267, S-278
  calibration curve for prism spectrophotometers, 452
  crystals of diamond structure, S-208
  derivative spectrophotometry, 361
  duplication of spectra on reduced scale, 432
  evaporated films, spectra of, 193
  ferroelectrics, S-37, S-145

induced absorption in gases, 747, S-52, S-53, S-55, S-172, S-214, S-218, S-221, S-258

inorganic substances, 4, 56, 91, 169, 170, 227, 324, 338, 391, 433, 448, 488, 489, 490, 496, 506, 507, 561, 567, 592, 603, 612, 613, 627, 651, 666, 671, 690, 754, 772, 781, S-34, S-50, S-71, S-75, S-77, S-102, S-131, S-154, S-167, S-169, S-172, S-207, S-229, S-230, S-234, S-268, S-288, S-289

intensity of transitions, S-51, S-73
    and the nature of the chemical bond, S-115

low temperature solid solution spectra, S-189

metal-oxygen bond frequency, S-151

metals
    optical and volume absorptivity, 253, 772
    optical properties, S-205

microspectroscopy, 325

molecules
    adsorbed on glass, 435
    adsorbed on silica, 709
    adsorbed on silicates, 692
    linear triatomic, S-287
    M(XY)$_4$ type, 668
    M(XY)$_6$ type, 667
    octahedral molecules, S-119
    pyramidal, 181
    spherical top, 626
    S$_2$X$_2$ type, S-80
    symmetric (mathematical), 608
    tetrahedral, 764
    XY$_2$ type, S-286
    XY$_4$ and XY$_3$Z types, S-285

salt effects, on bands of isotopic varieties of water, 618

semiconductors, 342, 461, 686, 737, 738, 739, 740, 773, S-10, S-11, S-25, S-43, S-126, S-213, S-238, S-241, S-242

sodium chloride-type lattices, 766

solid state studies, 63, 108, 143, 229, 709, S-215

solids condensed from discharge, S-204

techniques and instrumentation, 86, 126, 217, 231, 237, 244, 284, 298, 310, 327, 328, 350, 352, 355, 373, 380, 388, 394, 403, 420, 447, 628, 642, 673, 691, 722, 752, 761, 776, S-81, S-257, S-297

Germanium, 1, 42, 52, 53, 85, 133, 149, 164, 165, 180, 187, 189, 218, 234, 247, 257, 265, 289, 339, 377, 393, 396, 486, 504, 505, 523, 527, 650, 708, S-15, S-83, S-90, S-107, S-160, S-186, S-231
    deuterated germanes, 537
    digermane, 477, 478
    dioxide, 344
    germanate glasses, 358
    germanes, substituted, 386, 387
    germania, S-100
    monochlorogermane and mono-chlorogermane-d$_3$, 280
    tetrafluoride, 13, 55, 119

Gold, 305, S-269, S-270
    blacks, 155
    cyano-complex, 162, 260, 261
    monocyanide, 762
    smoke deposits, 75

Hydrazine, 69, 777, S-299
    hydrochloride and hydrobromide, S-273
    monobromide and monochloride, normal and deuterated, 141

Hydrogen, 47, 57, 215, 319, 334, 368, 381, 638, S-2, S-52, S-53, S-55, S-166, S-170, S-217, S-219, S-222

Hydrogen (*cont.*)
  bonding, spectroscopic evidence for, 636
  bromide, 112, 154, 372, 376, 622, 718
  chloride, 89, 129, 154, 176, 222, 264, 334, 372, 375, 718, 728, 729, S-2, S-216, S-290, S-291
  chloride-bromide crystals, 734
  cyanide, 3, 38, 78, 142, 445, 472
  exchange, with deuterium, 679
  fluoride, 41, 60, 221, 263, 406, 441, 532, 533, 718, 724, 748, S-87, S-133
    complex with chlorine trifluoride, 296
  halides, 251
  HO₂ radical, 589
  hydrazine, 69, 777, S-299
  hydrides, 285, 383, 483, 675
  hydronium ion, S-18, S-157
  hydroxylamine, 68
  iodide, 51, 372, 376, 416
  peroxide, 194, 286, 335, 735
  persulfide, S-300
  selenide, 417, 418
  sulfide, 5, 25, 48, 74, 89, 161, 199, 200, 414, 442, 443, 493, 522, 680, 729
    deuterated, 335, 336
  telluride, 574, S-118
Hydroxides, 174, 262, 332, 434, 467, 496, 506, 719, S-79, S-109, S-133, S-142, S-152, S-162, S-177, S-295
  type (XO·OH), 616, S-161
Hydroxylamine, 68

Indium
  antimonide, 190, 203, 208, 211, 223, 254, 266, 295, 317, 378, 427, 431, 455, 597, 689, S-23, S-122
  arsenide, 254, 295, S-104
  borate, 585

phosphide, 223, 294, 295, S-116
  telluride, 641, S-76
Iodine, 150
  cyanide complexes, S-248
  effect on properties of selenium, 703
  ferroelectric compounds, containing, S-37
  iodides, 9, 51, 79, 122, 343, 372, 376, 416, 437, 539, 659, 783, S-121
  monoxide, 625
Iridium
  hexafluoride, 404
Iron
  ammine complexes, 468
  carbonyls, 621, 623, 630, 760, S-54
    hydride, S-182
  cyano-complexes, 617, S-265
  ferric hydrate, S-197
  ferrites, 436
  ferro- and ferricyanides, 232
  oxide, FeO, 49
  pyrite, 42

Lanthanum
  borate, 585
Lead, 105
  bromate, S-260
  chlorate, 571
  fluoride, 80
  hyponitrite, 653
  metaborate, 62
  nitrate, S-20
  selenide, 43, 331
  sulfamate, 453
  sulfide, 33, 43, 58, 148, 183, 195, 331
  telluride, 43, 58, 331
Lithium, 324
  azide, 727
  fluoride, 80, S-59, S-78, S-89
  hydride, 383

hydroxide and deuterated analog, 262, S-134, S-177, S-295
nitride, 613
perchlorate, 765
peroxide, 612
potassium sulfate, 402
sulfate, 349, 691

Magnesium
bromate, S-260
bromide, S-255
chlorate, 571
chloride, 717, S-255
ferrite, 436, S-111
hyponitrite, 653
hydroxide, 174, S-79, S-152
nitrate, S-21
nitride, 613
orthoborate, 62
oxide, 103, 177, S-109
hydrated, 466
stannide, 326
sulfate, 691
tetrametaphosphate, 775
Manganese
ammine complexes, 468
carbonyl hydride and deuteride, S-171, S-182
cyanocomplexes, 617
decacarbonyl, 471
ferrites, 436
manganites, 624
molybdomanganates, 681
orthoborate, 62
Mercury
amido-bromide, 670
ammine halides, 712
bromide, 531
chloride, 531
cyanide, 647
complexes, S-251
Minerals, 4, 67, 81, 152, 160, 170, 204, 256, 491, 499, 510, 511, 512,

S-24, S-38, S-64, S-100, S-101, S-147, S-226, S-227, S-266
afwilite, $Ca_3(SiO_3OH)_2 \cdot 2H_2O$, 562
glasses, 225, 236, 273, 358, 515, 516, 769, S-101
mica, 108, 768, S-280
quartz, 67, 204, 422, 423, 501, 700, 770, S-22, S-140, S-203
Molybdenum
boride, 613
hetereopoly acid derivatives, 681
hexacarbonyl, 667
hexafluoride, 11, 54, 147
octacyanocomplexes, 715
pentacyanonitrosyl complex, S-202

Neodymium, 649
chlorate, 571
Neptunium
hexafluoride, 399
$N_PO_2^+$ ion, 72
ions in heavy water solution, 779
Nickel, S-259, S-269, S-270
bromate, 260
carbonyl, 374, 713, 743, S-35, S-249
tricyanonickelate ion, S-201
chlorate, 571
chloride, S-255
ferrites, 436, S-111
fluosilicate, 83
hexacyanodi-nickelate ion, 485
tetracyano-nickelate ion, 704, S-150
manganite, 624
orthoborate, 62
oxide, NiO, 259
salts, complex, 385, 389, 468
sulfamate, S-12
Niobium
pentachloride, 633
Nitrogen, 47, 120, 139, S-2
acid, nitric, 658, S-28

Nitrogen (*cont.*)
    monohydrate, 130, 131
    nitrous, 20, 32
  azide ion, 345, 346, 348, 548, 637, 727
  cyanogen, 755, 767
  dinitrogen tetraoxide, 101, 594, 685
  dioxide, 179, 526, S-36, S-69
  hydrazine, 69, 777, S-299
  hydroxylamine, 68
  isotope ratio, N^{15}/N^{14} in N_2O, 274
  nitrates, 56, 186, 269, 501, 559, S-21, S-70, S-71, S-148, S-261, S-262, S-288, S-289
    transition metal, anhydrous, 702, S-148
  nitrato complexes, 632
  nitrides, 613
  nitrites, 17, 95, 590, 698, S-281, S-282
  nitrito and nitro complexes, S-114
  NO_4 complex, 514
  nitrosyl bromide, 379
    chloride, 64, 379
    fluoride, 24, 88, 118, 379
  nitryl chloride, 303
    fluoride, 475
  oxide, nitric, 304, 312, 411, 558, 576, 591, 631, 778
    nitrous, 12, 28, 44, 45, 70, 127, 182, 192, 201, 216, 226, 304, 312, 390, 534, 558, 563, 635, 710, S-1, S-72, S-176, S-196
  oxides, frozen, S-185
  pentoxide, 191, 309
  tetrasulfide, 172
  transition metal—nitric oxide complexes, S-74, S-97, S-209
  trichlorides and chloramines, 92
  trifluoride, 117, 198, 415, 605, S-128, S-129

various types of nitrous oxide compounds, 733

Osmium
  hexacyanide, S-265
  nitrogen compounds, 749
  tetroxide, 509, 596, S-253
Oxides, 12, 28, 34, 35, 36, 37, 44, 45, 61, 67, 71, 77, 97, 99, 101, 103, 104, 111, 113, 114, 116, 123, 127, 129, 140, 177, 179, 191, 192, 201, 216, 222, 226, 230, 233, 241, 248, 259, 279, 290, 292, 297, 302, 304, 307, 309, 311, 312, 313, 314, 344, 356, 364, 369, 390, 391, 406, 411, 412, 421, 424, 441, 446, 451, 460, 471, 484, 494, 499, 529, 534, 550, 551, 558, 563, 572, 573, 576, 591, 594, 595, 596, 613, 625, 631, 635, 661, 663, 682, 683, 685, 701, 706, 710, 744, 746, 771, S-1, S-2, S-4, S-5, S-6, S-36, S-65, S-69, S-72, S-86, S-108, S-115, S-118, S-143, S-149, S-173, S-174, S-175, S-176, S-185, S-191, S-192, S-194, S-196, S-243, S-244, S-253, S-279
  per-, 166, 194, 286, 335, 612
    hydrates, S-284
Oxonium ions, 145, 357
Oxygen, 47, 120, 139
  absorption in silicon, 644
  discharge products, 730
Ozone, 554, 557, 730, S-175

Palladium
  complexes, 566, S-112
Peroxidates, S-284
Phosphorus
  alkali pyrophosphates, 756
  anhydride, 682
  biphosphine, 555
  deuterophosphine, 780
  fluorides, 73, 117, 198, 560, S-178

inorganic phosphorus compounds, 219, 220, 270, S-254
molybdophosphates, 681
oxyfluoride, S-178
pentachloride, 699
PH_2 and PD_2 radicals, 569
phosphates, 81, 98, 333, 392, 463, 464, 669, 775, S-37, S-94, S-136, S-137, S-247
phosphine, 175, 239, 544, S-115
phosphites and hypophosphites, 353
phosphonium and deutero-phosphonium iodides, 659
phosphoric acid derivatives, nitrogen containing, 688
pyrophosphates, S-272
silyl phosphine, S-224
sulfide, P_4S_3, 655
tribromide, 723
trichloride, 723, S-225
tungstophosphates, 681
Platinum
complexes, 566, 568, S-49, S-112
hydride, S-49
tetracyanoplatinate ion, 587
Plutonium, 640
hexafluoride, 370, 399
PuO_2^{++}, 72
Potassium, 324
acid carbonate, 283
antimonates, S-271
azide, 727
bifluoride, 14, 29, 528
bromate, S-260
bromide, 678
    and iodide, influence of ultraviolet radiation on infrared absorption, 437, S-47
carbonyl tricyano-nickelate, S-201
chlorate, 106, 107, 185, 571
chloride, 66, 678
cyanide, cupro-, 611, S-85
    ferro-, 329, 456, 458, 459

gold, 162, 261, 520, 646
molybdenum octa-, 457
silver, 518, 645
cyanocobaltate, 629, S-8
fluoborate, 15
fluosilicate, 83
glasses, silicate, 146
hexafluorides, complex, 21
hydroxide, S-134
iodide lattice, cyanate ion in, 753
nitrate, 340
nitrite, 698
perchlorate, 59
permanganate, 79
peroxide, 612
phosphates, KH_2PO_4 and KD_2PO_4, 270, S-94
ruthenicyanide, 714
selenosulfate, thiosulfate, amine sulfonate, S-16
sulfate, 691, S-16
tellurates, S-271
thiocyanate, 519, 742
tri (sesqui-) oxide, 241
Praseodymium
zinc nitrate, S-21

Rhenium
decacarbonyl, 471
Rubidium
azide, 727
chloride, 678
hydroxide, S-134
uranyl nitrate, S-70
Ruthenium
cyanide complex, 714, S-265

Selenium, 16, 19, 547, 703, 720, S-164
hexafluoride, 147, 465
selenides, 43, 331, 417, 418, 695, 782, S-9, S-110, S-181, S-294
selenious acid, S-63

Silicon 1, 42, 85, 135, 189, 218, 234, 339, 377, 397, 523, 687, 773, S-84, S-183
  carbide, 184, 613, 660, S-96, S-237, S-274, S-275
  cyanates, S-198
  disiloxane, S-57, S-106
  indium—doped, 410
  molybdosilicates, 681
  monoxide, 248
  silanes and related structures, 156, 157, 178, 202, 243, 330, 407, 546, 549, 552, 553, S-138, S-211, S-239
  silica, 67, 152, 204, 240, 344, 422, 423, 426, 575, 606, 745, S-100, S-105, S-146, S-187
    gels, 137, S-101, S-153, S-298
  silicate glasses, 146, 236, 273, S-168
  silicates, 81, 273, 619, 774, S-38, S-130, S-220
  silyl amines, S-61, S-91
    cyanides, 750
    iodide, 343, S-99
    isothiocyanate, 395
    phosphine, S-224
    selenide, S-181
    sulfide, S-98, S-181
  tetrafluoride, 8
  thiocyanates, 726
  tungstosilicates, 681
Silver, 305, 454, S-205, S-270
  bromate, S-260
  bromide, S-88
  chlorate, 571
  chloride, S-88
    cell windows, 577
  chromite, S-17
  cyano complexes, 260
  nitrite, 698
  perchlorate, 765
  sulfamate, 453

  sulfate, thiosulfate, selenosulfate, and amine sulfonate, S-16
  telluride, 320
Sodium, 324
  antimonate, S-271
  azide, 727
  bifluoride, 528
  bromate, S-260
  bromide, 115, 678
  chlorate, 185, 571
  chloride, 678, S-47
  fluoborate, 15
  fluorides, S-89
  hexafluorides, complex, 21
  hydroxide, 332, S-134
  iodide, 678
  metaborate, 62
  nitrate, 186, 269, 501, 732, S-21
  nitrite, 590, 698, S-281
  pentacyanoferrates, 371
  perchlorate, 601
  peroxide, 612
  phosphates, 463
  pyrophosphates, 756
  selenosulfate, thiosulfate, amine sulfonate, S-16
  sulfate, 691, S-16
  tellurate, S-271
  tetrametaphosphate, 775
Strontium
  bromate, S-260
  carbonate, 757
  chlorate, 571
  fluoride, 80
  peroxide, 612
  sulfate, thiosulfate, selenosulfate, and amine sulfonate, S-16
  titanate, 281, 293, S-193
Sulfur, 128
  acid sulfites, 580
  dichloride, 321, 556
  dioxide, 188, 297, 307, 406, 494, 550, 551, 594, 595, 661, 744, S-6, S-115, S-175

fluorides, 18, 65, 84, 147, 405, 476, S-14, S-26, S-27
oxyanions of, 705
persulfide, hydrogen, S-300
SOF_2, 413
sulfamates, 453, 480, 481, 482, 610, 696, S-12
sulfamic acid, S-113
sulfates, 56, 81, 170, 349, 362, 402, 434, 440, 508, 691, S-16, S-93, S-137, S-179
sulfides, 25, 39, 43, 48, 58, 74, 89, 148, 161, 172, 183, 195, 199, 200, 214, 245, 331, 365, 366, 382, 414, 442, 443, 444, 479, 522, 599, 600, 656, 680, 763, 782, S-5, S-98, S-110, S-163, S-181, S-192, S-200, S-263, S-264, S-301
sulfuryl bromofluoride, S-56
    chloride (and thionyl chloride), 282
    fluoride, 100
thiocyanato sulfur groups, 469

Tantalum
  oxide, 424
Thallium
  sulfate, thiosulfate, selenosulfate, amine sulfonate, S-16
Tellurium, 22, 93, 173, 212, 213, 278, 720, S-164
  decafluoride, S-14
  hexafluoride, 147, 360, 465
  oxide, 103
  tellurates, S-271
  telluric acid, S-271
  telluric ozone, 524
  tellurides, 43, 58, 320, 331, 574, 641, 782, S-110, S-118
Tin, 105, S-205
  stannates, S-145
  stannides, 326
  tetrachloride, 778

Titanium
  boride, 613
  molybdotitanates, 681
  oxide, 61, 288, S-65, S-174
  tetrachloride, 258
  titanates, 281, 293, 652, 751, S-29, S-145, S-193
Tritium
  bromide, 521
  chloride, 521
  cyanide, 583
  oxide, plain, hydrogenated, and deuterated, 584
Tungsten, S-259
  hexafluoride, 54, 147
  octacyanocomplexes, 715
  oxide, S-145
  tungstates, 351

Uranium
  hexafluorides, 54, 147, 242, 249
  uranyl and transuranium V and VI ions, 163
    complexes, 741
    halides, S-123
    nitrate, 559, S-70, S-148, S-262

Vanadium
  corundum, S-124
  hydroxide, 467
  oxytrichloride, 662
  vanadia-silica gels, S-298

Water, 50, 89, 111, 125, 138, 169, 170, 171, 441, 495, 529, 615, 672, 718, S-48, S-67, S-82, S-144, S-165
  as solvent for quantitative spectroscopy, 565
  ethanol—solutions, 588
  hydrogen-bonding of, 693
  hydronium ion, S-18
  ice, 286, 759, S-3, S-117, S-236

Water (*cont.*)
  in complexes, S-125
  in organic solvents, S-127
  of crystallization, 26
  of hydration, 539
  water-silica gel system, S-153
  vapor, 76, 210, 224, 341, 356, 473, 474, 517

Zinc
  arsenide, 367
  bromate, S-260
  chlorate, 571
  ferrites, 436, S-111
  fluorinated salts of hydrates, 543

fluosilicate, 83
nitride, 613
oxide, 706, S-65, S-108, S-149, S-279
praseodymium nitrate, S-21
selenide, S-110
selenosulfate, thiosulfate, and amine sulfonate, S-16
sulfamate, S-12
sulfate, 691, S-16, S-21, S-179
sulfide, 365, 501, 763, S-110
telluride, S-110
Zirconium
  boride, 613
  zirconates, S-145